Hot, steamy, sizzling…
Mixing with the ~~rul~~ ~~cicty~~
the fabu~~l~~

One ~~night~~
BUENOS AIRES

Three vivid, passionate and dramatic
novels by three favourite writers

One night in
MILAN

MICHELLE REID   INDIA GREY   KATE HEWITT

One night in
RIO

ANNE MATHER   JENNIE LUCAS   OLIVIA GATES

One night in
BUENOS AIRES

MAGGIE COX   CHANTELLE SHAW   SARAH MORGAN

One night in
MADRID

KATE WALKER   JENNIE LUCAS   ABBY GREEN

One night in
BUENOS AIRES

SARAH MORGAN

MAGGIE COX

CHANTELLE SHAW

Harlequin Mills & Boon Limited, Eton House,
18-24 Paradise Road, Richmond, Surrey TW9 1SR

ONE NIGHT IN BUENOS AIRES
© Harlequin Enterprises II B.V./S.à.r.l. 2011

The Vásquez Mistress © Sarah Morgan 2008
The Buenos Aires Marriage Deal © Maggie Cox 2009
Argentinian Playboy, Unexpected Love-Child
© Chantelle Shaw 2009

ISBN: 978 0 263 88743 3

009-0511

Harlequin Mills & Boon policy is to use papers that are
natural, renewable and recyclable products and made from
wood grown in sustainable forests. The logging and
manufacturing processes conform to the legal environmental
regulations of the country of origin.

Printed and bound in Spain
by Litografia Rosés S.A., Barcelona

The Vásquez Mistress

SARAH MORGAN

Sarah Morgan trained as a nurse and has since worked in a variety of health-related jobs. Married to a gorgeous businessman, who still makes her knees knock, she spends most of her time trying to keep up with their two little boys, but manages to sneak off occasionally to indulge her passion for writing romance. Sarah loves outdoor life and is an enthusiastic skier and walker. Whatever she is doing, her head is full of new characters and she is addicted to happy endings.

Don't miss Sarah's exciting new novels in June and July from Mills & Boon® Medical™ & Modern™. Also look out for *Summer Fling* in July.

CHAPTER ONE

SHE sat straight as a warrior on the horse, her hair gleaming like liquid gold under the baking Argentine sun.

When he'd first noticed her in the distance his reaction had been one of irritation, partly because the horse had been galloping hard in the ferocious heat, but mostly because he'd been seeking solitude, not company. And if there was one thing that the Argentine pampas offered in abundance it was the opportunity for solitude.

Endless grassland stretched far into the distance, the horizon so perfectly straight and flat that it might have been drawn with a ruler.

Irritation had turned to concern as horse and rider had drawn closer and he'd recognised the animal she was riding.

He felt a flash of anger towards whomever had allowed her to take that particular horse out alone and made a mental note to find the culprit. And then anger faded to slow, simmering masculine appraisal as he scanned the delicate lines of her features.

He had spent his life surrounded by exceptionally beautiful women, all of them more groomed than this girl, and yet he couldn't drag his eyes away from her face. She was fair-skinned and delicate, her body a mouth-watering combination of slender limbs and perfect curves. It was as if she'd been created by the gods and thrown onto Earth for the simple purpose of tempting man.

Her creamy skin and flushed cheeks gave her an air of innocence and he gave a wry smile, surprised that he was even capable of recognising that particular quality given how rarely he'd met with it before.

In fact his cynicism was so deep-rooted that his first thought when he'd noticed her on the horizon had been to assume that she'd somehow tracked him down and followed him. But he'd dismissed that possibility instantly, knowing that her presence could only be coincidence.

A happy coincidence, he thought idly, his eyes resting on her soft mouth. A very happy coincidence indeed.

The horse flattened his ears, arched his back and gave a ferocious buck that should have unseated her.

Faith gritted her teeth and managed to stay glued to the saddle. 'You really are in a horrible mood today, Fuego. It's no wonder everyone is afraid of you,' she muttered. 'I'm not falling off here. We're miles from home. Wherever you go, I go and the sooner you realise that the better for both of us.'

The heat was stifling and she reached for her bottle of water and then froze as she caught movement out of the corner of her eye. She turned her head, the breath jamming in her throat as she saw a man watching her.

She'd been concentrating so hard on not falling off the horse, that she hadn't noticed him.

But she noticed him now.

He was the most staggeringly handsome man she'd ever met and since she'd arrived in Argentina, she'd met quite a few. His body was lean and hard, his shoulders broad and powerful but what really disrupted the steady rhythm of her heart was the sheer raw sexuality that surrounded him like a forcefield.

'You're staring, *signorina*.' His deep, male voice trickled through her veins like a drug and her limbs weakened.

Her horse, sensing a lack of concentration on her part, chose that moment to give another determined buck and Faith flew into the air and landed on her bottom in the dust.

'For crying out loud!' Pain shot through her and she sat for a moment, working out whether anything was broken. 'That horse needs a psychiatrist.'

A pair of strong male hands closed around her waist and lifted her easily to her feet. 'He needs a male rider.' His eyes blazed fiercely into hers and she felt her heart stumble and trip.

'There's nothing wrong with my riding. It's your fault for jumping out on me with no warning…' Her voice tailed off because the sudden narrowing of his beautiful, sexy eyes drove all thoughts from her head.

'I assumed you'd seen me. The Argentine grassland hardly offers a large number of hiding places.'

'I was concentrating on my horse.'

'You were riding too fast.'

'Tell that to the horse, not me. I suppose that's why they called him Fuego—my Spanish isn't great, but I know it means "fire".' Faith dragged her gaze away from his handsome face in the hope that not looking at him might help her slow the crazy beating of her heart. 'I didn't choose the pace. With that particular horse, you always get more than you bargain for.' *What was the matter with her?* She felt lightheaded and dizzy and her body felt alarmingly lethargic.

It was the heat, she told herself quickly. Just the relentless, baking heat that turned the entire landscape into a throbbing, sultry outdoor sauna.

'You are staying at the Estancia La Lucia?' He glanced behind him even though the elegant colonial house was over an hour away. 'You shouldn't be riding alone. What happened to the rest of your party? You should have a groom with you.'

'Oh, please.' Baking hot from the relentless sunshine and aching from her fall, Faith shot him a warning look. 'I'm just not in the mood for all that macho Argentine-man thing. Not right now.'

He lifted an eyebrow in silent mockery. 'Argentine-man thing?'

'You know what I mean.' She rubbed at the dirt on her breeches. 'The mega-macho approach. The "sling a woman over your shoulder" method of communication.'

'Interesting description.' His eyes laughed into hers. 'This is South America, *cariño*. Men know how to be men.'

'I'd noticed. Ever since I stepped off the aeroplane I've been surrounded by so much testosterone that it's driving me mad.'

'Welcome to Argentina.' There was gentle mockery in his sexy, accented drawl and suddenly she felt impossibly awkward and shy and her reaction to him infuriated her because she'd always thought of herself as a confident person.

'Do you work here?'

His hesitation was so brief she decided that she must have imagined it. 'Yes.'

'Lucky you.' She assumed he must be one of the *gauchos*, the cowboys who worked with the nine-hundred head of cattle that grazed this land. Dragging her eyes away from his, she wondered why this particular man was having such an effect on her. Yes, he was good-looking but so were many of the men she'd met since she'd arrived in South America.

But there was something about him…

'Your English is amazing.'

'That's because I sometimes talk to women before I throw them over my shoulder.' He studied her for a long disturbing moment, a powerful, confident male totally at home in his surroundings. Then his gaze dropped to her mouth and lingered there, as if he were making up his mind about something.

The heat went from oppressive to unbearable and the chemistry between them was so shockingly intense that she actually felt herself sway towards him in anticipation.

She *desperately* wanted him to kiss her and the strength of that need shocked her because she'd been pushing men away since the day she'd arrived at Buenos Aires. She was here to work, study and learn, not to meet a man. But suddenly her lips were tingling with anticipation and she found herself trapped by the lazy, knowing expression in his dangerously attractive eyes. It was as if he was savouring the moment and she knew that he'd read her thoughts. Her sense of anticipation exploded into an all-consuming sexual excitement that she'd never before experienced.

She waited breathlessly, knowing that she was poised on the brink of something wickedly exciting and sensing that this man was going to change her life for ever.

But instead of kissing her he gave a slow, expressive smile and turned his attention to her horse. 'Your horse needs a drink.'

Released from the force of his gaze, Faith felt her entire body go limp and her face flood with colour. 'My horse needs a lot of things.'

What had happened just then?

Had she imagined the connection between them? Had it all been in her head?

Her eyes slid to his broad shoulders and the long, lean length of his strong legs as he led her horse to the river.

No, she hadn't imagined it. But this was no teenage boy eager for a quick grope and instant satisfaction; she was dealing with someone else entirely. He was all man, from the glossy black hair and darkened jaw to the powerful muscle that hardened his unmistakably male physique. He was cool, sophisticated and experienced and her stomach curled inside her because he carried himself with such confidence and she knew, she just *knew*, that he was playing with her.

Feeling as though the temperature had just shot up by a hundred degrees, Faith glared at his broad back and then bit her lip, wishing she could get rid of the agonising sizzle that was burning inside her.

Angry with herself *and* with him, she lifted her chin and strolled towards him, determined not to let him see how much he'd affected her.

'I need to be getting back.' She took Fuego's reins and vaulted into the saddle, taking some satisfaction from the way the man's eyes lingered on her slim thighs.

She hadn't imagined the chemistry. *The searing attraction wasn't all on her side.*

'Wait.' He closed a hand over Fuego's reins, preventing the horse from moving. 'You say that you work at the *estancia*. In what capacity? Do you work in the guest quarters?'

'You're showing your prejudices again.' Agonisingly aware of him, she rubbed a hand over the horse's neck to focus herself. 'All the Argentine men I've met so far seem to think that a woman's place is in the—' She stopped herself just in time, but he lifted an eyebrow, his eyes gleaming with wicked humour.

'You were saying? We Argentine men think a woman's place is in the…?'

He was so desperately attractive that for a moment she couldn't speak and she certainly didn't want to finish her sentence. It would draw the conversation towards an extremely dangerous area that she knew was best avoided. 'Kitchen,' she said lamely. 'Kitchen.'

His smile deepened. 'Kitchen? If that's what you think then you obviously haven't yet deciphered the workings of the average male mind here in South America.'

That smile connected straight to her nerve endings and she was infuriated with herself for being so susceptible to his charm and masculinity.

'The average male mind is of absolutely no interest to me,' she said sweetly, 'unless the mind belongs to a horse.'

'Is that what brought you to Argentina? Our horses?'

Faith glanced around her, at the endless sweep of grassland that surrounded them. 'I came because I read about Raul Vásquez.'

The man stilled. 'You travelled thousands of miles to meet Raul Vásquez?' There was a coolness to his tone that had been absent before. 'You are hoping to catch yourself a billionaire, perhaps?'

Faith gazed at him in astonishment and then burst out laughing. 'No, of course not. Don't be ridiculous. Billionaire polo-patrons aren't exactly my style, and anyway, I've never even met the man. He's off in the States at the moment, negotiating some high-flying deal or other and he employs thousands of people. I don't expect our paths are ever going to cross.'

He studied her with disturbing intensity. 'And that would disappoint you?'

'You misunderstand me. I'm not interested in the man, but I *am* interested in his polo *estancia*. That's why I'm here. Raul Vásquez breeds horses and trains them and his vet facilities are the best in the world. I read a paper in a journal written by Eduardo, his chief vet. I contacted him. Landing a job here is my dream come true.'

'Eduardo employed you?' That statement was greeted by incredulous silence. 'You're a *vet*?'

'Yes, I'm a vet.' Watching the frank astonishment in his eyes, Faith gritted her teeth. 'Welcome to the twenty-first century. Women do become vets, you know. Some of us can even walk and talk at the same time, although news of that accomplishment clearly hasn't yet reached South America.'

'I'm aware that some women become vets,' he said smoothly, 'But this is a busy, commercial stud-farm, not some small-animal practice in the city.'

'I wasn't interested in a small-animal practice. For me it's always been about horses.'

His gaze slid to her arms and lingered. 'I don't doubt your commitment or your enthusiasm, but sometimes physical strength is required, especially out here in the pampas where we deal with powerful stallions and hormonal mares.'

Her heart rate suddenly doubled. 'Here we go again. You think it's all about muscle, aggression and domination, but what you need to realise is that there's more to horsemanship than brute strength. And Raul Vásquez understands that. He has some revolutionary training methods.'

'I'm fully aware of his training methods. Answer me one question…' His tone was soft and deadly and his gaze returned to her face. 'Who was in charge when you were galloping across the pampas with the wind in your hair? You or the horse?'

'Oh, the horse,' Faith admitted, her eyes sparkling with humour. 'But brute force wouldn't have changed that fact.'

'He needs to be ridden by a man. A man with sufficient skill and strength to control him.'

Faith came back at him instantly. 'He needs to be understood. If you want to change behaviour, then you have to first try and understand the reason behind that behaviour. Horses do things for a reason, just like humans.'

She'd spent her life studying and all her spare time around horses. No man had ever captured her attention.

Until now.

His confidence and sophistication tied her in knots and she felt horribly self-conscious and more than a little confused by her own reaction.

She would never in a million years have described herself as shy, but suddenly she was agonisingly aware of her own naivety when it came to men like him.

'I'd better be going. I have to ride back and…' Her voice tailed off and she wondered whether he was going to stop her.

But he didn't.

He let his hand drop from Fuego's bridle and stepped away. 'Ride carefully,' he said softly and she gave a puzzled smile because she'd been so, so sure that he was going to stop her or at least suggest that they meet again.

And she'd wanted him to.

She'd really wanted him to.

The Vásquez Polo Cup was an important annual part of the Argentine polo circuit and it was the most glittering, glamorous affair Faith had ever attended.

She was only there in her official capacity as a vet of course, but she couldn't help glancing towards the spectators who were gathering in the stands. 'How come the women are all so stunning?' she wondered out loud. 'And how do they achieve such straight hair? In this heat my hair just curls.'

'You are looking at the elite of Buenos Aires,' Eduardo replied, breaking off to shout instructions to one of the grooms before turning his attention back to Faith. 'They would have spent the whole of the day preparing in the hope that they catch the boss's eye.'

'The boss?' Faith glanced around her. 'Raul Vásquez? He's playing today isn't he? Is he here?'

'Not yet.'

'But the game is due to start in five minutes.' She couldn't take her eyes off the women in the stands, her attention caught by the glint of diamonds against designer silk. They were like a flock of exotic birds. 'They're very dressed up considering they're spending their afternoon around horses.'

'This is polo,' Eduardo drawled. 'The most glamorous game in the world. Everyone dresses up.'

The men thundered onto the field on lithe, agile horses and Faith tried not to be overwhelmed by the sheer glamour of the spectacle.

She'd just stooped to examine a horse's fetlock when she heard the noise of a helicopter in the air.

'Here he comes,' Eduardo murmured, glancing upwards and narrowing his eyes against the glare of the sun. 'Match starts in two minutes. He's cutting it fine as usual.'

Faith was too busy with the pony to pay any attention to the helicopter landing. 'He isn't fit.'

Eduardo frowned. 'He's the fittest man I've ever met.'

'Not the boss, this pony!' Faith stared at him in exasperation. 'Does everyone here only think about Raul Vásquez?'

There was a sudden roar from the crowd and Faith realised that the game had started. She glanced over her shoulder, watching as horses and riders thundered down the pitch.

Before arriving in Argentina she'd never been to a polo match and the speed and danger of the game still left her breathless.

She turned to one of the grooms. 'Which one is Raul Vásquez?'

'The one taking all the risks,' he muttered and Faith's eyes narrowed as she turned her attention to the game.

From this distance it was impossible to distinguish anyone's features under the protective helmet, but one man stood out from all the others. Lithe and muscular, he controlled his horse with one hand while he leaned out of the saddle to hook the ball, apparently indifferent to the danger inherent in such a manoeuvre.

Watching in disbelief, Faith braced herself for him to crash to the ground with disastrous consequences. He had to fall, surely? But with a mixture of sheer muscle-strength and athleticism, he stayed with the horse, swung his mallet with lethal accuracy and hit the ball through the posts.

The crowd erupted in ecstasy and Faith suddenly realised that she'd been holding her breath.

'The tension of this game is unbelievable,' she muttered and the groom grinned at her.

'It is very aggressive, yes. But the horses love it.'

Turning her attention back to her job, Faith worked her way down the pony lines, checking each animal and talking to the grooms, and at half time one of the grooms tapped her on the shoulder. 'Time to stomp the divets. It's tradition. Everyone joins in.'

Spectators and players strolled onto the pitch and started treading in the lumps of turf that had been dislodged by the horses' hooves. It was a social occasion, with much laughter and conversation, a chance for the audience to mingle with the players.

Faith stretched out her foot to push down a lump of grass but a large black boot was there before her and she glanced up into the laughing eyes of the man she'd been watching on the polo field.

Raul Vásquez.

The man from the river.

For a moment she just stared. Then she swallowed and her tongue seemed to tie itself into knots. 'I didn't know. You didn't introduce yourself.'

'I didn't want to,' he drawled softly and hot colour flooded her cheeks because he was just so, *so* attractive and although they were surrounded by beautiful, glamorous women, he was looking at *her*.

'You should have told me who you were!'

'Why? You might have behaved differently and I wouldn't have wanted that.' His smile was sexy, distracting and impossibly intimate.

'How did I behave?'

He stamped down another piece of turf and his leg brushed against hers in a deliberate movement. 'You were delightfully natural.'

She glanced around her at the poise and confidence of the women around her. 'You mean I don't spend all day being pampered. Why are you talking to me?'

'Because you fascinate me.'

'You prefer your women with no make-up and covered in dust?'

He laughed. 'I'm interested in the person, not the package.'

'Oh please!' She stared up at his impossibly handsome face. 'Are you seriously telling me that you would look twice at a woman who wasn't stunning?'

'No, I'm not telling you that.' His eyes didn't leave hers and she felt as if the air had been knocked out of her lungs.

'You're saying that—you're implying that—'

'Yes.' His tone was amused. 'I am. And you're not usually short of a sharp reply. What's the matter? Hasn't anyone paid you a compliment before?'

The chemistry between them crackled and sizzled like a high-voltage cable and she was conscious of what seemed like hundreds of eyes looking at her. 'Everyone is staring.'

'And that matters because…?'

'Well, you might be used to being the centre of attention, but I'm not.' Not knowing what to say and frustrated with herself for being so gauche, she glared at him. 'It doesn't matter who you are, I still think you're macho and sexist.'

He threw his head back and laughed. 'You're absolutely right, *cariño*. I am macho and sexist. And I want to spend some time with you. Come to the Beach House.'

The Beach House was his private residence, a beautiful architect-designed villa that faced the Atlantic coast and opened onto a perfect stretch of sand. And it was strictly out of bounds to the staff.

What exactly was he suggesting?

But one glance at his wicked dark eyes told her exactly what he was suggesting and the colour rushed into her cheeks like fire.

Unsettled by how much she wanted to say yes, Faith stepped away, conscious that all the women on the pitch were watching her enviously. How on earth was she supposed to say no to a man like him? Worried that part of her didn't even want to say no, she spoke quickly before she could be tempted into doing something she just knew she'd regret. 'No. But thanks.'

'I wasn't asking you a question.'

She was suddenly so aware of him that her entire body was burning inside. 'You were giving me an order?'

His gaze was lazily amused. 'A strongly worded request.'

She could hardly breathe. 'I have a job to do. I'm working until ten.'

'I'll arrange for you to have the evening off.'

Just like that.

The power of a billionaire, Faith thought helplessly. 'No. That wouldn't be fair on the others.' She was swamped with disappointment and suddenly wondered what she would have said if she *hadn't* been working. Would she have gone with him? Her insides fluttered with nerves. 'I'm afraid we're going to have to postpone my Cinderella moment for another occasion. It's Eduardo's night off and we have a mare due to foal any minute. I can't leave the yard.'

The humour died in his eyes and her words were met by a tense silence. 'One of the mares is due to foal?' Easy seduction was replaced by sharp efficiency. 'Which one?'

'Velocity.'

He inhaled sharply and ran a hand over the back of his neck. 'If she is foaling then Eduardo should be here.' His cool declaration punctured her bubble of happiness.

'Well, thanks for that vote of confidence. Nice to know you trust me.'

'It isn't personal.'

She gave a short laugh. 'You mean you'd feel like this about any woman?'

His eyes narrowed dangerously. 'Velocity is my most valuable mare. This is an enormous responsibility,' he said softly, and she lifted her chin and looked him straight in the eye.

'I can handle responsibility. I don't spend my days straightening my hair and applying my make-up. I've trained for seven years so that I can meet the responsibility head-on.' Suddenly she felt angry and frustrated. Maybe she'd been wrong to think she could pursue her career in this part of South America. It was an uphill battle to get anyone to take her seriously. 'I can handle the work. What I can't handle is dealing with men who don't think women are capable of having a career.' She was so upset she was afraid she might burst into tears. *And that would undermine her credibility even further.* 'If you'll excuse me, I have work to do.'

Trying not to think about Raul Vásquez, she worked in the stables until ten. Then she went to check on the mare, Velocity, one more time before returning to her room in the staff quarters.

A single glance was sufficient for her to see that the mare was in difficulty.

The groom was in the corner of the stall, his hands shaking as he fumbled with his mobile phone. 'I can't get hold of Eduardo. He isn't answering.'

'You should have called *me*, not Eduardo.' Faith dropped to her knees beside the horse. Cursing herself for relying on them to let her know how the mare was progressing, she reached for her stethoscope.

The groom was sweating. 'You better not touch that horse. She's the boss's favourite mare. If anything happens to her…' He broke off, panic in his eyes. 'We need to get hold of Eduardo somehow. If anything happens to the animal, Raul Vásquez will hit the roof. I'll lose my job.'

Faith gritted her teeth. *None of the Argentine grooms had faith in her.*

'At the moment I don't care about the boss's temper or your promotion prospects, but I *do* care about the horse and you need to do as I tell you.' Keeping her voice calm so it didn't disturb the animal, Faith gave him a string of instructions but he just stood there, staring at the horse with terrified eyes.

'If that mare dies—'

'It will be my responsibility,' Faith said coldly and then she sighed. 'Oh for goodness' sake, just get out. If you can't work with me, fine, but I need you to find someone who *can*. I need help and I need it now.'

'I will help you.' Raul Vásquez stood in the doorway of the box and the groom shrank into the shadows, too intimidated to even defend himself.

Faith was too worried about the mare to feel intimidated. With barely a glance in his direction, she told Raul what she wanted him to do and he immediately dropped to his haunches next to the mare and spoke to her softly in Spanish.

Faith had no idea what he said but his words had an immediate effect on the frightened animal and finally she was able to concentrate, which was just as well because it was the most difficult foaling she'd ever attended.

Finally the mare heaved a sigh and the foal slipped out onto the straw.

'Clever girl,' Faith breathed quietly and glanced up, suddenly aware that Raul was watching her intently.

'I think *you* are the clever girl,' he murmured quietly, a thoughtful expression in his dark eyes as he scanned her face with disturbing intensity. 'I underestimated you and for that I apologise.'

The atmosphere in the box was charged with tension and for a moment they just stared at each other. Then she suddenly realised that he was wearing a dinner jacket. 'I'm sorry I interrupted your evening,' she said stiffly, hating herself for caring that he'd clearly found another woman with whom to spend his evening.

It could have been her.

Remembering the sleek, beautifully groomed women who had vied for his attention during the polo match, Faith wondered which of them had caught his attention. Then she gave herself a mental shake. It could *never* have been her. Men as rich, successful and handsome as Raul Vásquez wanted trophy women, not career women.

Descending back to earth with a bump, she gave a tired smile. 'Your mare is going to be fine, Raul, but I'll stay with her tonight just to make sure. Thanks for your help. It made all the difference.'

'You are planning to sleep in my horse's stall?' At some point he had undone his top button and she caught a glimpse of bronzed male skin and a hint of curling dark hair.

'Yes.' Faith looked away quickly. *He was impossibly masculine.* 'That way if anything happens, I'll be here.'

He frowned sharply. 'You have been working since six this morning.'

'I'll take tomorrow off. I don't want to leave until I'm sure she's all right.' Her attention was back on the mare and her foal. 'You should understand that. From what I've heard, you're the original workaholic.'

'That is different.'

'Because you're a man and I'm a woman? Don't start that again, Raul.' Suddenly exhausted, she just wanted him to leave so that she could stop dreaming. 'I won't leave halfway through a job. And you were obviously in the middle of dinner or something, so perhaps you'd better go back to the woman in question in case she gives up on you.'

There was a long silence. 'You hide behind your job, don't you?' Raul asserted. 'Why is that?'

'I don't hide. But I love my job, if that's what you're asking.' She glanced at him briefly and then looked away again, her heart thumping and her mind spinning fairy-tales.

'This thing between us—' his voice was soft '—it frightens you, doesn't it?'

She was too honest to pretend she didn't know what he was talking about. 'Yes, it frightens me. Because it's not real. The mere idea of you and I is—' She waved a hand. 'It's crazy. I mean, we couldn't be more different. You're used to women who spend all day making themselves beautiful. I'm a working girl. I love my career and I definitely don't want a relationship.'

'If you don't want a relationship, then you are my perfect woman,' he drawled softly. 'What about fun, *cariño*? Do you object to having fun?'

The colour poured into her cheeks. 'Raul—'

'Why are you blushing? When it comes to your job you are supremely confident, but whenever we are alone…' He stroked a leisurely finger down her cheek. 'Why is it that you are so confident with my horses and so shy with me?'

'Blame it on the testosterone again. I'm not used to macho men.' She tried to make a joke, but he wasn't smiling. Instead his gaze was curiously intent.

'You are very inexperienced, aren't you?'

'I've had boyfriends,' she muttered defensively and a smile played around his firm mouth.

'But what about *men*, *cariño*? Men are a whole new experience for you, isn't that right?'

She gazed at him, her heart pounding and her mouth dry. 'What does *"cariño"* mean?'

His smile widened and he strolled towards the door. 'I'll teach you tomorrow,' he answered softly. 'Along with the facts of life. Finish your job and get some rest. You're going to need it.'

CHAPTER TWO

SHE spent the night with the mare and emerged from the box to find Raul Vásquez in conversation with Eduardo.

Raul turned his head and looked at her and the look of blatant masculine appreciation in his dark eyes made her stomach flip. 'You are now officially off duty and you're coming with me.' He took her hand firmly in his, said something in Spanish to Eduardo and led her towards the helicopter pad at the far side of the polo fields.

'I was going to bed,' she mumbled and he flashed her a smile of such devastating charisma that for a moment she was blinded.

'That can be arranged.'

She didn't know whether to laugh or gasp with shock. 'I really don't do this sort of thing—'

'What sort of thing?' His eyes teased her and she glanced at the sleek lines of the black helicopter and then back over her shoulder towards the safety of the *estancia*.

'I don't fly off into the sunset with men I don't know.'

'You can spend your day sleeping in your room and then you can eat dinner with the grooms, if that is what you would prefer.' He paused and his gaze drifted to her mouth. 'Or you can have dinner with me.'

She licked her lips. 'Where?'

'Somewhere we can talk without disturbance.' He opened the door of the helicopter and she scrambled inside, wondering what on earth she was doing.

This wasn't her life.

She didn't climb into helicopters with dangerous billionaires.

While she was wrestling with self-doubt and nerves, Raul settled himself in the seat next to her and flicked several switches with swift, confident fingers.

Faith stared at him. '*You're* flying it?'

'I'm a control freak,' he confessed in a dry tone. 'I prefer to be in the driving seat and anyway, for what I have in mind, I don't need an audience.'

His words sent a shiver of anticipation through her body. 'I don't know why you're doing this. And I don't know why I'm doing this either.' She licked her lips. 'I don't own a silk dress or diamonds.'

'Then we'll have to do something about that.' He turned towards her and there was laughter in his wicked dark eyes. 'Relax.' His voice was surprisingly gentle. 'You're going to have a nice time. This is my thank-you for saving my horse and my apology for not having more faith in you. You were impressive.'

His praise was as surprising as it was welcome. 'Your groom didn't think so. Perhaps you could have a word with him.'

'That won't be necessary. He no longer works for me.'

'You fired him?' She was shocked. 'Isn't that a little extreme?'

'You asked for his help. He didn't give it.'

Faith felt a flash of guilt. 'I didn't mean to get him fired. Shouldn't you give him another chance?'

'I gave him one chance. I employed him.' His smile didn't falter but there was something in his eyes that hinted at a more

ruthless side of him. *The side that had made him a billionaire by the time he was thirty.*

Sensing that the subject was best dropped, Faith glanced
around her. 'Where are we going?'

'You'll find out.' Without answering her question, he
turned his attention back to the controls and the helicopter
lifted into the air.

Terror soon turned to exhilaration as they swooped above
the pampas. 'The view is amazing from up here,' she breathed,
her eyes fixed on the landscape beneath her.

They flew over grassland, interspersed with lagoons and
wetlands. Occasionally Faith saw cattle being herded by men
on horseback, but this was a vast landscape and the sheer size
of it took her breath away.

Eventually a large lake came into view and Raul landed
the helicopter.

'We're here. This is the boundary of the *estancia*.' He
jumped down from the helicopter and led her towards a luxurious lodge that nestled between water and trees. 'My secret
hideaway.'

Faith stopped dead, her heart bumping against her chest.
'We're alone here?'

He turned, his eyes on her face. 'Does that bother you? Are
you nervous?'

She swallowed. 'Maybe. Just a little.'

'You were alone with me on the pampas on that first day,'
he said softly, strolling back towards her and taking her face
in his hands. 'And you weren't nervous then.'

'That was an accidental meeting.' The skilled brush of his
fingers set her pulse racing and nerves fluttered like butterflies in her stomach. 'I don't do this sort of thing, Raul. I
shouldn't have come.'

'Stop panicking. You haven't done anything yet,' he
pointed out gently. 'And you won't be doing anything you

don't want to. All I ask is that you allow yourself to be spoiled. This is a thank-you for having saved my favourite horse. Treat it like a spa day.'

'A spa day?'

His mouth hovered tantalisingly close to hers and then he stepped away and smiled. 'I want to spoil you. And we're not alone here. You can shout for help any time you feel the need and a hoard of staff will come running and beat me away with sticks.'

He led her up a few steps, onto a wooden deck that was suspended over the water and into a large bedroom filled with natural light. 'This is your room. Have a rest, you deserve it. When you're ready for a massage or whatever takes your fancy, just pick up the phone and dial zero.'

Faith blinked. Her head was full of questions but she had no chance to ask any of them because he'd left the room.

It was like being dropped into paradise.

She slept in the enormous, comfortable bed and then lay in the shade on the deck while a girl rubbed scented oils into her skin, the skilful stroke of her fingers removing all the last strands of tension from Faith's body.

After the massage, she sat and gazed across the tranquil water of the lake while someone tended to her nails and another did her hair.

There was no sign of Raul and when she eventually walked back into her room, she wondered how she was supposed to contact him.

A splash of colour drew her eye and she glanced towards the bed, her eyes widening as she saw the beautiful silk dress laid carefully on the cover. The exquisite fabric shimmered in the late-evening light and Faith stepped towards it, puzzled. *Had Raul left this for her?* And then she saw the diamond necklace, draped almost casually across the bodice, the stones sparkling and glittering like shards of ice.

She was so stunned that it took her a few moments to notice the card. Her fingers shaking, she opened the envelope and read the dark, bold scrawl: *Every woman deserves to be given a silk dress and diamonds at least once in her life. Enjoy. R.*

Completely out of her depth, Faith stared at the dress and the necklace. It was an enormously generous gift. *Obviously* she couldn't possibly accept it.

She stood for a moment, her lip caught between her teeth, her eyes on the dress. Tormented by indecision, she stepped away from the bed and then immediately stepped back again. Then she let the dressing gown slip from her shoulders, the feminine side of her completely unable to let her ignore such a gorgeous dress.

She was just going to try it on. Nothing more than that.

Just for a minute.

The silk slithered over her skin and she gave a moan of indulgence as she realised that it was a perfect fit.

How had he guessed her size?

Feeling as though she was living someone else's life, Faith fastened the dress and then tried to secure the clasp of the necklace. Strong fingers covered hers and swiftly finished the job.

Stifled by sexual awareness, she turned slowly and found herself looking into Raul's laughing eyes.

'So how is your day going?' His fingers lingered at the base of her throat. 'Do you feel properly thanked?'

'I can't possibly accept any of this.'

'Of course you can. It is nothing.'

To him, maybe, but she suspected that the necklace alone was worth more than she earned in a year. 'I'm just trying it on, that's all. And then I'm taking it straight off.'

'Why would you want to do that?'

'Because this is *not* my life.'

He turned her gently until she was facing the mirror. 'So who is that, if it isn't you?'

Faith barely recognised herself. Her hair fell past her shoulders like sleek, polished gold, the diamonds glinted against her pale skin and the dress hugged her figure. She felt like a princess. 'Maybe I'll wear it just for this evening.' She almost laughed at her own weakness. 'But then I'm giving it back.'

Acknowledging her internal battle, Raul smiled. 'We'll have dinner on the terrace. The view is very pretty.'

'So do you do this often?'

He dismissed the staff with a discreet movement of his head and reached over to pour her another glass of wine. 'Eat dinner? Yes. All the time.'

'No, I mean—' She glanced down at herself. 'Play the part of the fairy godmother.'

'It's fun buying gifts for a woman who appreciates them.' He watched her across the table. 'You're not eating. Aren't you hungry?'

Her stomach was churning so badly that she just couldn't touch the food. 'No. No, I'm not. Sorry. It looks really delicious but—'

He gave a slow smile. 'You don't need to apologise for the fact that I'm putting you off your food. I take it as a compliment.'

'You're very sure of yourself.'

'And you're very nervous, and I can't understand why. Don't they have men in England?'

Not men like him. 'I've been too busy working to notice men,' she said lightly and his eyes narrowed.

'You are very dedicated to your work. Why did you choose to become a vet?'

'I always wanted to. My father was a vet and I grew up helping alongside him. Even when I was small, he'd involve me in some way and he always encouraged me.'

'He is proud of you, I'm sure.'

Faith hesitated. 'He and my mother died two years ago,' she said quietly. 'That's one of the reasons I came to Argentina. I missed them so much and I knew I needed to do something different. I thought combining travel with work might be the distraction I needed.'

'What about marriage and babies?' His tone was casual but when she looked at him his gaze was sharp and incisive as if the answer to that question mattered to him. 'When women think about the future it almost always contains a wedding ring.'

'That's a typically Argentine-male comment,' she teased, giving up on her food and putting her fork down. 'Be honest—you don't think a woman can do anything except stay at home and breed, do you?'

'It's what most women want. Don't you?'

'No. Not right now. In the future? Who knows?' She glanced towards the stillness of the lake. 'The future feels miles away when you're out here. I'm too young to even think about that. I have my whole career ahead of me. In another ten years or so, maybe.' She shrugged. 'It just isn't what I want. I love my job.' She watched the sunset, admiring the shimmering red glow that was reflected in the still water of the lake. 'What about you? No wife? No babies?'

Something flickered in his dark gaze. 'Absolutely not.'

'You mean, you don't want it now.'

His long strong fingers tightened ruthlessly round the wine glass. 'I don't want it ever. Remember that, Faith.' There was a steeliness in his voice that made her look at him more closely but his handsome face revealed nothing.

She frowned, sensing undertones that she didn't understand and feeling puzzled by them. 'Why would I need to remember it?'

'It's just something that I like to make clear,' he said softly, 'early in a relationship.'

Heat rushed through her body. 'Are we having a relation-ship?'

'I don't know,' he replied softly, his dark eyes fixed on hers. 'Are we?'

CHAPTER THREE

Ten months later

'SHE just stepped in front of the taxi without looking. According to a man who witnessed the accident, she's lucky to be alive.'

Lucky?

Lying in the hospital bed, listening to those words, Faith decided that it was better to keep her eyes closed. *She didn't feel lucky.*

'Any news on next of kin?' The doctor spoke again and Faith felt the dull pain inside her intensify to serious agony.

No next of kin.

She'd lost *everything* and it was hard to know whether her injuries were more severe on the outside or the inside.

'None. She had no identification on her when she was brought in—they assume someone must have stolen her bag. Her dress was expensive, though,' the nurse murmured enviously. 'Some flashy designer label I couldn't afford in a month of Sundays. Take it from me, she's either got a good job or a very rich and generous boyfriend.'

'Well, we can't discharge her until we know she has a home to go to. It's very inconvenient because she's blocking a bed.' The doctor sounded impatient. 'Someone should have missed her by now.'

Only if someone cared, Faith thought bleakly. In her case, no one did.

'Faith? Are you awake?'

Resigning herself to the fact that they wouldn't go away until she'd spoken, Faith reluctantly opened her eyes and the doctor gave a wintry smile.

'How are we today?' He spoke in the faintly patronising tone that he obviously reserved for patients.

'I'm fine.' *No point in telling the truth.* 'Much better.'

'I expect you're longing to go home.'

Home? Where was home? For the past year it had been Argentina and she'd thought...

Faith turned her head away, realising with a sickening lurch of horror that she was going to cry. The misery had been bubbling up inside her for days and suddenly it felt almost too enormous to hold back.

With a huge effort of will, she tried to focus her mind on something neutral. She wasn't going to think about Argentina, she wasn't going to think about the fact that she didn't have a job or a home any more, but most of all she wasn't going to think about...

She gave a tortured groan and curled into a foetal position, her thoughts so agonising that she just wanted to remove them from her head.

'Are you in pain?' The doctor leaned towards her, frowning. 'I can give you something for it.'

Not for this type of pain. Faith squeezed her eyes tightly shut. 'It's all a hideous mess.'

'Your head? It's nothing that time won't heal. Your hair will cover the scar.'

'Not my head,' Faith muttered. 'My life.'

'She's obviously worrying about her head—how's the wound, nurse? Everything healing?'

Realising that no one was remotely interested in how she

really felt, Faith kept her eyes closed, wishing they'd go away and leave her alone.

'Last time I saw it everything was healing beautifully,' the nurse said briskly. 'It will be a very neat scar.'

On the outside, maybe, Faith thought to herself. But on the inside it was a deep, ugly gash that would never heal.

Clearly oblivious to the true extent of his patient's trauma, the doctor gave a nod of approval. 'You've made a remarkable recovery considering the condition you were in two weeks ago. We need to start talking about discharging you.' He cleared his throat and glanced at the chart again. 'You need to go home to family or friends. You can't be on your own at the moment.'

Faith's lips were so dry she could hardly speak. 'I'll be fine on my own.'

Just saying the words intensified the sick throbbing in her head.

How had she ended up at this point?

The doctor gave an impatient sigh. 'You haven't given us details of your next of kin. There must be *someone*. Or do you think it's possible that you are suffering some degree of memory loss after all?'

Faith opened her eyes. 'My parents died nearly three years ago and I'm an only child,' she said wearily, wondering how many times she had to repeat herself. 'And my memory is fine.' *Unfortunately.* Given the nature of her memories, she would have paid a great deal for a serious bout of amnesia. Nothing too dramatic. As long as she lost all knowledge of the last couple of months, she'd be happy.

She wanted the whole nightmare erased from her head for ever.

But in her case it wasn't forgetting that was the problem, it was remembering.

She remembered *everything* and the memories tortured her.

All she wanted to do was cover herself with the duvet and just sob and sob and the fact that she felt like that was terrifying because it was so unlike her.

Where was her energy and drive? What had happened to her natural inclination to fight problems with grit and determination?

She'd always been resilient. Life could be tough, she knew that.

But although she'd always known that life could be tough, she'd had no idea it could be quite *this* tough.

Panicked by how truly awful she felt, she rolled onto her back and stared up at the cracked ceiling—but somehow the cracks looked like the curve of a beach and soon the images in her head were of a laughing, naked woman and a spectacularly handsome man.

She gave a groan of denial and covered her face with her hands. It didn't matter what she did or where she looked, the memories were everywhere. She felt drained and empty, lacking the physical or emotional energy to drag herself out of the dark pit of despair that was sucking her down and down.

In the bed opposite, an old lady rambled and muttered, confused and disorientated by her surroundings. 'Doctor, doctor!'

Muttering something under his breath to the nurse, the doctor turned. 'Yes, Mrs Hitchin?' His manner and tone were a study of exaggerated politeness. 'What can I do for you?'

'You can marry me, that's what you can do!' The old lady's tone was sharp. 'No more messing me around! Do what you promised to do and stop running away from your responsibilities.'

The nurse covered her mouth with her hand to conceal the laugh and the doctor's face turned a deep shade of beetroot.

'You're in *hospital*, Mrs Hitchin!' He raised his voice and separated each syllable, as if he were speaking to a very slow child. 'And I'm a doctor!'

'Well, I'm glad you finally made something of yourself.' The old lady waggled a finger at Faith. 'Don't believe a word he says to you. Men are all the same. They want all the fun and none of the responsibility.'

Faith gave a choked laugh. 'I could have done with that advice a few months ago, Mrs Hitchin.' Then perhaps she wouldn't have made such a complete and utter wreck of her life.

Another nurse hurried into the room, her cheeks flushed and her eyes glowing. Excitement radiated from her like a forcefield and she had the look of a woman just bursting with serious gossip.

Her eyes slid to Faith and her expression changed to one of awe and fascination. 'I know you think your memory is fine, Faith,' she said sympathetically. 'But I'm afraid we now have evidence that you are suffering from amnesia.'

Faith gritted her teeth. 'My memory is fine.'

'Really? Then why can't you remember that you're married? You're married to a billionaire,' the nurse said faintly. 'And he's standing outside right now waiting to claim you. I mean, he's gorgeous, sexy—'

'Nurse!' Dr Arnold interrupted her with a scowl and the nurse blushed.

'All I'm trying to say,' she muttered, 'is that he just isn't the sort of man any woman would ever forget. If she really doesn't remember him, then she *definitely* has amnesia.'

Simmering with impatience, Raul glanced at the Rolex on his wrist, oblivious to the fact that the force of his presence had brought the entire hospital ward to a standstill. Like a thoroughbred racehorse at the starting gate, he radiated coiled, suppressed energy, as confident and unselfconscious in this environment as he was in every other, his powerful legs planted firmly apart, his intelligent dark eyes fixed on the room straight ahead of him.

Female members of staff suddenly found reasons to hover around the central nurses' station, distracted by the unexpected presence of such a striking man.

Raul didn't notice.

He was entirely focused on the task in hand and this brief, unexpected delay in reaching his final objective was a thorn of irritation under his richly bronzed skin.

A lesser man might have spent the time worrying that the information he'd received might be wrong, *that it wasn't her*. Raul had no such concerns. He only employed the best. His security team had been hand-picked and the possibility that they might have made a mistake didn't enter his head.

Barely containing his impatience, he stood still for a full thirty seconds—which was twenty-five seconds longer than he'd ever waited for anything in his life before—and then took matters into his own hands and strode purposefully across the corridor and into the six-bedded side ward.

The doctor greeted his sudden entrance with a murmur of disapproval that Raul ignored. His gaze swept the room and came to rest on the slender figure of the woman lying in the bed by the window.

The anger that had been building inside him erupted with lethal force and he ran his hand over the back of his neck in order to stop himself from punching something. And then he took a closer look at the solitary figure staring up at the ceiling and the anger died, only to be replaced by a surge of very different emotions.

Emotions that he didn't want to feel. Primitive urges that mocked his belief in his own sense of discipline and self-control.

Raul almost laughed. The weakness of man was woman, and that hadn't changed since the beginning of time. From

Eve in the Garden of Eden and Pandora with her box, for every man there was one woman who seemed to be designed for the express purpose of complicating life.

And for him, that woman was lying in front of him.

He could negotiate the most complex business deal without once losing his clarity of thinking but here, in the same room as her, a witch's cauldron of emotions stirred to life, clouding everything.

'Faith.' His strong voice reverberated round the small room and her head turned, her expressive green eyes widening with horror and disbelief as she saw him.

'No!' Immediately she shrank under the blankets and her reaction was like a fist in his gut but the biggest shock was seeing the remains of the bruises on her face and shoulders before they vanished under the covers.

'What happened to you?' Two weeks before her mouth had been permanently curved into a happy smile and her blonde hair had rippled down her back. Now it was cropped short in a rough, jagged style that made her eyes look huge and her face pale and vulnerable. And there was no trace of the cheeky, teasing smile that was so much a part of her.

Kiss me, Raul, go on. You know you want to. Forget about work.

That one brief glance had been enough to show him that she'd lost weight. She'd always been fine-boned and delicate but now her skin seemed almost preternaturally pale and her jagged haircut gave her face an almost ethereal quality. When had that happened?

Why hadn't he noticed?

Something tugged at him and he ruthlessly pushed the feeling away.

She'd brought this on herself. And on him.

The doctor cleared his throat. 'We were forced to cut her hair when we were dealing with her injuries.'

'*Dios mío*, she's skin and bone.' Caught broadside by emotions that he hadn't expected, Raul directed the full force of his anger towards the doctor. 'Don't you *feed* your patients in this hospital?'

Clearly unaccustomed to such full-on confrontation, the doctor fiddled nervously with the charts he was clutching. 'Faith suffered a head injury,' he stuttered. 'She was unconscious for a while. Her rapid recovery is nothing short of remarkable. We saved her life.'

'Good,' Raul said coldly, his eyes focusing on the doctor's badge as he committed the name to memory. 'Because if you hadn't then your days of practising medicine would now be over. How was she injured?'

The nurse stepped forward swiftly, obviously hoping to smooth the situation. 'According to witnesses, she walked in front of a car just outside the airport terminal. It was as if she wasn't looking.'

Raul strode over to the bed, his mouth tightening as she turned her back on him and pulled the covers even higher.

That simple gesture said more than words ever could and suddenly he was gripped by the unfamiliar tentacles of guilt. He thrust them aside, reminding himself that he had no reason to feel guilty.

She'd done this to them.

He'd been up front and honest from the start. *She* was the one who'd chosen to play elaborate female games. And it was time she acknowledged that. 'Look at me!'

The lump in the bed didn't move and he gave an exasperated sigh. 'Running from a problem solves nothing. *Have you any idea how worried I've been?*'

The anger had burned inside him day and night for the past two weeks and he'd promised himself that when he finally caught up with her he would make sure that she was left in no doubt about his feelings.

For a moment he thought she wasn't going to respond and then the figure in the bed moved slowly and she sat up.

The words died in his throat.

There was something about her appalling fragility that prevented him from venting the full force of his wrath. She looked as vulnerable and shaky as one of his newborn foals and Raul felt something twist inside him.

He'd always thought of her as strong and vibrant, but there was no sign of the energy and enthusiasm that he'd come to expect from her.

The shapeless hospital nightdress hung from her narrow shoulders, her eyes were shaded by dark bruises and there were scratches on her shoulders and arms.

The usually irrepressible sparkle in her green eyes had been extinguished and she stared straight forward, refusing to meet his gaze.

She looked like a woman who was broken.

Apart from that one, anguished word—'No!'—she hadn't spoken or glanced in his direction since he'd entered the room. It was as if she was pretending that he wasn't there.

Reflecting on the damage she'd caused, Raul felt another monumental surge in his tension levels.

Was she sorry? *Did she regret what she'd done to their relationship?*

He stared in brooding silence at her frozen profile. If it had been any other woman he would have walked away and left her to deal with the situation she'd created. But Faith wasn't any other woman and something kept his feet nailed firmly to the ground.

Pandora, Eve, *Faith*…

Exasperated with his own display of weakness, Raul turned back to the doctor who was now eyeing him with trepidation. 'What are her injuries?'

'Well—er—' The doctor cleared his throat. 'Despite the

seriousness of the accident, she has made a remarkable
recovery. She experiences some headaches and a little dizziness from time to time, but the wound on her head is healing
well. There is, however, the issue of her memory.' Accustomed to relatives who were suitably submissive and respect-
ful, he was obviously struggling to cope with Raul's direct,
forceful approach. 'We have found it difficult to assess the
extent of her amnesia.'

'She doesn't have amnesia.' It had taken only one glance
for Raul to know that she remembered absolutely everything
that had happened between them.

The doctor looked taken aback. 'But—she doesn't appear
to remember you.'

Raul's mouth tightened into a grim line and he transferred
his gaze to the frozen profile of the woman on the bed. 'Oh,
she remembers,' he said softly. 'If her memory was impaired,
she wouldn't be ignoring me. She'd be firing sparks and
demanding to know why I took so long to get here. The
reason she is refusing to look me in the eye is because her
memory is perfectly intact and she's suffering from a severe
attack of guilty conscience, isn't that right, *cariño*?'

Her head turned at that, her gaze locked with his and
although she didn't say a single word her eyes sent him
straight to hell.

The past swirled and bubbled between them like a dangerous beast just waiting to swallow them whole.

Then she looked at the medical staff. 'I don't know who
he is,' she said, her voice remarkably steady. 'I've never seen
him before in my life and I don't like the look of him. It would
be quite wrong of you to release me into his care.'

Raul gave a bitter laugh. Ignoring the notices about not
sitting on the bed, he settled his powerful frame only inches
away from her body. 'They have no choice but to release you
into my care. I'm your only family.' He thought her eyes

grew brighter but when he looked more closely she was staring straight ahead, still studiously ignoring him.

The doctor cleared his throat. 'You have to admit that her memory seems cloudy where you're concerned—'

'I've discovered that Faith's memory is most adaptable,' Raul drawled. 'Occasionally she can forget the most important facts. Like an agreement between two people.' His words had the desired effect and he watched with grim satisfaction as the last of the colour drained from her cheeks.

'There was no agreement. I am *not* one of your business deals. I wish I'd never met you. I *hate* you, Raul. You are a heartless, cynical, insensitive…' Her voice tailed off and the doctor gave a small, embarrassed cough.

'Well—it does appear that she at least knows your name so that's good. And—er—a little bit about your personality. She told us that she had no family—'

'I don't have family.'

The doctor glanced at her and then at Raul. 'I suppose—' He coughed nervously. 'Well, over to you, really.'

'That's it? Are you just going to stand there and let him bully you?' Faith glared at the doctor and when the man didn't reply she made a sound of disgust. 'You're all spineless. I'm telling you, he's *not* my family. If I was the last woman left on the planet and he was the last man, then the human race would die.' Having drawn the battle lines, she turned her head back to Raul and her eyes locked with his in fierce combat.

Raul felt a surge of relief because for a moment he'd wondered if her lack of spirit was something to do with the head injury. But the dangerous shimmer in her eyes reassured him that her accident hadn't done any permanent damage and despite everything that had happened between them he felt the instantaneous response of his body.

Passion. Hot, searing, blinding passion.

It was always there between them, whatever they were doing.

And that was the problem of course. Their astonishing physical compatibility had made it all too easy to overlook the truth.

They were two people who should never have been together.

Both of them had known it, but the extraordinary chemistry had bound them together when common sense should have dragged them apart.

She was *entirely* wrong for him. *He* was *entirely* wrong for her.

Somehow that hadn't made a difference.

Aware that the medical staff were rooted to the spot, staring, he rose to his feet and took charge.

'She has family,' he said in a driven tone. '*I'm* her husband. And I'll take over from here.' Detaching himself from the emotional, he concentrated instead on the practical, his mind shifting into problem-solving mode as he reached into his pocket for his mobile phone.

'Oh, here we go,' Faith muttered. 'Let's just make another million while we're hanging around.'

Having accessed a number with a decisive stab of his finger, Raul turned with a mocking smile. 'I wouldn't bother switching the phone on for a million, *cariño*. You should know that by now.'

The doctor cast them both a despairing glance. 'The two of you clearly have some problems.'

Rising to his feet, Raul dealt the other man a glance that would have silenced a football stadium in full voice. 'Unless you're adding psychiatry to your list of questionable medical skills, I suggest you don't tread where you are bound to lose your footing. She is no longer your responsibility. I'll be removing her from this place in the next ten minutes.' Having delivered that missile directly to its target, Raul turned his attention to the man on the end of the phone and switched to his native Spanish.

By the time he'd ended the call, the nurse had retreated and the doctor was sifting through paperwork with shaking hands, clearly worrying about his own position.

'If you're taking her then you'll have to sign something. I won't be held responsible if anything happens to her. She *needs* to be in hospital—'

'Maybe. But not this one.' With one disdainful sweep of his eyes, Raul took in the state of the ward. 'What exactly *is* this place and why hasn't it been shut down before now?'

'Shut down?' The doctor looked scandalised. 'This is the oldest hospital in London. We have been treating patients in this building since the time of King Henry the Eighth!'

'It's a shame no one has bothered to clean the floors since his last visit,' Raul said coldly and the old lady in the bed opposite Faith clapped her hands in delight.

'Oh, well said! I do so love a man who is dominant *and* handsome. These days most men have forgotten how to be *real* men. If she turns you down, I'm available.'

Amused, Raul turned and flashed her a smile. '*Gracias*, I will remember that.' His response clearly goaded Faith because she gave a strangled laugh.

'He's the worst of a bad bunch. If you're looking for a man who shoulders responsibility, then don't look at this one, Mrs Hitchin.'

'I could look at him all day,' Mrs Hitchin said happily, adjusting her hearing aid. 'I think he's *gorgeous*.'

'Actually he's a sex-mad control freak,' Faith muttered and Raul gave a twisted smile.

'One wonders why, with that glowing opinion of my qualities, you were so grimly determined to drag me to the altar by any means at your disposal.'

Faith lifted her chin and her beautiful eyes flashed at him.

'I did *not* drag you. Since when have you ever done *anything* that didn't suit you? Your life is one long selfish, self-indulgent ego trip.'

'You put me in an *impossible* position!' His tone thick-ened, Raul felt his tension levels soar into the stratosphere. He hadn't intended to tackle the issue here but even without spelling it out it was there in the room with them, hovering between them.

He saw that she was shaking and his eyes scanned the pale flesh of her smooth, slender arms, his treacherous mind turning to thoughts of sex. Those arms had been entwined round his neck, curved round his body as she'd urged him on. Those eyes that now flashed in anger had softened and tempted as she'd lured him on an erotic journey from which neither of them had emerged unscathed.

What they had shared was so powerful that even now he could taste it in the air. Even now, with all that lay between them, he knew that he could turn her from spitting hell-cat to purring kitten with one skilful touch of his mouth.

Only with supreme effort of will did Raul prevent himself from reaching out and flattening her against the bed.

And she knew.

She'd always known the effect she had on him. And she'd loved to tease and prolong the agony for both of them, using those jewel-bright green eyes of hers to raise the temperature from hot to raging inferno. With sideways glances, slow smiles and the sensuous swing of her hips she'd stoked the fire of his libido, pushing and pushing until his control had finally cracked. And when it had, she'd taken him into her soft, pulsing body, her desperation matching his.

In some ways their entire relationship had been a power struggle.

And for a while she'd won.

Only she was showing no signs of celebrating her victory.

'Just get out, Raul,' she said, and her voice held a quiver of vulnerability that he hadn't expected. 'It's over. You wanted an escape, well, I'm giving you one. Get out.'

'It would have been a great deal better for both of us had you realised that a few months ago. As it is, your timing is unfortunate. I'm your husband, *cariño*, although you could be forgiven for forgetting that fact, given that we were married for all of two hours before you ran away.'

'I didn't run away. I'm not a child or a convict. I left because I discovered what a *monumental* mistake I'd made about you. I wouldn't have married you at all if I'd known what you were like.'

Remembering the circumstances of their wedding, Raul gave a bitter laugh. 'I think we both know that isn't the case. Anyway, you made your bed and fortunately for you it's a great deal more comfortable than the one you're lying in at the moment.'

'I'm not going with you, Raul, and you can't make me. I'm not one of your staff.'

'If one of my staff had behaved the way you did,' he snapped, 'they would no longer be working for me. Unfortunately we are now legally bound, so firing you isn't an option. Believe me, I've considered it.' His phone rang and he took the call, simmering with dark, deadly emotion, his eyes on hers as he listened and then broke the connection.

'My plane has been refuelled, a medical team is now on board and we take off in an hour from now.'

She shrank away from him. 'I'm not well enough to go with you. I haven't fully recovered.'

'Then you can complete your recovery in the sunshine by my pool,' he returned in a cool tone and she flopped back against the pillows, looking drained and exhausted. Raul wondered grimly whether her pallor was a reflection of the effort the confrontation had required, or the fact that she was contemplating the reality of being back in a marriage that she never should have entered in the first place.

You wanted a war, my beauty, he thought bitterly, and you fired the first shot. *Now live with the consequences.*

CHAPTER FOUR

TWENTY-FOUR hours later, Faith was lying on a sun-lounger under the shade of a huge umbrella. In front of her lay the perfectly still waters of the most stunning pool she'd ever seen and all around her a profusion of exotic plants and trees gave her the impression of being deep in a lush rainforest.

Once they'd landed in Buenos Aires she'd expected him to take her straight back to the *estancia*, but instead he'd taken one look at her pale face and given instructions for them to be taken straight to the Vásquez building, his corporate headquarters in the smartest district of the vibrant South American city.

She'd swiftly discovered that his corporate headquarters was crowned by a breathtaking penthouse apartment, complete with a lush, exotic roof garden.

He'd taken her straight up to this outdoor paradise but she found herself wondering about the apartment. When did he use it? And what for?

Already aware of just how little she knew him, this further question gnawed away inside her but she forced herself not to think about it. She had other, more pressing issues demanding her attention: like the reason he'd brought her back to Argentina.

When she'd stumbled away from him on their wedding

day, she hadn't thought for a moment that he'd follow her. Why would he, when he'd made it perfectly clear that he didn't love her?

Remembering the things that he'd said to her, she gave a shiver.

She'd been so utterly shocked by what had happened that her only thought had been to get as far away from him as possible.

For the sake of her own mental health, she'd known that she could have nothing more to do with him. She'd felt dead inside, as if the most important part of her had been gouged out. She'd loved him *so* much and the ten months they'd spent together had been the happiest of her life.

It was almost impossible to believe that it had all gone so dramatically wrong.

That she'd been so wrong about him.

Faith reached for the glass of chilled lemonade that had been left within her reach and took a sip, completely unable to relax because she knew that Raul would reappear at some point.

What was he doing? Was he working? How could he work when their marriage was in its death throes?

She glanced up and saw him strolling across the sun-baked terrace towards her. He'd showered and changed after the flight and was now wearing a pale shirt with lightweight trousers. An air of leashed power emanated from his tall, athletic frame and Faith's mouth dried.

For a moment she had no idea what to say to him. She wanted to shout at him, she wanted to hit him until she made dents in that spectacular body of his, but most of all she just wanted to lie down and sob because it just never should have been like this between them.

In the end she just stayed on the sun-lounger and didn't move, too drained to do any of the things in her mind.

The fact that he looked perfectly groomed despite the pressure of the situation came as no surprise to her. Raul had been born and bred in Buenos Aires and if there was one thing that her travels in South America had taught her, it was that the body-conscious Brazilians were nothing compared to the pride of the average Argentine male.

In fact, Raul was less obsessed than most but she'd long ago come to the conclusion that that was because he was so much more beautiful than most. He didn't have to try. Even if he never glanced in a mirror again, he would still be unable to walk down a street without attracting an almost stifling degree of dazed female attention.

'Next time you decide to run away, stop when you reach the end of the drive,' he advised in an acid tone. 'I have just spent the entire morning unravelling problems that occurred while I was chasing you across the globe.'

'I didn't ask you to come after me.'

'You left me no choice. If you wanted an open marriage, you shouldn't have picked a South American male.' He turned his head and miraculously a team of staff appeared.

Faith watched in silence as they laid a table and served lunch. 'I'm not hungry.'

'You need to eat.'

She glanced at him then and immediately wished she hadn't because it was immediately apparent that the way he'd treated her hadn't done anything to reduce the physical impact of the man.

He was well over six feet tall, lean and hard muscled and he moved with a predatory grace that was unequivocally male. Strong and athletic, he pushed himself to the limits in every aspect of his life—work, play, exercise, *sex*—for Raul it was all about being the best and he accepted nothing less.

'Don't let me hold you up,' she said politely. 'I'm sure you're dying to eat and return to your work.'

'Having solved the immediate crisis I have no intention of working this afternoon.' His expression grim, he sat down on one of the chairs and served himself. 'There are more important issues at stake.'

'More important than your work?' Despite everything that lay between them, she found herself laughing but she stopped herself quickly because she couldn't be sure that it wasn't going to end in a sob. 'And I thought I was the one who had the bang on the head.'

She felt strangely disconnected, making polite conversation with a man who didn't know the meaning of the term, when beneath the surface of conventional chat there lay a deep chasm of trouble and turbulence.

They'd never resorted to 'polite' before.

Their entire relationship had been a full-on explosion of exquisite passion, so uncontrolled and ferocious in its intensity that it had burned everything in its path.

She'd been crazy about him. And crazy to get involved with him when she had known his reputation for hurting women.

What had made her think she would be different?

What had made her think she could handle him when plenty of women before her had tried and failed?

She'd thought she understood him but she'd discovered too late that she'd barely scratched the surface. Raul Vásquez was a complex, volatile man, his character so full of dark, hidden corners that she suspected no woman would ever know him.

And now she was seeing a different side to him—the side that had made him a billionaire.

He was sharply intelligent but instead of his usual dry observations and smart comments, he was focused and on his guard. *Intimidating.* She'd been brought up to question and challenge and never to be afraid of anyone, but there was something about the harsh lines of his impossibly handsome features that made her want to just shrink into silence.

Over the past couple of weeks she'd gone from lover to adversary and no one in their right mind would choose Raul as an opponent.

His sexy mouth was set in a grim line and the unshakeable confidence that had made her weak at the knees made him seem more formidable than ever.

No wonder everyone just rolled over and played ball when he walked into a room, Faith thought hopelessly as she watched him take a sip of wine. In his current mood he wasn't a man that anybody would bother challenging.

Faith felt her stomach drop and told herself it was just part of the head injury. Hadn't they warned her she'd feel nauseous from time to time? It was nothing to do with Raul's presence. She couldn't possibly still feel anything for him. Not after what he'd said to her. What he'd *believed* of her.

Their relationship was dead in the water.

And she really didn't know what he was doing here.

He rolled his shoulders to ease the tension and despite all her determined resolutions, Faith's eyes were drawn to the swell of muscle visible beneath the fabric of his shirt. He had an incredible body. Hard, strong, powerful and capable of encouraging an unbelievable response from hers.

Raul caught the look and his eyes darkened. '*Don't,*' he warned and his eyes seemed to deepen in colour to a dangerous, stormy shade of black. '*Don't* look at me like that and *don't* bring sex into this or so help me I'll—' He broke off, his emotions so close to the surface that he clearly didn't trust himself to finish the sentence.

'Do you seriously think I'm lying here thinking about sex?' Her defence was attack, but the truth was that she *had* been thinking about sex and she knew that while she was still able to breathe, this man would always have that effect on her. *And she on him.* There was something between them that transcended all the rules.

One look was all it took.

One look was all it had ever taken.

And that was why they were here, of course, in this horrible mess.

If the physical attraction hadn't been so overwhelming, perhaps they would have discovered their fundamental differences a great deal sooner.

Abandoning the food on his plate, he made an impatient sound and dropped the fork with a clatter. 'I don't know what you're thinking and I've given up guessing,' he growled. '*Why* did you run?'

She gasped and suddenly her palms literally ached with the desire to swipe the arrogant look from his indecently handsome face. 'If that is a serious question then you're even more insensitive than I think you are.'

'I am not insensitive.' He pushed the chair back and it scraped on the terrace, the dark flash in his eyes hinting at the degree of volatility that lurked beneath the veneer of control and sophistication. 'But I fail to see why anyone would go to the lengths you went to and then just walk away.'

'The lengths I went to?' Her voice shook. 'You make me sound like some sort of manipulative gold-digger.'

He looked at her and the derisive glint in his eyes spoke volumes. 'Yes?'

She swallowed, determined not to cry in front of him. How could he think that of her? 'I walked away because the things you said to me were *awful*! Heartless, callous and cruel. Did you really think I'd stick around for second helpings? I was hurt and sad—I needed support—and all I got was a double helping of blind, cynical insensitivity.'

His gaze locked on hers with the deadly accuracy of a heat-seeking missile. 'You created the situation. You should have stayed to see it through.'

'What was the point of that?' she forced herself to answer.

'You made your position more than clear. Hearing it once was bad enough.' *Enough to kill her dreams and her childish, naïve belief that they'd had something special.*

'If you are going to run at the first sign of trouble, our marriage is going to be extremely interesting.' He was infuriatingly sure of himself, forceful and arrogant, if he thought he could make her bow to his will by simply applying sufficient psychological pressure. 'If you'd talked to me, we could have sorted it out.'

'You weren't "talking" Raul. You were accusing! Judge and jury rolled into one—only you weren't prepared to listen to my defence.' She broke off in horror, unable to believe what she'd just said. 'You see what being with you has done for me? You've turned me from a rational, questioning human being into a meek, subservient blob with no brain! I don't need a defence because I've done *nothing wrong*!'

'You are the least subservient woman I have ever met,' he said through gritted teeth. 'And I have never questioned your intelligence.'

'Then why are you behaving like this, Raul? Why are you so willing to believe the worst of me? You're talking as if I committed a crime, but you were there too!'

'You assured me that you were protected.'

'I thought I was!'

There. It was out. The subject that both of them had been avoiding since he'd first strode into her hospital ward.

She was trembling now despite the blazing sunshine, tiny shivers that took over her whole body, but whether it was as a reaction to her accident or his words, she didn't know. 'I didn't mean to get pregnant.' And she wasn't prepared to have this conversation. *Hadn't thought that he'd follow her.* 'Go away,' she croaked. 'Go back to your work because that's all you really care about. We no longer have anything else to say to each other.'

Her response sent shards of hostility cracking through the air and Raul rose to his feet and walked away from her, as if he were considering precisely that option. But he didn't leave the terrace. Instead he stood still, all coiled, suppressed tension like a jungle cat ready to leap on the first unwary animal that crossed its path.

She knew him well enough to know that he was at the outer limits of his patience and that surprised her because it was his razor-sharp thinking and icy control in all situations that had driven him to billionaire status. Where his competitors just cracked and folded under pressure, Raul showed nerves of steel.

But she still didn't understand why he had brought her here.

Searching for clues, she studied his taut, handsome profile through a hot haze of tears, noticing with almost detached curiosity that the hard lines of his jaw were darkened by stubble. Since when had Raul ever forgotten to shave?

Somehow that observation made her feel better.

If she was suffering then she wanted to know that he was suffering, too.

He turned back to her, control firmly back in his grasp, his tone icily formal. 'How are you feeling, physically? Have the medical staff I employed treated you well?' Deliberately he'd stepped aside from the unstable, shifting surface of their emotions.

'They've been fine.' She was equally polite. 'Offhand I can't think of a single person you need to fire or sue.'

A ghost of a smile touched his firm mouth as he acknowledged her accurate assessment of his personality. 'I think that comment confirms that your brain is still in perfect working order.'

'My brain is fine. *I'm* fine. You can let them all go now. They must be costing you a fortune.'

'"They" are one of the perks of being my wife, *cariño*.'

'I was never interested in your money and you know it.' The first time they'd met she hadn't even known about his money. It was only after she'd been scorched alive by the chemistry between them that she'd discovered his real identity. And by then it hadn't mattered. Nothing had mattered, not even the fact that he was difficult and complex. She'd thought she had what it took to handle him.

She'd been wrong.

She lifted her chin. 'When I met you, I had a career. Don't insult our relationship by implying that your money was ever part of what we shared.'

'So why are you worrying about cost? We have enough problems piled up between us. Let's not add more.' His tone harsh, he swept aside her protest with a single, decisive stroke and she sank against the sun-lounger, all the energy draining out of her.

'I'm worrying because we're not together any more and I don't want to owe you anything.'

'Now I'm starting to wonder whether your brain might be damaged after all.' He stood looking at her, his legs planted firmly apart in a stance that shrieked control. 'Did you walk under that car on purpose?'

She gasped with shock. *'No!* How can you ask me that?'

'Because I don't shirk from the difficult or the awkward,' he ground out. 'Unlike you. You were upset.' His hard stare allowed her no escape and Faith felt a sudden stab of agony.

Upset?

It was such an insignificant word to describe the utter devastation inside her. 'Of course I was upset. And that's why I didn't look where I was going.' She'd been blind with misery, her brain disconnected from everything except the enormity of her loss.

'You told the hospital that you had no next of kin. I can't

believe that you were capable of such unbelievably selfish behaviour. *Why didn't you call me?*' His tone was thickened by raw, red, molten anger and this time when she looked at him her eyes were dry.

'Why would I have called you?'

His features were set and grim. 'It should have been obvious to you to let me know that you were safe.'

'I had no reason to believe you'd even care.'

'Now you're being childish.'

'I'm being honest! Our last meeting was hardly a loving encounter—you hurt me, Raul. *You hurt me so much.*'

'I was honest about my feelings.' His savage rejoinder showed no hint of self-reproach or apology and her shivering intensified, as if someone had dropped her in the Arctic wearing nothing more than her underwear.

'You don't have feelings and I can't do this, Raul. I don't know you any more. You're not the man I was with.' Her head was spinning alarmingly and her stomach rolled and lurched. 'Go away. Just go away. It's over, Raul.'

He swore softly and fluently and turned away from her, as if he didn't trust himself to look at her and not explode. 'Perhaps you didn't *want* to know me. This is who I am, Faith. The real me. You saw only what you wanted to see. What suited you.'

'That isn't true. I know you can be ruthless in business, but you're *not* cruel, I know you're not.' The threat of tears was back with a vengeance and she blinked rapidly to clear her vision. 'Up until our wedding day you were—'

'What?' He turned, his dark eyes glinting hard. 'I was *what*? A complete fool? A trusting idiot?'

'I don't think it's foolish to trust the person you—' She just stopped herself saying the word 'love' because she knew now that he'd never loved her. 'Marry,' she said flatly. 'It's not foolish to trust the person you marry.'

'Oh really?' His tone was heavy with sarcasm. 'Perhaps that depends on the reason for the marriage. In our case it was based on deceit. Hardly a firm foundation for trust.'

'I did *not* deceive you! And I don't even understand why you would think that. Is this because of your money? Is this some sort of billionaire thing? What, Raul? You have so much money and you're such a fabulous catch that women are going to go to any lengths to trap you? Is that what this is about?'

Raul ran a hand over his face. 'We will leave this subject aside for now.' His voice shook with emotion. 'You're not up to discussing it and frankly I'm not sure I am either.' It was a measure of his focus and determination that he was capable of moving on from a subject that was burning both of them up inside. 'You could have been killed.'

'And that would have solved your problem, Raul.'

'*Dios mío*, that comment is *totally* unjustified.' His tone was savage and loaded with contempt. 'Never at any point in this whole miserable mess have I wished you dead.'

Her head throbbed and her mouth was dry as a desert. Seeking any excuse to look away from him, Faith reached for the lemonade again but her hand was shaking so much that half of it slopped over her dress.

Raul stood still, exasperation flickering across his handsome face as he watched her efforts. Then he gave a soft curse and took the glass from her hand, his mouth compressed into a thin line as he held the glass to her lips. 'Drink.' His sharp command made her flinch but although there was no sympathy in his tone, he held the glass carefully, allowing her to take small sips before placing the glass back on the table.

But his attentiveness, albeit reluctantly given, simply made things worse.

He was so close to her and she breathed in his clean, male scent and felt her insides stir. It was as if her body recognised him and despite the heat, her shivering intensified.

Why couldn't he be less of a man?

Maybe then her brain and body would have worked in harmony instead of battling like opposing forces.

'Stop shivering.' Raul delivered the order in a driven tone but when his demand had no effect he reached for his phone. 'I will get the doctor back up here.'

'No.' Her teeth chattering, Faith shrank away from him, exhausted and wishing that he was easier to understand. He'd made it obvious that he bitterly regretted their wedding and yet he'd sought her out and brought her back to Argentina. 'Why did you bring me back here, Raul? Why?'

'You're my wife. You belong by my side and in my bed.'

That simple statement encompassed everything it meant to be married to an Argentine male and she closed her eyes briefly. So it was all about possession. There was no love there at all.

'I didn't want this to happen to us—'

'Yes, you did.' His words and his tone were brutal, leaving her no escape. 'You made this decision. You rolled the dice and you gambled. At least have the courage to face what you did to our relationship.'

The sick throbbing in her head intensified. 'I don't want to talk about it.'

He gave a bitter laugh. 'And that from a woman? Talking is what women are supposed to do best, isn't it, Faith? You think that every problem can be solved if it's talked through.'

Not every problem.

'I have nothing more to say to you, Raul. You're angry and bitter and I just don't know you any more.'

Something flickered across his dark, handsome face— dangerous shadows, a suggestion of something ugly lurking deep, deep inside.

'I can't be married to a man who doesn't love me,' Faith whispered. 'I want a divorce. Give me whatever you need me to sign and I'll sign it.'

Her flat statement drew no response from him and in the end she looked back at him, only to find that he'd walked towards the pool and was standing with his back to her.

Faith stared at him helplessly. Even from the back he was spectacular. His shoulders were wide and powerful, his legs strong and well-muscled. He carried himself with confidence, the astonishing success he'd made of his life evident in every aspect of his demeanour and behaviour.

Once, she'd believed he was hers.

She'd truly believed that they shared something special and the knowledge that for him their relationship had been empty hurt more than any of the wounds she'd incurred in the accident.

He turned suddenly, feeling her gaze on him with that instinctive awareness that had always bound them together. 'You went to all those elaborate lengths to get me to the altar and now you want a divorce?' His mouth twisted into a mocking smile. 'You're giving up extraordinarily easily. Take some advice—if something is worth fighting for, it's worth fighting to the death.'

It was a remark so typical of him that in the old days—*the days before marriage*—she would have smiled and teased him unmercifully. She would have told him to chill out and not be so driven. 'I never saw our relationship as a war, Raul.'

'You started the war. You manipulated me into marrying you,' he said coldly. 'So it seems absurd for you to abandon your goal so easily.' His supreme self-confidence and the chill in his tone simply added to her pain.

'I didn't have a goal, Raul!' Feeling at an even greater disadvantage lying down, Faith sat up. 'I'm not one of your companies!! I don't have a mission statement or a five-year plan! I did not manipulate you!'

'No? So who's fault is it that we are in this position? Marriage was *not* part of *my* plan. I was clear about that from the beginning.' He stepped forward, his voice throbbing with emotion. 'No marriage. No babies. You entered into our relationship with your eyes wide open.'

His words were so uncompromisingly harsh that for a moment she had trouble breathing.

They were *so* different. How could she ever have thought that their feelings for one another would be enough to bridge the gulf between them?

'It wasn't like that. We were just having fun, Raul. I wasn't even thinking about marriage.' Faith sank back against the sun-lounger. 'I thought we shared something special.'

'We did. But it wasn't enough for you, was it? Like a typical woman, you wanted more and more.' His tone was an angry growl, his words so heavily loaded with accusation that she shrank. 'You thought that you knew what I wanted better than I did. Well, you were wrong *cariño*. I knew *exactly* what I wanted and it wasn't this.'

Every word he spoke was designed to destroy any last tender shoots of hope that might have survived the initial blast of his anger.

'You're still talking as if I had some sort of master plan. I didn't create this situation, Raul. I didn't lie to you.'

'You truly expect me to believe that it was an accident? Contraception is not a hit-and-miss affair.' He spelled it out with brutal lucidity and Faith felt her heart suddenly bump erratically.

He stood there like a mythical god—lean, arrogant and impossibly handsome, seeing everything from one point of view only.

His own.

'One day you'll learn that you can't control everything in life, Raul. Accidents *do* happen,' she said hoarsely. 'I am living proof of that, but it doesn't matter any more, does it?'

He drew breath, ready to challenge that remark as he automatically challenged everything and she lifted a hand in a defensive gesture.

'No!' She cut him off before he spoke. 'Just don't say what's on your mind, Raul, because frankly I don't think I can sit through another session of your thoughts on the subject.'

'You don't know what I was going to say.'

'Oh yes I do. It would have been something along the lines of "if you hadn't got pregnant we wouldn't be married now" or "it's lucky for both of us that you lost the baby."' She'd been trying so hard not to think about the baby, but now there was no escaping it and her eyes filled with the tears that she'd been choking on for the past couple of weeks. 'Well, do you know what? I don't feel lucky. I know it wasn't what you wanted and to be honest, I was surprised myself—but I don't feel lucky, Raul. I *minded* that I lost the baby.'

He was so tense that every muscle in his powerful frame throbbed with it. 'I know.'

'*You do not know!* How could you know? I protected you from it. You were in New York on business. I was *devastated* but I kept it to myself because you were tied up with that meeting, takeover—'

'It was a merger.'

'*I don't care what it was!* I just knew it was important to you and I didn't want to cause you extra stress. But I shot myself in the foot, because you decided that the reason I didn't tell you about my miscarriage was because I was afraid you might call off the wedding.'

'It was a natural assumption.'

'Only for a man like you, Raul. Any other person would have thanked me for being so thoughtful and selfless.' She turned her head, her voice a whisper. 'Go away. Just go away. Why are we even talking about this, anyway?'

'Because we are married,' he bit out harshly. 'And we have to sort this out.'

'Some things just aren't fixable. And this is one of them. Do you realise that you haven't once thought about *my* feelings? All you've thought about is yourself. You think I trapped you. Well, do you know what?' Her voice rose. 'I wish you *had* ditched me at the altar. You would have been doing us both a favour.'

'I would not have done that. Despite what you think, I do have a sense of decency.'

'*Decency?* Where was your sense of decency when you said it was a good thing I'd lost the baby?'

He stiffened, his handsome face pale despite his tan. 'You are taking my words out of context.'

'I wish I was, but I'm not. And frankly, I would have preferred you to have broken it off, than to find myself married to a cold, insensitive bastard.'

He inhaled sharply. 'I've never heard you use language like that before.'

'Well, if you stick around, you'll be hearing more of it.'

Raul ran a hand over his face. 'You are *extremely* upset—'

'Yes. Funny that, really. I lose a baby, discover that my husband is a cold-hearted, ruthless pig, get run over—' Her heart was pounding so rapidly that she felt dizzy. 'I can't imagine why I'd be upset.'

'You need to calm down. The doctors said you shouldn't be subjected to any more stress.' Raul lifted a hand in what presumably was a gesture of conciliation. 'Why are we going over this again? *No me importa.* I don't care. It's history now. We have to move on.'

'Where to, Raul?' Faith choked, holding it together by a thread. 'You're relieved, but that isn't how I feel. I feel terrible. You have no idea. Our relationship is dead and so is—' She broke off with a whimper of pain, unable to finish the sentence. 'I wish there *had* been a baby.'

'I know you do.' Raul's tone was grim and his face was white with the strain. 'Which is why you should have left me six months ago for some homely, domesticated male whose sole desire was to reproduce and spread his seed. You should have ended it instead of forcing me into something I didn't want.'

'*It was an accident.*' She covered her face with her hands to hide the tears but clearly she was less than successful because she heard Raul swear and then felt his thigh brush against hers as he sat down next to her.

'*Stop* crying. I've never seen you cry before. You're the strongest woman I've ever met.' His strong fingers closed around her wrists and he pulled her hands away from her face, as if he could ease her distress simply by the force of his will. 'And you wonder why I am so against marriage as an institution! Until we exchanged vows, we were happy together.'

She sniffed. 'It isn't marriage. It's *you*—the way you are—'

'And you always knew the way I was. We both knew it, Faith.' Raul's tone was rough. 'There was never any future for us. Eventually you would have wanted marriage and babies. It was inevitable.'

'I hadn't even thought about it.' Furious with herself for crying, Faith wiped her eyes with the palm of her hand. 'I had a career when I met you. The last thing I was thinking of was playing happy families.'

'When you discovered how badly you wanted a baby, you should have left.'

'How are you so successful at negotiation when you don't even listen to the other person?' Faith bit back a hysterical laugh. 'That wasn't how it happened! I did not plan it. I had a whole career ahead of me. Plans! When I discovered that I was pregnant, I was in shock. But then I realised how much I wanted our baby.' And *him*. She'd realised how much she wanted him.

'And the fact that I didn't wasn't of importance to you?'

'You asked me to marry you!'

'Because you left me no choice.'

His blunt admission sliced through her control and brought the tears to the surface. 'Well, that's romantic. And having admitted that you married me because I "forced" you, you now want to continue this relationship? Are you mad, or what?' The tears trickled down her face and Raul's sensual mouth tightened.

'Don't cry.'

'Why?' The tears fell harder. 'Because it makes you feel bad? Well, good. At the moment, I *want* you to feel bad.' The utter desolation echoed in her voice and she saw his emotional turmoil.

After a moment's hesitation he reached out a hand towards her but she shrank away from him and he let it fall to his side. 'How did our relationship reach this point?'

'I don't know. I was so in love with you.' Her voice was thick with tears. 'I didn't think anything could ever damage what we had. I thought we were invincible.'

'And presumably that's why you did it.' His voice grew several degrees colder and she knew that she would never convince him that she hadn't become pregnant on purpose.

'So just divorce me,' she whispered, wiping her eyes with the back of her hand. 'Divorce me for unreasonable behaviour.'

'There won't be a divorce.' His tone was hard and icy cold. 'You chose this path, *cariño*. Now walk it. I have some calls to make. Make sure you rest before dinner.'

CHAPTER FIVE

WHAT was she supposed to wear for dinner?

She'd fled from Argentina with nothing more than her passport. She certainly hadn't stopped to pack a wardrobe.

Glancing at her watch, she realised that there were still several hours until dinner, so she picked up her bag and stepped into the elevator.

They were in the centre of Buenos Aires. How hard could it be to find something simple and practical to wear?

She pressed the button for the ground floor, thinking of Raul. He'd changed *so* much and she didn't have to look far to discover the cause of their problems.

By becoming pregnant she'd committed the ultimate sin.

The lift doors opened and she gave a gasp of shock because Raul was standing there, anger shimmering in his dark eyes.

'Do you have a death wish? You are supposed to be resting.'

For a long, agonising moment the tension throbbed between them momentarily blinding both of them. She was painfully aware of his sexuality and her stomach swooped and spun like a ride at a funfair.

Suddenly, looking at his rigid shoulders, she realised that they'd never stood a chance.

They were worlds apart; not just in terms of wealth, but in life experience and culture.

They'd talked all the time, but never about his past, and she was only now realising how little she knew about him.

The phone in his pocket rang and he removed it, scanned the number and then took the call. '*Sí*—I am aware of that.' He switched between Spanish and English with effortless ease and Faith listened with reluctant admiration, trying not to be impressed but failing because his razor-sharp intellect had always given her a buzz. She'd loved arguing with him because his brain was so fast and challenging him had always resulted in lively debate.

As if sensing her scrutiny, his eyes locked onto hers and a muscle flickered in his jaw. 'No—cancel... I don't care, I'm busy right now. They can wait until I'm ready.'

Faith watched as he broke the connection with a decisive stab of one long finger and dropped the phone back into his pocket. She cleared her throat. 'If you were cancelling a meeting because of me then you shouldn't have bothered.'

'How else am I supposed to stop you from doing something foolish? If I don't watch you personally you will no doubt vanish again, and I have no desire to scrape you off the floor after yet another accident.' He'd obviously come from a meeting because he was dressed in a dark formal suit but the white cuff of his shirt had ridden up slightly and she found her eyes drawn to the hairs that darkened the bronzed skin at his wrist. That tantalising hint of masculinity was sufficient to trigger an uncomfortably vivid image of him naked and Faith turned her head away quickly, wondering how a physical connection could possibly endure when everything else was so catastrophically wrong between them. It was true that Raul exceeded the most exacting woman's standards of masculinity, but after everything that had happened, *she shouldn't be feeling this way.*

The brain was supposed to be connected to the senses, so why were hers humming and buzzing instead of freezing him off?

Glancing over his shoulder, Faith saw two burly men standing in the opulent lobby. 'Who are they?'

'Security.' Raul stepped into the elevator with her and slammed his hand against a button. He controlled his privacy with the same ruthless efficiency that he used on every other aspect of his life.

'I need to go shopping—'

'You were never interested in shopping.'

'I don't have anything to wear. All my clothes are at the *estancia*.'

He stared down at her for a moment. 'I apologise,' he said stiffly. 'I hadn't realised. You should have said something sooner.'

The doors slid closed and Faith suddenly found herself trapped with him in a small, intimate space.

Erotic images swirled around her brain and she stared straight ahead, trying to concentrate on something else. The utter stillness of his powerful body told her that he was doing the same thing and she knew instinctively that his brain was playing the same tricks.

So how could *not* looking intensify the connection between them?

In this closed-in space Faith was agonisingly aware of the latent power of his lean, strong body and she realised with a stab of pain that this was the first time she'd stood this close to him and not touched. In their relationship she'd been the affectionate one and he'd always teased her about it.

'*You can't go five seconds without checking I'm still here.*'

And it had been true. She'd adored him and it wouldn't have occurred to her to not show it.

But now she envied his emotional detachment and wished she'd kept part of herself back.

If she'd done that, would it hurt less?

Probably not. Despite everything that had happened

between them, part of her wanted to take that final step towards him and feel his arms close around her in that decisive, possessive way that had always thrilled her.

And it *horrified* her that she still felt that way.

She couldn't be with a man who didn't trust her, could she? For her, trust was as fundamental as breathing. And she couldn't be with a man who had such little regard for her feelings. *A man who knew her so little.*

Did she have no self-respect?

Or was it just that she'd totally underestimated the power of love?

Desperate to interrupt the uncomfortable flow of her thoughts, Faith struggled to make conversation. 'I didn't know you had an apartment in Buenos Aires.'

He loosened his top button and jerked at his tie, the intimate confinement clearly affecting him in a similar manner. 'Sometimes I work late.'

The lift rose smoothly upwards and she stared at the view. 'It's stunning.'

'Actually it's on the market,' Raul said stiffly. 'I've discovered that a glass lift isn't a good choice if you want privacy.'

And Raul was fiercely protective of his privacy, she knew that. This particular billionaire wasn't about to become public property, and he invested time and effort into keeping his profile as low-key as possible. His extreme wealth had protected their relationship from the intrusion of the outside world.

She'd been spoiled, cosseted, protected and most of the time she hadn't even been aware of that fact because everything in his life ran so smoothly and discreetly.

His main residence was the Beach House in the grounds of the *estancia*, ten thousand acres of prime real-estate that stretched from the Atlantic coast of Argentina into the grasslands. Under Raul's watchful eye, his dedicated staff, which had once included her, bred and trained polo ponies, and the *estancia* was the first port of call for the super-wealthy who enjoyed that particular sport.

With typical flare and vision, Raul had tapped into a market where the very, very rich would pay for the privilege of receiving the very best polo instruction and advice on the purchase of a string of ponies, safe from the prying eyes of the world's press. It also allowed Raul to indulge his dare-devil streak—as one of the country's most daring polo players, he thrived on the thrilling adrenalin rush of the game.

But the stud-farm was only a small part of an empire that encompassed hotels, finance and export. Applauded by the financial pages of the world's newspapers for his astonishing vision, Raul had diversified sufficiently to ensure that any change in the markets would have no effect on the overall profitability of his business.

The lift doors opened and Raul strode out, as if he couldn't wait to get away from her. After a moment's hesitation Faith followed, knowing that if she didn't do so voluntarily, he'd simply haul her out himself.

The penthouse apartment spread over the top of the building, a dazzling, soaring living-space designed to give the occupant breathtaking views over Buenos Aires.

'It is stunning,' she muttered weakly. 'Another world.' And at that moment she almost laughed at herself.

It *was* another world. The world he lived in. How had she ever thought she could just step into his life with no problems?

A frown touching his strong, dark brows, Raul turned his head and stared out of the window, as if the view wasn't something he'd noticed before. 'It's a city.'

His reply was so rigidly polite that Faith felt as though she was on a blind date with a stranger. 'If you didn't buy it for the view, why did you choose it?'

He gave a careless lift of his broad shoulders, as if he considered it an odd question. 'I needed somewhere to shower and change in between meetings. And it's an investment.'

He was standing still but she could feel the energy pulsing from every centimetre of his powerful frame. She'd never met anyone as driven as Raul. 'Does money come into every decision you make?'

'Not always.' His charcoal-dark eyes locked on hers, his gaze boldly explicit and she understood the unspoken message in that one blistering look.

If he'd been thinking about money, he wouldn't have chosen her.

Looking at him now, at the careless arrogance he wore with the same ease as his expensive clothes, she wondered how she'd ever felt comfortable with him.

Everything about him screamed power and success but on top of that he possessed a raw, dominant sexuality that had always rendered her breathless.

For a moment his burning gaze held her captive, the sheer force of his personality preventing her from looking away.

In the end it was Raul who broke that connection, turning from her with a sudden movement that suggested an underlying tension of almost unbearable proportions. 'I haven't shown you round properly, but the bedroom is up the stairs.' His voice was tight, clipped, as if he were restraining himself not to say a great deal more. 'Take a shower and help yourself to some clothes from the wardrobe.'

Clothes? Her heart lurched and the dull, sick feeling in the pit of her stomach returned. Since when did he keep a spare set of clothes for female guests? She'd never been here, which could only mean that...

Reminding herself that the way he chose to live his life was no longer any of her business, Faith curled her fingers into her palms.

'Upstairs?'

'It's a duplex penthouse.' With a spare, minimal gesture he angled his glossy, dark head and she belatedly noticed a curving staircase in one corner of the room.

'Fine.' Not trusting herself to stay cool in front of him, she stalked across the apartment and up the stairs, horribly conscious of his eyes tracking her every movement.

She found herself in a sumptuous master-bedroom suite that extended over the whole of the top floor. Gripped by the sharp claws of jealousy, she kept her eyes firmly averted from the enormous bed. Raul had had women before her, she knew that. But she'd always told herself that they were part of his past.

Only now was it dawning on her that she'd never really known this dangerous, complicated, hotly sexual man. When he'd flown to Buenos Aires for meetings, had he been alone? Could Raul deprive himself of sex for a few nights? Remembering his almost insatiable hunger for her body, she doubted it. He was a man of apparently limitless stamina in every area of his life and the demands he placed upon himself would have exhausted a lesser man.

Reminding herself that none of that was supposed to matter to her any more, she made straight for the bathroom.

Even there she couldn't escape the vagaries of her imagination because the amazing glass bath was easily large enough for two, as was the shower.

And she knew enough of Raul's sexual appetites to know that he wouldn't have restricted his activities to the bedroom.

Trying to block out the distressing image of those skilled, bronzed hands on another woman, she stripped off her damp clothes and stepped under the shower. Why would she care that he had another woman? She didn't want him, did she? Not after what he'd believed of her. He was right—they were *totally* wrong for each other. She was a modern, thinking woman. He was a ruthless tycoon who inhabited a world she hadn't even known existed. And that world had made him cynical and hard.

She probably *should* have ended the relationship and maybe she would have if it hadn't been for the one small fact that he'd overlooked when he'd delivered that piece of advice.

She loved him.

Totally, completely and utterly. To the point where the mere idea of leaving would have been laughable.

And he'd taken that love and crushed it.

Closing her eyes, she let the hot water scald her skin, finding the warmth strangely soothing. After the clinical scent of the hospital it was pure bliss to lather indulgent products into her hair and body. She could have stayed under the shower for ever, but she knew that if she didn't emerge soon Raul would come looking for her and she didn't want that. Reluctantly she stemmed the flow of hot water, dried herself on one of the heated towels and walked into the dressing room.

Steeling herself for seeing a range of glamorous dresses, she was taken aback to see nothing but male clothing, both formal and casual.

Suits, shirts, ties, shoes—nothing remotely feminine or glittery.

Relief swamped her, closely followed by exasperation because she didn't want to feel anything. She didn't want to care. Shaking her head in despair, she wondered how she was ever going to divorce herself from this man. It wasn't the legal side that worried her—that would be simple enough. The real problem was the mental agony of accepting that he was no longer in her life.

Faith stared at the contents of his dressing room, realising with a sense of resignation that there was absolutely nothing that was going to fit her.

Abandoning ideas of boosting her flagging courage with a touch of power-dressing, she gave a shrug and reached for a crisp white shirt. She wasn't trying to make a good impression anyway, so what did it matter how she was dressed? The shirt fell to mid-thigh and she had to roll up the sleeves, but after she'd added a belt she decided that she was more or less respectable.

Feeling ridiculously self-conscious, she walked back into the luxurious living area.

Raul was standing with his back to her, phone to his ear as usual, his hand braced against the glass window as he listened to the person on the other end. For a moment Faith just watched him, her eyes feasting on every tiny detail from the fit of his shirt to the bold confidence that was so evident in everything he did. He was spectacular. Sleek, handsome and every inch the successful billionaire.

How had she ever thought that their relationship could work?

He was used to driving over everything in his path and she'd never been meek and submissive.

They'd been an accident waiting to happen.

Sensing her presence, he turned, issued a set of instructions and then terminated the call and dropped the phone onto the nearest available surface. His eyes swept over her in one swiftly assessing glance. 'You've lost weight.'

His comment shot like a spear through her self-confidence. 'Lost weight' good, or 'lost weight' bad? 'It's your shirt,' she muttered. 'It's too big for me. There weren't any female clothes.'

'Why would there be?' His tone was heavily laced with sarcasm. 'On the whole I don't find the financial sector take me seriously if I arrive at a meeting wearing a dress.'

The question burned inside her and she looked at him, desperately wanting to ask and *hating* herself for that weakness. Their relationship was in its death throes. Why demean herself by voicing the fears that had been gnawing at her insides since he'd dragged her into the apartment?

The apartment she hadn't known about.

Raul shot her a look of sizzling impatience. 'You are *totally* transparent. But I don't play those games, Faith, I told you that when we first met. I was with you. I didn't want anyone else.'

The fact that he'd read her so easily should have bothered her but she was too lacerated by his use of the past tense to care. 'Women want you—'

'I'm an adult, not some hormonal teenager,' he said curtly. 'Do you think I jump into bed with every woman who looks at me?'

Obviously not, or he'd never get any work done.

Faith tried to breathe evenly. 'I just thought—'

'I know what you thought,' he snapped. 'And for your information I have never brought another woman here. This is convenient accommodation, not a love nest. When I'm here, I'm working.'

Wishing she hadn't exposed so much of herself, or her *feelings*, Faith looked away. 'This is so difficult.'

'You're the one who made it difficult.'

'You expect my trust but you don't give it in return.' She turned to him. 'What did I ever do to make you believe that I'd lie to you? And lie about something so enormously important?'

He stilled, his face ashen beneath his tan. 'You cannot walk around Buenos Aires wearing one of my shirts.'

So he was going to stampede right over the issue, then. Her legs gave way and she plopped onto the sofa. 'I didn't have any luggage.'

'You left Argentina with nothing?'

She wanted to turn the conversation back to the subject that he'd abandoned but her woman's intuition warned her that it was best left. If Raul was avoiding it, then he was avoiding it for a reason.

And suddenly she wanted to understand that reason.

Only now was it occurring to her that she was being punished for someone else's sins.

'When I left, I was upset, Raul.' In fact she'd been in such a state when she'd fled to the airport that it was fortunate her passport had been in her handbag or she wouldn't have gone far. 'I wasn't thinking.'

'Evidently.' The mockery in his voice was sharp as a blade. 'As you evidently weren't thinking when you stepped in the path of a taxi. You don't need luggage, *cariño*, you need protection. From yourself.'

'That's not true. And I wouldn't have taken any luggage, anyway.' She bit her lip. 'I didn't want to take anything that was yours.'

'*You* were mine,' Raul said with lethal emphasis, his thick dark lashes veiling the expression in his eyes. 'You were mine. And unlike you, I take incredibly good care of my possessions.'

CHAPTER SIX

'I'M NOT *your possession, Raul.'*

Raul watched her and wished he'd had the foresight to send out for some clothes for her. At least then he might have stood a chance of being able to concentrate.

He'd never considered a plain white shirt to be sexy, but Faith managed to turn it into something that could have become a top seller in a sex shop.

It wasn't the shirt, he decided grimly, it was the woman.

Faith would have looked sexy dressed in her grandmother's clothes.

And she was looking straight at him, her green eyes wide and intelligent. '*Talk* to me, Raul,' she urged softly, all the fight suddenly leaving her. '*Tell* me why you're thinking like this. Is there something I need to know? Did someone hurt you? *Did someone betray your trust?*'

She'd changed tactic in mid-fight but this alternative, gentler assault was infinitely more deadly than the fierce blast of her temper.

She was getting close. Too close. Closer than any woman had ever dared tread before.

'We've been talking non-stop,' he said coldly, retreating mentally and physically from the question he saw in her eyes.

'Maybe we haven't been talking about the right things.'

Swiftly, he sidestepped an issue he had no intention of exploring further. '*You* betrayed my trust.'

'No.' She shook her head slowly. '*Why* would you even think that?'

'Because you went to astonishing lengths to drag me into this marriage.'

'That is *not* what happened!'

'Then what did happen, Faith? Why are we standing here, as husband and wife, because I sure as hell don't know!' His words thickened, his usually faultless accent tinged with a hint of his South American heritage.

She stood in front of him and he could actually see her slim legs shaking. In fact she was shaking so badly that for a moment he wondered whether she might actually collapse. Her face had lost every last hint of colour and she looked as though she were in shock. 'We're here because I thought it was what you wanted. You proposed, Raul. You asked me to marry you.'

'Because you gave me no other option! Have you listened to anything I've said over the past ten months?' With a supreme effort of will, he kept his voice level even though the temptation to vent his wrath was extreme. 'Right from the beginning I made it clear to you—no marriage, no babies. If that's what you had planned then you should have been with another man.'

But even as he uttered the words he knew them for a lie. *He would never have let her go to another man.*

'I didn't have anything planned. I didn't *plan* any of this!' Some of her spirit returned. 'I came to your wretched *estancia* because the job was interesting and I wanted to see something of South America. All you were to me was a name. A guy who knew about horses!'

Watching her trembling and shaking in front of him, Raul frowned. 'Calm down.' She looked impossibly fragile and he watched with a mixture of concern and exasperation as she grew more and more agitated, her slender hands clasping and unclasping by her sides.

'Don't tell me to calm down! How can I possibly calm down when you're accusing me of planning as though I'm some sort of s-s—' she stumbled over the word '—scheming woman, out to trap you. I'm *not* scheming. I never planned or plotted. I had an accident! It happens to millions of women every day! And it wasn't just my fault! You were there, too! You're very quick to blame me, but I wasn't alone in this. I didn't have sex by myself. You were there, Raul, every time. You were there in our bed every night. You were there in the shower, in the stables, in your office, in the fields—wherever I was, you were. *I didn't do this by myself!*'

Her passionate diatribe conjured up images of such disturbing clarity that it took him a moment to formulate a response. 'You assured me that you were protected.'

'Well, it seems that nothing is foolproof. I've thought about it and thought about it.' Faith swallowed. 'I was sick, if you remember. I picked up that bug when we spent the night in that hotel outside Cordoba, when you were looking at a horse. I didn't even think of it at the time, but it was probably enough—'

He digested that information in silence. 'It's history now.'

'No, it isn't history. I can't be with a man who would think that badly of me!'

'All marriages hit sticky patches.'

'But not within hours of the ceremony! I hate you, Raul.' The tears spilled down her cheeks and she started to sob. Not delicate, controlled sobs designed to win a man round, but tearing, anguished sobs that seemed to place great strain on her slender frame. 'I hate you for not believing me, I hate you for marrying me when that wasn't what you really wanted, but most of all I really, *really* hate you for not caring that I lost the baby.'

Raul swore fluently and stepped towards her but she held up a hand to stop him.

'Don't come near me,' she choked. 'Don't you *dare* touch me or I'll injure you.'

He stiffened. 'You're obviously distressed—'

'And you are the reason for that distress! Make up your mind, Raul. You can't accuse me of lying and manipulating one minute and then offer to support me the next. When I told you that I'd lost the baby—*that* was when I needed your support.' Her voice was thickened and clogged with tears. 'But what did you do? You accused me of having become pregnant on purpose to trap you into marriage. I didn't just lose the baby, I lost *you* because I realised then that I couldn't be with a man who would think me capable of something like that.'

'What was I supposed to think?' Infuriated by her totally unjust accusations, Raul felt his own tension levels soar.

'*You were supposed to think that I wouldn't have done that to you. To us! That was what you were supposed to think.*' Her face was streaked with tears but for some reason she didn't look pathetic or sorry for herself, just angry and passionate and very, very beautiful. 'I know you find it hard to show your feelings, but I *assumed* you loved me. I assumed you cared about me. It didn't occur to me to even question that because I thought we were happy together. So at the time, all I was really thinking about was the baby and how sad I was.'

Raul turned away and raked his fingers through his hair. 'It might have helped if you'd told me about the miscarriage *before* the wedding.'

'Well if I'd known how jaded and cynical you are then perhaps I would have done, although goodness knows when!

You arrived five minutes before the ceremony! If I'd talked about it then I would have broken down and I thought it would be bad for your image to be seen marrying a woman who was sobbing.'

'Faith—'

'Answer me honestly, Raul.' Her voice trembled and shook with emotion. 'Why did you propose to me? If you were truly so against marriage, *why* did you propose? If you remember, when I first discovered I was pregnant I told you that I did not expect you to marry me.'

'Yes, that was clever.'

'It wasn't clever! It was how I felt.' Increasingly agitated, Faith paced across the floor, her back to him as if she couldn't bear to look him in the eye. 'It was bad enough finding myself pregnant and knowing that you were going to blame me for that. Do you know how much courage it took to tell you I was pregnant? Do you know?' She turned, her eyes flashing. 'I could have vanished into the sunset and brought your baby up on my own, but I didn't do that because I decided that it wasn't right or honest. I decided that it wouldn't be fair to you.'

Raul stilled, black clouds from his past rolling towards him like a deadly storm. 'I would not have wanted you to do that,' he said hoarsely, sliding a finger round the neck of his shirt in an attempt to ease his breathing. 'I wouldn't have allowed that.' *Never.*

'Why not? If you're really so allergic to the thought of parenthood, then that would have been a perfectly reasonable option to consider.'

Not for him. Ruthlessly battling to rein in emotions that he hadn't experienced for years, Raul rubbed his fingers over his temples in the hope that touch might erase the memories. Not now. He wasn't going to think about this now. And not later, either. It was gone. Done. Finished.

'I'm *trying* to understand you, Raul.' Her eyes glittered like jade. 'And you're not helping.'

He inhaled deeply. 'When you told me that you were pregnant, I did *not* react badly.'

'You stood there, looking as though you'd been shot through the head at close range.' She turned away from him and he saw her chest rise and fall under the soft fabric of his shirt. She looked traumatised, fragile and desperately upset. 'What is going on here, Raul? Is this some sort of billionaire hang-up? Is that it? Woman gets pregnant so it must be because she wants your money?'

Raul watched her in tense silence. Their relationship was in shreds around them and he had no idea how to fix it because he'd never actually bothered fixing a relationship before. If it wasn't right, it ended. Simple as that.

So why wasn't he ending this one? 'You need to calm down—'

'*Stop* telling me to calm down! I don't feel calm. I'm angry, Raul. Angry with you. And angry with myself for believing that we had something special. It was bad enough telling you that I was pregnant, but I reassured myself that our relationship was strong enough to take it. We loved each other, or so I thought. I really believed that we'd weather this and make it work.' Her voice faltered and she gave a tiny intake of breath. 'And then I lost it.' That last statement was an anguished gasp and Raul felt his own tension rocket and every muscle in his body tensed in readiness for more female tears.

'Why didn't you tell me? I called you that night,' he reminded her. 'I called you every night I was away on business. You had ample opportunity.'

'I just couldn't do it over the phone…' Her voice faded to a whisper and she dropped back onto the sofa as if her legs had lost their strength. 'How do you do that? I don't know—

I mean, should I have said, "How was your day, dear? By the way, I lost the baby"?'

'Faith—'

'I was *devastated* and you hate emotional scenes, you know you do. Look at you now—you're standing there thinking to yourself, "I hope she doesn't cry again. Once was enough."'

'That isn't true,' Raul lied swiftly but her soft, derisive laugh told him that he'd been less than convincing. He paced to the furthest end of the living room although why, he didn't really know. There was already an enormous gulf between them. Physically and emotionally they were as far apart as it was possible for two people to be.

'It's all irrelevant. What matters now is that we're married. And we have to find a way of moving forward from here.' He thought of the past year and the passion they'd shared. He'd loved the fact that she hadn't known who he was at their first meeting. Loved the fact that the chemistry between them had been raw and explosive and *nothing* to do with who he was.

And even when she'd discovered his identity, it hadn't changed her. She'd continued to be herself, challenging him constantly without guarding what she said. Surrounded by people who deferred to him, he'd found Faith a revelation. *And then there had been the sex.*

'Raul, it's over.'

'You're my wife, Faith. I want you back in my bed.'

She gaped at him. 'You *have* to be kidding.'

Taken aback by her less than enthusiastic response to his statement, Raul frowned. 'Every relationship goes through rocky patches.'

'This isn't a rocky patch, Raul, it's a mountain range!'

'I told you earlier that there wouldn't be a divorce.'

'I assumed you didn't mean it.'

'We were good together.'

'At sex. You're just being ridiculously possessive and macho. You're doing it again—that whole Argentine-man thing.' Her face was terrifyingly pale and she rose to her feet so suddenly that her body swayed.

With a sharp frown, Raul stepped towards her but before he could reach her her legs gave way and she sank to the floor, unconscious.

'These things happen after a head injury, but it's important that she avoids any unnecessary stress.'

Faith woke to find herself lying on the bed with a doctor hovering over her and groaned. *Not more doctors.*

'She really needs peace and quiet,' he was saying and Faith struggled to sit up.

'What happened?'

'You fainted,' the man said calmly and Faith frowned.

'I never faint.'

The man closed his bag. 'You can't expect to return to full health immediately. You need to take it gently.'

'I intended to take her back to the *estancia* tomorrow.' Raul's face was strained and the doctor nodded.

'It's only a short drive. She will be fine, I'm sure. But you need to remember that a miscarriage followed by a head injury—it's a lot for anyone to cope with.' He picked up his medical bag and left the room with Raul.

A few moments later Raul was back, a wary expression on his handsome face.

Faith lay still, just watching him. 'Why are you staring at me like that? I'm not about to break in two.'

'The doctors think that the reason you're so emotional could be because of the miscarriage,' he said tightly. 'They think you should be encouraged to talk about it.'

'Talk?' Faith gave a weak laugh. 'They don't know you very well, do they? Now I understand why you're looking green around the gills. You're afraid I suddenly want to expose you to my inner feelings. Relax, Raul. I wouldn't discuss it with you if you were the last person on earth.'

He absorbed the insult without attempt at retaliation, his face grim as he studied her in silence. Then he dropped something into her lap.

Faith looked at it and her heart stopped dead.

'It's your wedding ring,' he said in a harsh voice. 'The wedding ring you threw at me only two hours after I'd placed it on your finger. Put it on. You're mine and don't ever forget it again.'

Remembering how she'd felt when she'd removed it, Faith felt the lump return to her throat. 'Do you know something?' she said in a shaky voice that didn't sound like her own. 'Until I met you, I could never understand why a woman would be so stupid as to cry over a man. And here I am, doing exactly that.'

'Put it on. You should never have taken it off your finger.'

'You should never have put it on my finger, feeling the way you felt.' She took the ring in her hand but didn't put it on.

'I did not intentionally upset you.'

'Don't say that, Raul, because if you've achieved this level of devastation without even trying, I don't even want to think about what you might manage if you really applied yourself.'

'I'm willing to admit that I was thinking of my feelings rather than yours.' His surprising admission left her speechless and he sat on the edge of the bed, his dense lashes lowered as he studied her. 'I *am* trying.'

'Are you?'

'I'm here.'

'Claiming your "possession"; wasn't that the word you used? Give me one reason why I should even think about putting this ring back on my finger.'

'Because you love me.'

His arrogant statement rocked her to the core. *Did she love him?* Was she really such a poor judge of character? 'Go away, Raul. You heard the doctor—I'm not supposed to be subjected to any stress and you definitely fall under the category of stress.'

'You love me, Faith.' His voice was dangerously intimate and she glared at him angrily but the anger was as much directed towards herself as him. She shouldn't be listening to him. She shouldn't be giving him air-time.

'Do you want to have to explain to the doctor why I've collapsed again?'

His response to that was to take her cold fingers in his warm, strong grip and slide the ring onto her finger in a decisive gesture. '*Don't* take it off again. And now I want you to tell me how you feel.'

'No, you don't.' She gave a hollow laugh. 'Trust me, you really don't want to go there. And anyway, we both know that you would sooner eat glass than discuss my feelings.'

'That is *not* true.' His fingers tightened on hers. 'Whatever you may think, I do care about you. The doctors say you need to talk about the miscarriage. I explained that the pregnancy was an accident, but they didn't seem to think that would make any difference to the emotional impact.'

'And that was news to you?' Her voice shook as the pain shot through her. 'You think that made any difference to my feelings? Do you think that made it hurt any the less?'

'I don't know.' His tone was cool and detached. 'I have no experience in this area.' And he hadn't wanted any experience; that much was obvious from every taut, stiff line of his powerful frame.

'I don't know why we're talking about this.'

'Because the doctors seem to think it might help you. Did it hurt, physically?' His voice was gruff and she stared at the ceiling, feeling as though the bottom was dropping out of her world, yet again.

'Raul, I really don't—'

'*Talk to me!*'

'Why? So that you can watch me unravel like a ball of wool?' Her strangled laugh was like a warning bell, indicating that the volumes of tension building inside her were reaching danger levels. 'Is that what you're asking?'

'*Dios mío*, do *not* attack me when I am trying to help! *Tell* me what is in your head.'

His hand rested close to hers and the fact that her own fingers tingled with the need to touch shocked her. He wasn't capable of giving comfort, so why was she hoping for it? 'I'm angry. That's how I feel.'

'*Sí*, that much I can see for myself,' he growled. 'What else?'

'Sad,' she whispered, curling her fingers into the soft duvet that covered her. 'And guilty. Because I was so worried about what the baby would do to you and to us. It didn't occur to me that I might lose it. And now I'm wondering—'

'It was *not* your fault.' The fact that he'd read her mind surprised her because she hadn't thought he was capable of being so connected with her thoughts.

'You don't know that. It feels as though it is.' Her voice was clogged with tears. 'Perhaps that baby knew that it had stirred up a hornet's nest between us. Perhaps it knew, Raul.'

'You are torturing yourself for no reason.'

'You wanted to know how I feel. I'm telling you. I feel guilty. Sad. Disappointed. Angry with you.' She swallowed painfully and her voice dropped to a whisper. 'And empty. Really, really empty. Because I've lost something that was part of me. Part of us. And I know it wasn't planned, but once I found out about it I just wanted it.' It was too much. Letting a tiny drop of emotion escape was dangerous when so much of it was bottled up.

'You always were maternal. I watched you delivering foals

and I knew then that you were trouble.' His tone was gruff and she knew he was acknowledging what they'd both known: *that this was always going to be an enormous issue between them.*

'I didn't think it would be a problem,' she admitted hoarsely. 'I had no plans to settle down and get married. Children were something in the far-distant future so when you told me that wasn't what you wanted, I suppose it just didn't really seem relevant. We were having fun and we were happy. That was what mattered.'

'The problem was always there.'

'Only if you were thinking in terms of marriage and a future, and I wasn't.' Her fingers tightened on the duvet. 'I didn't see it as a problem.'

'You mean you hoped I would wake up one morning longing to be a father.'

'No, I mean I wasn't thinking about parenthood. I was just enjoying our relationship.'

His gaze didn't shift from her face. 'And now?'

'Well, I don't think this is the most fun we've ever had together, if that's what you're asking me,' she croaked and he rose to his feet and gave her a long, speculative look that made her stomach tumble and turn.

'I never wanted to hurt you.'

'Raul, don't—'

'I love being with you.'

It was as close to a declaration of love as he'd ever come, and for a moment she couldn't breathe. Afraid that she'd make a fool of herself, she squeezed her eyes tightly shut. 'Getting soppy on me, Raul?'

'Perhaps.'

She gave a soft moan of agony. 'It's easier to deal with you when you're angry and unreasonable. Why are you doing this to me now, when it's too late for us?'

'It isn't too late.'

If she'd thought she was confused before, she was doubly so now. 'How can you claim to care about me when you *hurt* me?'

'If I didn't care, I wouldn't be here now.' He didn't try and touch her but somehow that made his simple statement all the more compelling and she screwed her eyes tightly shut.

'We make each other miserable.'

'Until we married we were extremely happy together.' His voice was tense. 'We need to put all this behind us and move on. Concentrate on our relationship.'

'I can't just put it behind me—'

'So what are you going to do?' His voice was brutal. 'Carry on like this? Walking under cars, winding yourself up to a state of such anxiety that you pass out?'

Numb, she looked at him. 'What do you *want* from me?'

'You,' he said simply. 'Back in my bed where you belong.' It was such a typically macho declaration that she closed her eyes tightly, hating herself for even considering it.

'You hurt me, Raul.'

'And you hurt me.'

Accepting that as a truth, she opened her eyes. 'You seriously expect to carry on with our marriage?'

'You are getting upset again and you are very pale. Last time we talked about this you collapsed on the floor at my feet,' he bit out. 'So we're going to leave the subject until you're feeling stronger. In the meantime you'll just have to accept the fact that we're married and that we're staying that way. We're not going to talk about this again, now.' He turned and strode towards the bedroom door. 'Get some rest. I need to do some work.'

Too exhausted and drained to argue with him further, Faith collapsed against the pillows, feeling as though she'd been run over all over again. Now what?

Part of her was worried that she felt so lousy, but another

part of her was far too distracted by her relationship with Raul to pay much attention to her own health.

Why was he so determined that they should stay married when it was clear that he'd only married her because of the baby?

What hope was there for them?

And then she remembered just how good their relationship had been—how much she loved him.

Just how much could a person forgive?

Did she dare try to make their marriage work?

If she chose that path, how much pain lay ahead of her?

Her head full of doubts and questions, she couldn't relax or lie still so she slid out of bed and padded on bare feet out of the bedroom and into the living room.

Raul was sprawled on the sofa, his eyes closed. His shirt was undone at the collar, his sleeves were rolled up and dark stubble emphasised the lean, hard lines of his handsome face.

He looked exhausted and Faith felt her heart twist. Five minutes earlier she'd wanted to slap him. Now she wanted to put her arms round him and hug him.

Confused and infuriated with herself, she was about to turn away when his eyes opened and he saw her.

For a moment they just stared at each other and she felt her cheeks burn as she saw the sudden flare of heat in his eyes. Every feminine part of her exploded with awareness and she knew from the sudden tension in his shoulders that he was experiencing the same powerful reaction.

Acknowledging the strength of the force that drew them together, he gave a cynical laugh. 'Complicated, isn't it?'

'Yes.' It would have been foolish to pretend that she didn't know what he was talking about. She stood for a moment, trying to catch her breath, needing to speak and not knowing how to say what needed to be said. 'I didn't mean to force your hand. I thought we were good together.'

'We were.'

'But—you never would have wanted marriage.'

'No.' His face was closed, uncommunicative and she looked at him with mounting frustration.

'Why? If a relationship is good, marriage just makes it better.'

His laugh hurt more than any harsh words. 'And we're a case in point, are we?'

'Is there anything left between us?'

His answer was to rise to his feet and stride across to her. Without bothering to speak, he closed his fingers around her wrist, pulled her hard against him. 'How can you ask that, when this thing between us has been choking us since the day we met?'

Without giving her a chance to reply, he brought his mouth down on hers.

As kisses went, this one wasn't gentle but she didn't even care. It was an explosion of mutual need, an acknowledgement of the passion and chemistry that kept both of them locked together when external forces might have driven them apart.

Excitement swamped her, her head swam with a rush of dizzying pleasure and she would have slid to the floor if he hadn't wrapped his arms around her.

They kissed with desperation, their mouths locked together in a furious, reckless urgency that exploded away the flimsy barriers that had been erected between them.

It was only when his hand touched her breast that Faith regained sufficient mental ability to realise what she was doing.

'We can't fix problems with sex,' she groaned, but the erotic skill of his mouth stole the words and her body shivered against his. 'Raul, this is just too complicated to solve in this way—'

'Life is complicated,' he muttered, his lips trailing down the line of her jaw. 'In real life, people are complicated and they behave in complicated ways.'

'You didn't think about my feelings.'

He lifted his head and looked at her. 'Both of us were guilty of that.' His return shot scored a direct hit and she stiffened.

'With hindsight I can see that I should have told you I'd lost the baby, but my reasons for not telling you *were* unselfish.' Her stumbled admission received no more response than a raised eyebrow and a careless lift of his shoulders.

'If there's one thing that the last few months has proved, it's that neither of us knows the other as well as we thought.' His handsome face was grim. 'That is common. It's the reason that so many marriages end in divorce. We can change that, Faith. But not if you run.'

She looked at him, torn by indecision, her head full of problems and questions. Logic told her to do one thing, her heart another.

'If I stay, I won't let you hurt me again,' she warned in a voice that shook with emotion. 'Don't *ever* hurt me again.'

CHAPTER SEVEN

IT FELT strange being back when she'd thought she'd never see the place again.

Faith sat in silence in the back of the limousine as it drove through the ornate iron gates that guarded the entrance of the *estancia*.

She couldn't quite believe she was actually here.

What if she was making the biggest mistake of her life by giving their marriage another chance?

She sighed and stared out of the window. Obviously she was just a pushover for a big, arrogant South American male.

But she knew it was more than that.

She loved him and she couldn't just switch that off.

And she loved Argentina.

Despite the nagging ache in her head and the dull feeling of nausea in her stomach, part of her felt lighter just for being here. After the noise and bustle of Buenos Aires, the wide open space of the pampas was a welcome refuge.

It was an incomparably beautiful place.

Grassland stretched into the distance and a herd of Criollo ponies galloped and bucked, manes and tails flying, clearly enjoying the freedom of the wide, open planes.

As the car purred along the tree-lined avenue and curved round the final bend, Faith held her breath in expectation.

Raul had once told her how he'd bought the place piece by piece.

He'd shown her photographs and she'd barely recognised the tumbledown, dusty buildings.

The ranch had been restored to its former colonial glory and now the dusky-pink stone walls of the main residence were covered in tumbling bougainvillea, the colours so bright that at a glance it seemed as if someone had gaily splashed paint against the walls. Three perfectly manicured polo lawns were bordered by pristine white fences and in another field a herd of exquisitely beautiful horses galloped and pranced, the quality of their bloodline indisputable.

Faith's eyes slid to the row of expensive cars parked in the far corner of the immaculate yard.

Money, money and more money…

Raul had barely spoken during the journey, instead working on his laptop and fielding a never-ending series of calls, the subject of which had revolved around the purchase of a neighbouring *estancia*.

'You're buying more land?'

A strange expression flickered across his face and she sensed immediately that this was one deal he didn't intend to discuss. 'Are you making small talk or are you suddenly interested in the nature of my business?'

Four days had passed since they'd first arrived in Buenos Aires and apart from that one kiss, he hadn't touched her. Once he'd put the ring back on her finger, he'd turned his attention to work, dividing his time between the phone and the computer. The only time they'd met up had been for dinner by the pool, a stiff, uncomfortable affair for Faith, an opportunity to refuel for Raul. He'd never lingered, instead opting to return to the room he used as an office. His desk faced the glass window and she'd caught glimpses of him lounging in his leather chair, long, muscular legs stretched out in front of him as he'd given hell to the person on the end of the phone.

Faith had immediately retreated to her favourite place, the cosy sofa that took advantage of the same view that Raul enjoyed from his office. She'd cradled a book in her lap, but hadn't read a single word. Instead she'd stared out of the window, her thoughts far removed from the printed page of a book.

She'd always thought that the physical side of their relationship was the one area where they would never have a problem. But apart from that one, searing kiss, Raul hadn't touched her. When he'd slept, which wasn't often, he'd slept in the spare room and she hadn't questioned him because she hadn't wanted to appear insecure.

But she couldn't help wondering *why*.

Was it because her hair was short?

Was it because she'd lost weight?

Halfway through her second day in his apartment, a delivery had arrived for her and she'd opened the various boxes and discovered an entire wardrobe. Dresses, shoes, casual wear, underwear, nightwear—the fact that it had been lacking nothing was a testament to Raul's experience of women but she'd tried not to think about that as she'd riffled her way through the various boxes.

If she was seriously going to give their marriage another go, then she needed to stop thinking like that.

So now, as she arrived at the *estancia*, she was wearing a cool summer dress in soft, muted shades of green and a simple pair of sandals. Lifting her hand to her head, she fingered her hair self-consciously and he caught the gesture and gave a frown.

'Don't. I like it.'

It was the first compliment he'd paid her since he'd stormed into the hospital on that first day and Faith gazed at him in surprise. 'You do?'

'Yes.' He gave a smile that was faintly mocking. 'You look like a pixie.'

'Oh.' She wanted to ask whether he found pixies sexy but then realised that she already knew the answer to that question. *Obviously not, since he hadn't been near her for the past four days.*

And she was relieved about that, she told herself firmly, because she wasn't ready to make love with him yet. Yes he was impossibly sexy, but for her it was more complicated than that. Her feelings were bruised and damaged and before she committed herself emotionally, she needed to know that he cared about her.

She needed him to show it.

Maria, the housekeeper, hurried across the courtyard towards them and Raul gave her a warm smile.

'*Buenos dias*, Maria, *qué tal*?'

Wistfully remembering a time when he'd smiled at her with the same warmth, Faith also greeted the older lady and then followed her towards the luxurious Beach House that was Raul's private residence.

He could have lived in the thirty-two-roomed *estancia*, but instead he'd turned it into his corporate headquarters, complete with suites of rooms for entertaining and overnight guests. For his own personal use, he'd chosen the privacy and intimacy of the Beach House, well away from the busy commercial world of the *estancia*.

The first time she'd seen it, Faith had been unable to believe that such paradise actually existed.

It was hidden from the main house by trees and fencing, and opened onto a private beach so breathtakingly idyllic that the world outside seemed not to exist and the only sound was the gentle hiss of waves breaking onto the perfect curve of white sand.

'Everything is ready for you,' Maria told Raul as she opened the door for them. 'Just as you instructed.'

Dragging her gaze from the sea, Faith gave a gasp of surprise. The elegant Beach House was filled with the scent of flowers and someone had obviously given a great deal of thought to their return. On the table, a basket was piled high with exotic fruit and a bottle of vintage champagne lay chilling in an ice bucket.

'All Raul's idea,' Maria said, her approval evident in her smile. 'Newlyweds deserve something a little special.'

Faith felt the colour pour into her cheeks. Just what did Raul's staff know about the last few weeks? Had they guessed about the state of their marriage?

Clearly keen to leave them alone, Maria said something else in Spanish to Raul and then left the Beach House, closing the door behind her.

Faith glanced around her, her mouth dry. 'You asked for this?'

'To prove that I *am* capable of being thoughtful,' he drawled softly, reaching for the bottle of champagne and tugging out the cork.

Faith was on the verge of pointing out the fact that she would have preferred a conversation, but decided that this wasn't the time to dent the atmosphere.

'What do your staff know about the last few weeks?'

'I have no idea.' Raul poured the glistening liquid into two glasses. 'I'm not in the habit of discussing my personal life with the staff.'

'Well, you must have given them some explanation for the fact we haven't been living here.'

'Why?' Genuinely puzzled by her question, Raul unbuttoned his shirt and walked towards the bedroom. 'I have no idea what they think and I couldn't care less. And neither should you.'

They were *so* different, Faith thought helplessly, watching as he slid the shirt from his shoulders. 'Actually I *do* care what they think,' she muttered and he gave a wolfish smile.

'Then learn not to, because most people in this world are not that generous-spirited. If you really want to know, they're thinking you're obviously extremely hot in bed or there is no way you'd be wearing that ring on your finger.'

She flushed to the roots of her hair. 'Oh.'

His smile widened and he walked into the bedroom without giving her a chance to respond and she stared after him with exasperation.

There was so much that they still needed to talk about.

So much that she needed to know. 'Raul?' She followed him into the bedroom. 'We can't carry on like this. The past few days, you've been driving yourself into the ground, working until you're ready to drop. I don't know whether it's pressure of your business or whether you're just avoiding this thing between us, but we *have* to talk. Not rows and accusations, but *really* talk. It isn't going to go away and we can't just pretend it never happened.'

He stilled. Then he turned slowly and their eyes locked.

And that one, powerful, sizzling look was all it took.

Her stomach knotted with almost unbearable tension and she felt every nerve ending in her body tingle and buzz with shocking awareness. Her breasts tightened and deep in her stomach something burned, hot and dangerous as desire engulfed her.

He felt it too, she knew he did because she saw the betraying glitter in his sexy, dark eyes and the sudden flare of colour on his high cheekbones.

The attraction enveloped them like an invisible force, burning everything in its path like a forest fire, drawing them relentlessly towards an outcome that both of them had been fiercely resisting.

He strode back towards her and pushed her back against

the wall. His body trapped hers as he took her face in his hands, forcing her to meet his burning gaze.

'I think we're way past talking, Faith,' he said huskily, all sexually confident male as his thumb traced a sensual path across her cheek. 'All we've done for the past few days is talk and it's been driving me crazy.'

'But we haven't solved anything,' Faith gasped, turning her head to try and escape his agonisingly skilful touch. But they both knew it was a losing battle.

'Frustrating, isn't it?' He gave a harsh laugh and then lowered his head and drew his mouth along the line of her jaw where his thumb had been, sending the heat between them soaring higher still. 'You think it was easy to let you sleep alone, *cariño*? You think I found that easy? *A man like me?*'

It hadn't been easy for him? 'I didn't think about it,' she lied, her voice barely audible as it became harder and harder to speak. 'You hurt me so badly, sex was the last thing on my mind.'

He gave a cynical laugh. 'If only that were true, life would be a great deal less complicated. Unfortunately for you and I, chemistry seems to override common sense every time. You were thinking about it as much as I was. I could see it in your eyes every time you sat in that chair *not* reading that book on your lap.'

'That's not true,' she moaned, but the smouldering glitter in his eyes told her that the lie had been a waste of breath.

'You want honesty between us?' he breathed. 'Then let's have honesty. I have wanted you for every second of the day and night since the first time I met you and nothing has changed that.'

His words affected her so deeply that there wasn't a single part of her body that didn't react. 'So why did you let me sleep alone?' She tried to remind herself that it wasn't supposed to matter, that she wasn't supposed to care any more, but it was as if her body was tuned to respond only to his. 'I assume you were punishing me?'

'Punishing myself,' he said huskily, his hand curving over her bottom in an unmistakably possessive gesture that rocked her to the very core. 'The doctor told me that you were to avoid all stress. From the disapproving look in his eyes, I assumed he considered me to be the cause of your stress. I stayed away from you and I can tell you that doing so has caused havoc with *my* stress levels.'

His body was hard against hers and it was impossible to think. 'I wondered whether— You told me I was thin…' Overwhelmed by his sexuality, she tried to catch a breath, hating herself for giving voice to her very female insecurities. 'And you keep looking at my hair—you don't find me attractive any more.'

'No, you're right.' His voice was thickened as he hauled her closer still. 'I don't find you at all attractive.' But his words were loaded with self-mockery and she gasped as her body encountered the unmistakable evidence of his shockingly powerful arousal.

'We really shouldn't do this.' Faith's body was no longer her own. 'This is going to make things worse,' she moaned and he captured the sound with his mouth, the fierce demand of his kiss plunging her past the point of no return.

'Worse?' he murmured in a thickened voice. 'How in heaven's name can the situation between us be any worse, *cariño*? I'm made of flesh and blood, not stone, and the past few weeks have been intolerable.'

She tried to hang on to her sanity. 'You thought I became pregnant on purpose—'

'*Dios mío*, why are you bringing that up now? It doesn't matter any more! *This* is the only thing that matters.' His hands cupped her face and he kissed her until physical sensations completely overwhelmed her. She reached for his shoulders, excited and terrified by the sexual craving that threatened to consume her.

Even knowing that there was going to be even greater pain ahead, Faith was unable to do anything except respond. She was so lost in a wild maelstrom of sensation that she didn't even realise that he'd unzipped her dress until it slid to the floor, leaving her standing in her underwear. She clutched at his shoulders, feeling the hard swell of male muscle under her fingers, revelling in the strength and power of his body.

He was pumped up and aroused and she gave a choked cry as his hand cupped her breast through the thin, silken fabric and he stroked her with skilled clever fingers.

The delicious friction of his thumbs over her nipples sent intense excitement shooting through her body and it would have been impossible not to respond. She arched against him in desperate invitation, feeling the heavy, rigid thrust of his arousal and the immediate explosion of heat deep in the core of her femininity.

He kept his mouth on hers, his kiss demanding and shockingly intimate, but all the time his fingers teased her breasts, driving her wild. Only when her breasts ached and throbbed with almost agonising sensation did he slide his clever, confident hands down her shivering, quivering body.

Mindless and desperate, Faith slid one foot up his leg and he caught her thigh in his hand, lifting her leg higher and wider, exposing her to his touch. Once, such a wanton position would have brought a blush to her cheeks but she was too aroused to think about modesty or behaviour. The response of her body was outside her own control and as she felt his knowing fingers slide over the thin fabric of her panties she shuddered and pressed towards his hand. Only a layer of thin, flimsy silk lay between them but it was too much of a barrier and she gave a moan and shifted her hips, just desperate for him to touch her *there*.

But he didn't.

Instead he tormented them both by prolonging the moment that they craved so desperately, very much in control despite the hunger that consumed both of them.

Driven wild with excitement, her fingers slid downwards, reaching for him and he broke the kiss with a harsh groan as the flat of her hand brushed against his pulsing erection.

'Faith—'

Desperate and urgent, her fingers dealt with his zip, slid inside and encountered the warm throb of masculine power. Touching him so intimately, she felt an explosion of pure sexual need. He was so unashamedly male, so virile, that for a moment her heart seemed to beat double-time. She couldn't quite circle him with her hand and as usual she felt a flash of trepidation that he might be more of a man than she could handle.

'You're driving me wild, *cariño*,' he groaned and his hand moved again and this time he slid his fingers under the silken barrier that still protected her. The intimate stroke of his fingers was the touch she'd longed for and she whimpered his name, her eyes closing as his fingers slid deep, her damp, desperate body closing around him. She didn't know herself when she was with him. Didn't recognise the person she became. Devoured by sensation she was powerless to resist as his long clever fingers explored her with astonishing expertise. She felt the pressure build, felt her body race headlong towards completion and then he gently removed his hand and brought his mouth down on hers with punishing force.

His kiss made her so dizzy that she was only dimly aware of him lifting her, of him coiling her other leg around his hips. There was a brief moment of clarity when she felt the blunt tip of his arousal brush against her and then suddenly she felt a blind flash of panic and struggled against him. 'No, Raul. *No.*'

He froze, his breathing harsh, his body on the point of penetrating hers. 'No?' His voice was hoarse with disbelief, his entire frame straining with the tension of holding back. 'What do you mean, no?'

'We have to stop. Put me down!'

Two streaks of colour on his cheeks, Raul hesitated for a tense, pulsing moment and then lowered her gently and released her. Stepping away from her, he leaned both hands against the wall and breathed deeply, clearly struggling for control.

'Raul—'

'Don't.' His tone was raw and savage. 'Just give me a minute—'

Faith watched helplessly, not knowing what to do or say, her own body singing with unresolved passion. It didn't help that he was half-undressed, his bronzed back bared for her greedy gaze, his trousers riding low on his hips.

She closed her eyes with a groan because her only hope was not to look at him.

What was it about this man that made her forget herself every time?

Finally he drew in a breath and turned, his dark eyes burning with feverish intensity. 'So what was that all about?' His dark hair was tousled from the aggravated plunge of his fingers and he reached down and zipped his trousers with a purposeful movement. 'It was a joke or a punishment?'

'Neither.' Shivering and shaking, she stooped and retrieved her dress, holding it in front of her like a shield.

'Then *what*? You wanted it as badly as I did,' he said in a driven tone. 'So don't pretend that you didn't.'

'I'm not pretending anything.'

'So *why* did you stop?' His eyes were dark as a winter night and Faith licked her lips, trying to ignore the fact that her entire body was suddenly alive with anticipation.

'Contraception,' she croaked, watching as his expression

froze. 'For a man who doesn't want babies, you're extremely careless, do you know that?'

He stilled and a sudden silence screamed through the room.

'I am *not* careless.' His breathing suddenly shallow, he ran a hand over the back of his neck. 'Not usually. I did not intend to put you at risk—I forgot that you didn't use protection.'

And there it was, back again. This thing that lay between them. 'I *did* use protection,' she said flatly. 'But I stopped taking the Pill when I found out that I was pregnant. And I didn't start taking it again after I lost the baby.' She looked away from him but felt the tension levels rocket in the room.

'So, clearly that's something we need to address sooner rather than later.' His voice was rough, still laden with the passion that thickened the air and scraped along the edges of their nerve endings.

'No, we don't!' She took several steps backwards and found herself against the wall again. The same wall that just moments earlier she'd been pinned to under the weight of his body. 'We shouldn't even be *thinking* about sex when things are so complicated between us, Raul!'

'We have thought about nothing but sex since the first moment we met, *cariño*, and you know it.'

Faith wished there was a switch she could flick to turn off the responses of her body. *She didn't want to feel like this.* 'And that's our problem, isn't it?'

'Problem?' One dark eyebrow swooped upwards in sardonic appraisal. 'The fact that you are capable of satisfying me in the bedroom is the one thing that is absolutely *right* about our relationship. I certainly don't see it as a problem.'

His oblique reference to her abandoned response to him sent the colour flooding into her cheeks. 'You can't base a relationship on sex!'

'Never underestimate the importance of sex.'

Her heart rate doubled. 'I know it's important, but if sex

is the only thing that is right about our relationship then we're doomed, Raul. A marriage is about trust and caring. We need to talk.'

Casting her a glance laden with hot-blooded volatility, Raul stepped back from her. 'If you want to talk, phone a girl-friend.' Simmering with unfulfilled passion and male hormones, he strode into the bedroom, leaving her staring after him in disbelief.

Stunned by the suppressed violence she sensed in him, Faith followed. 'You can't just walk out in the middle of a conversation just because you don't happen to like the subject matter—'

'*Dios mío*, not now!' With a low growl of impatience he turned, his hand on the bathroom door, his eyes burning into hers. 'You're a highly intelligent woman. Surely you're not so naïve that you can't see what is happening here? Either get dressed or get out.'

'But—'

'Faith—' The word was a deadly warning, as if he were holding on to control by a thread. 'I'm telling you now that if you stand there naked, I *will* finish what we started, contraception or no contraception. You will be back against that wall and this time I will *not* be stopping!'

Stunned by the appalling frankness of his words and the barely subdued violence of his reaction, she gave a little gasp. 'But there are so many issues between us—'

'At the moment I'm not interested in the issues, I'm just interested in sex.' Interpreting her shocked expression, he ran his hand over his face and swore long and fluently in Spanish. 'Does that make me shallow? Yes, probably, but I warned you before that I wasn't anyone's idea of a good catch. Remember that before you start trying to change me.'

'I don't want to change you,' Faith said honestly. 'I just want to understand what you're thinking.'

'No, I don't think you do, because what I'm thinking right now this moment,' he said in a silky tone, 'is that it is either a long, cold shower or you on that bed, naked with your legs wrapped around my waist. Your choice, *cariño*.'

'You're being shocking on purpose.'

'I'm being honest,' he said harshly. 'Because I thought that was what you wanted. Maybe now you'd like to rethink that particular demand, given that the truth of what is on a man's mind is so rarely what a woman wants to hear.'

Shaken to the core by the savagery in his voice, Faith backed towards the door. 'I'll—I'd better leave you alone. I'll see you later.'

'You certainly will and by then I will have addressed the issue of contraception so you can knock that particular excuse off your list.' He gave a humourless laugh and opened the bathroom door. 'In the meantime, we have guests for dinner. They arrive in two hours, and in order to concentrate on business I have to *not* be thinking about sex all the time. So this is what you're going to do. You're going to delve into that expensive wardrobe of yours and find something that covers you from head to toe. I want nothing showing.'

'Raul—'

'If necessary, sew two things together. Wear a coat! But I don't want to see cleavage or leg or so help me, Faith, I'll show you in public just how important sex is to me.' And with that rejoinder he strode into the sanctuary of the enormous bathroom and slammed the door firmly shut behind him.

Dios, she was driving him wild.

In the fierce grip of dark, primitive sexual need, Raul slammed the palm of his hand against the shower controls and sent fierce jets of freezing water cascading over his tense, throbbing body.

He closed his eyes, his jaw clenched, his teeth locked as he tried to let go of the tension. Every muscle in his body was pumped up and hard, the hormones coursing round his blood like a dangerous drug.

Litres of cold water sluiced over his heated, throbbing flesh and he stood there with grim determination until he finally acknowledged that he would develop pneumonia long before the desperate need in him died.

Unaccustomed to feeling sexual frustration, Raul leaned both hands against the wall and breathed deeply, trying to use his brain to calm the overwhelming need that tortured his body.

He hadn't intended to touch her like that; not then. What had happened to him? He, who prided himself on his control. He had more finesse than to indulge in mindless, animal sex and yet the facts spoke for themselves. The moment they'd been alone he'd had her up against the wall, his hand on her flesh...

He was behaving like a man possessed and he didn't know what had angered him most: the fact that she'd stopped him or the fact that he'd been so crazy for her that he hadn't given a single thought to anything except the immediate satisfaction of being inside her.

Not even the subject of contraception.

Never, with any other woman, would he have forgotten contraception. It had been his mission, the single overriding fact that had governed the way he lived his life.

But with Faith...

Resigning himself to the fact that cold water was not going to cure his current affliction, he turned off the shower with another forceful punch of his hand and reached for a towel from the pile.

It didn't matter what she did, how she behaved, he wanted her more than any woman he'd ever met.

Acknowledging that fact with a growl of frustration, Raul wrapped the towel around his hips.

Marriage.

He'd avoided that institution all his life and yet somehow here he was, married.

And what had been a mutually satisfying relationship had been transformed into an emotional minefield that no sane man would attempt to negotiate.

He only had to think of her and the desire leapt inside him like a wild animal hunting its prey.

So now what? He mocked himself with the question. It was obvious that, like all women, she wanted him to talk. And given the look on her face when he'd given her a small taste of what was on his mind, he knew that if she really had access to his thoughts, their marriage would be over in a flash.

So perhaps now she'd learned her lesson and wouldn't risk asking him for his thoughts again, he thought grimly.

And he probably ought to do his bit for the relationship and prove that it wasn't all about sex. And that shouldn't be too hard. He might not believe in love, but he did enjoy the sparky, intellectual side of their relationship. He appreciated the fact that she was intelligent enough to challenge him in conversation. He was quite prepared to discuss the stock market, polo or any other subject that interested her.

In fact he was quite prepared to be thoughtful and caring, just as long as thoughtful and caring didn't involve an exchange of thoughts and feelings.

As long as they steered clear of that, their marriage should be fine.

CHAPTER EIGHT

FAITH stared at herself in the mirror, barely seeing her reflection.

What was she doing here? *How had she reached this point?*

She was an intelligent woman who could have been absorbed in her career, instead of which she was living at the whim of an extremely volatile billionaire, wondering whether she was wearing the right dress.

Impatient with herself, she turned sideways and took another look, wondering whether to go back and change into something different. Still on edge after their previous encounter, she had no idea how to handle Raul in his current mood.

They had entirely different ideas about marriage, she thought helplessly. *About life.*

For him, blistering sex was apparently enough. Was that just his macho, South American genes coming into play?

Still shaken by the explosion of passion that had consumed both of them, Faith lifted a hand to her lips, still tasting the lick of his tongue and the heat of his kiss.

He'd been out of control. *Seriously* out of control.

And so had she.

What had happened to her brain? What had happened to her ability to think clearly and logically?

Stopping had been the hardest thing she'd ever done, even harder than walking away from him because at the time, that had seemed the right thing to do.

And now? Did it seem right now?

She didn't know.

All she knew was that her body was buzzing and desire was racing round it like a dangerous drug.

With a groan of disbelief, she squeezed her eyes shut and tried to dispel the erotic images in her head. She had to stop him thinking about sex. And *she* had to stop thinking about sex. So, with that objective in mind, she'd been perfectly happy to comply with his command that she wear something discreet.

In the wardrobe he'd provided for her, she'd found a simple black dress that fell from a high neckline to the floor in a single sweep of soft fabric. She had no idea if it was too dressy for the evening ahead because he hadn't elaborated on what was expected of her. All she knew was that when she looked in the mirror, not one single part of her was on display except her arms.

Satisfied that she'd fulfilled his request, she walked into the living room on shaking legs. She was standing by the door looking across the beach, her stomach knotted in a turmoil of anticipation when she heard him enter the room.

Making sure that her defences were firmly in place, she took a slow breath and turned.

As always he exuded effortless style, his trousers superbly tailored to make the most of his physique, his jacket moulded to his wide shoulders. Tall, athletic and impossibly handsome, he looked every inch the wealthy and successful tycoon and the hint of arrogance in his bearing made her smile.

'I'm sure the other guy, whoever he is, will just give up on the spot when he sees you.' Her eyes slid over him. 'You look scary and intimidating when you dress for business, do you know that?'

'Appearance matters.'

'Spoken like a true Argentine male.'

His response to her light teasing was a careless shrug. 'I *am* an Argentine male, *cariño*. I have never denied that.'

But although she knew he was capable of using his looks when it suited him, she also knew that his success was due to his drive, energy and phenomenal intellect. Raul Vásquez was super-bright. His brain worked at twice the speed of most people's and he used his skills in that area to ruthless advantage, out-manoeuvering, out-negotiating.

He ran his eyes over her in silence and his eyes darkened. 'I told you not to wear anything provocative.'

Having been sure that her dress was perfect, Faith raised her eyebrows. 'This isn't provocative.'

'If you think that, then clearly you dressed without the aid of a mirror.'

Confused and exasperated, she glanced down at herself. 'You said no legs and no cleavage.'

'Your arms are showing.'

She lifted her head and looked at him. 'My *arms*?'

'Bare flesh, *cariño*,' he said huskily, a cool challenge in his eyes. 'If I see your arms, I can clearly imagine the rest of you. And if I'm imagining the rest of you, I'm not keeping my mind on business.'

Her heart had been behaving itself when he'd first walked into the room but suddenly it was bumping frantically against her chest. 'You're very basic.'

'Yes.'

'So don't take me with you. If I'm a distraction, then leave me here.'

He gave a faint smile. 'One of the benefits of having a wife,' he drawled, 'is being able to present her when the occasion demands it.'

'And does it?'

'This evening? Yes, it so happens that it does. Fetch a

wrap,' he commanded, dragging his burning gaze from her body. 'And keep it on.'

'Perhaps you'd rather I wore a long coat?' Faith suggested acidly, using direct challenge as a method of disguising how deeply his words had affected her. *He wanted her with him.* Surely that was a positive sign?

He surprised her with a smile that was achingly sexy. 'Good idea. Coat and no dress. Just underwear.' His voice was deep and impossibly male. 'Later on I undo the coat and take you. And yes, this time you will have no excuse to stop.'

The vivid image his words created sent a burst of excitement through her stomach and it took her a moment to catch her breath. Trying desperately to conceal her reaction, Faith gritted her teeth. 'You're sex-mad, do you know that?'

'Gracias.'

She looked at him in exasperation. 'I didn't intend it as a compliment.' He was impossibly, arrogantly attractive and he shrugged his shoulders in a careless dismissal of her observation.

'Liking sex is a healthy and natural drive for a man. What's wrong with that?'

Wishing she'd never pursued this particular line of conversation, Faith drew in a long breath. 'Nothing. It's just—there are other things apart from sex. We could have a conversation.'

'Sí.' His eyes mocked her gently. 'Talking can be very intimate, I agree. Before and after sex.'

Now he was teasing her and the fact that he could succeed in making her hot and bothered even though she knew what he was doing, really irritated her. 'Talking isn't part of sex.'

'What do you think this is, if it isn't foreplay?' He murmured the words softly, his voice so sexy that she felt her limbs weaken. 'We are talking, yes, but we are both thinking about sex—'

'Raul, please don't do this.' She couldn't think clearly, not with his dark eyes suddenly alight with dangerous promise and his powerful body so achingly close.

'We both know what is coming later,' he purred. 'Each of us is thinking "how will it be?" and "can I wait that long?"' His normally fluent English seemed considerably less fluent than usual but there was no mistaking his meaning and his words were such an accurate assessment of her thoughts that she stilled, a bloom of colour touching her pale cheeks.

'That's not what I'm thinking,' she croaked and he gave a faint smile.

'Liar.'

She dragged her eyes from his. Only when she wasn't looking at him was there a chance that her brain would work. 'For a man with legendary intelligence, your goals are very shallow.'

'Would you be flattered if I climbed into bed with you and reached for a book?' He curved his hand around her waist, and she felt the instant response of her body.

'Do you ever think of anything other than sex?'

'*Sí*—sometimes I think of business.' He leaned forward and kissed her mouth, the hot slide of his tongue deliberately erotic. 'And now you need to stop distracting me or I am never going to get through the evening.'

'It isn't me, it's you—you started this.' But she was starting to feel the strain and he must have noticed because he slid his fingers under her chin and lifted her face to his.

'You're pale.'

She gave a careless shrug, trying not to betray everything that he made her feel. 'Jet lag. I'm tired.'

'No, it isn't that. I've seen you with more colour in your cheeks when you've been up all night with one of the horses.' He studied her closely, his scrutiny more than a little disturbing. 'Are you dizzy? Do you need a doctor?'

'No.' She didn't confess that she was just as wound up as

he was. Every nerve ending in her body was reminding her that he was close by.

He watched her for a moment, and then increased the pressure of his hand and urged her towards the door. 'If this evening is too much for you, tell me and you can go back to bed.' He flashed her a confident, self-satisfied smile. 'You see how thoughtful and caring I can be?'

'Would that be an empty bed, or a bed with you in it?'

'We both know you would be mortally offended if I wasn't in it, *cariño*,' he purred, amusement in his eyes as he pulled her against him and stole a swift kiss from her parted lips. 'Then you would be accusing me of not finding you attractive, no?'

Tied into knots by his kiss, his smile and his words, she couldn't even respond.

She was a hopeless case, Faith thought weakly as she followed his direction and walked through the door on shaking legs. Desperately she tried to think about something, anything, other than him.

'These people we're meeting tonight—' she glanced at him briefly '—do I need to know anything about them? I don't want to say the wrong thing. Who are they?'

'They own land.' Raul took her hand in his and drew her close to him as they walked up the path that led from the Beach House to the main courtyard of the *estancia*. 'Land that I want.'

'You already own ten-thousand acres. Why would you want their land?'

'Why settle for less when you can have more?' But something flickered in the depths of his dark eyes and she had a feeling that there was more to this business deal than he was revealing.

'In other words, you have a good reason and you're not planning to share it with me.'

He laughed. 'I love the fact that you have a sharp brain.'

'Just as long as I don't use it,' Faith said tartly and his

answer to that was to bring his mouth down on hers again, his kiss so impossibly skilled that the rest of her sharp rejoinder died in her brain.

'You taste good,' he murmured against her lips and she groaned and dragged her mouth away from his.

'You always *do* this to me.' She put her hands on his chest to steady herself, and then looked up at him. 'You're infuriating, do you know that? You use sex to shut me up.'

'*Not* true.' He bent his head and his mouth brushed her neck, that simple touch sufficient to send a thrill of excitement rushing through her.

'You're doing it again,' she gasped, wishing desperately that her body wasn't so responsive to his. 'Stop it, Raul.'

His mouth lingered, warm and full of promise. 'You want me to stop?' The erotic flick of his tongue fired her blood.

'No. Yes…' Sinking into a trance, Faith closed her eyes. 'I don't know. Where did you learn to do that?'

'I was born knowing,' he purred softly, but the twinkle in his eyes softened the arrogance of the statement. 'In Argentina, men know how to be men. And part of being a real man is being an incredible lover.'

'Your ego is enormous.'

His eyes darkened wickedly. 'That isn't my ego, *cariño*…'

All too aware of the strength and power of his arousal, Faith dragged herself out of his arms. 'All right, enough.' Flustered and shivering with desire, she held up a hand like a 'stop' sign. 'Just stand there and don't move for a minute.'

His gaze was slumberous and deadly. 'I love the fact that you're such a sexual woman.'

Faith gritted her teeth. 'I said *enough*! And no more kissing. I can't have a conversation while you're kissing me.'

One dark eyebrow swooped upwards in sardonic mockery. 'Precisely.'

Confused, her entire body buzzing, Faith glared at him. 'Do

you know that you use sex to avoid every subject that is remotely difficult? You never talk about things that matter.' Her head was still reeling from the slow, seductive touch of his mouth and for a moment she wished that he wasn't quite so skilled in that area. If he had been less accomplished as a lover, she might have been able to concentrate on their relationship.

His beautiful eyes narrowed. 'I don't solve problems by committee.'

'I'm not a committee. I'm your wife.'

'Sí, and you knew the type of man you were marrying.' His tone hardened slightly but his gaze was still on her mouth. 'If you don't want me to think about sex, don't dress provocatively.'

'Well, what do I wear then, Raul? Tell me, because I certainly don't know.' Shaken by the depth of her own response to him, Faith smoothed the dress over her hips. 'You're staring at me.'

'Because I don't understand you,' he breathed. 'You would prefer that I don't find you attractive?'

'No, of course not. I'd just like there to be more to our relationship than sex.'

His thick lashes lowered slightly as he surveyed her. 'You don't like the fact that I want to make love to you day and night?'

His words made her stomach tumble and she dragged her gaze away from his, her breathing shallow. 'Of course I do. Any woman would, but—'

'So what is the problem?' The careless lift of his broad shoulders indicated that as far as he was concerned, there was nothing to solve.

'I feel as though I'm banging my head against a brick wall.'

'This is because of your accident perhaps.'

She turned to look at him, ready to thump him for that comment, and then she saw the twinkle in his eyes and realised that he was teasing her. 'You really like to live dangerously.'

His slow smile was impossibly sexy. 'Of course.'

She gritted her teeth. 'I hate you, do you know that?'

'Sí, cariño.' Ignoring her attempts to keep at a distance, he hauled her into his arms and brought her hips in direct contact with his. 'I know just how much you hate me. About as much as I hate you.' Sexual tension erupted with explosive force and Faith groaned a faint protest against his seeking mouth.

'I had a career before I met you,' she muttered, but he smothered her words with another assault on her lips, the skilled stroke of his tongue almost unbearably exciting as he kissed her until her head spun. Finally he lifted his head slowly and the look he gave her was one of pure, undiluted masculine satisfaction.

'I have no objection to your career. I'm very modern in my outlook.'

Faith would have laughed but she no longer had the energy. 'Modern? You make Neolithic men look progressive. Why am I with you? I used to have a brain.'

He smiled at that. 'You still have a brain, cariño.'

'So why am I standing here, kissing you?'

'Because I am the best at what I do,' Raul drawled with a trace of humour. 'And your brain is occupied in responding. I love your brain. Never think I don't.' He cupped her face possessively and looked into her eyes. 'And now, enough. We have guests arriving.'

And that was that, Faith thought helplessly. As far as he was concerned, that was the end of yet another conversation where he'd tied her in knots and revealed absolutely nothing about himself.

'If these negotiations really are important to you, then

why are you taking me?' She turned away from him, unsure whether she was more annoyed with herself or him. 'I obviously just distract you.'

'I want you to be there.'

Resigning herself to the fact that she was unlikely to be given more of an explanation than that, Faith picked up her bag that she'd dropped on the floor when he'd kissed her. 'What role am I playing? Am I allowed to speak? Or do I pretend I've had a lobotomy?'

'You're my wife.' Raul smiled and that smile held such charm that for a moment Faith caught her breath.

'I hate it when you do that,' she muttered and his smile widened as he took her hand firmly in his.

'Do what?'

'You know what,' she said crossly, picking her way carefully up the path. 'You always use that smile of yours when you're losing an argument.'

'Lose?' He frowned at her. 'What is this "lose"? It isn't a word I know.'

'Very funny.' Faith pulled a face but she left her hand in his, enjoying the contact more than she was wiling to admit, even to herself. 'Perhaps I'm going to embarrass you tonight. You know I'm not at all commercial. I don't think I'm capable of making a good impression on a businessman.'

'You made a good impression on me.' Raul adjusted his long stride to match hers. 'And I'm a businessman.'

Her heart turned over at the unexpected compliment. 'You're lots of different things.'

'Desperate,' he said dryly, his smile full of wry self-mockery as he glanced at her. 'That's what I am at the moment, *cariño*. Thanks to you.'

Awareness exploded inside her. 'I thought we were supposed to be avoiding the topic of sex.'

'We were.' He let out a frustrated sigh. 'It's *your* fault.'

She tried to ignore the electrified atmosphere and changed the subject swiftly. 'So what do you want me to do this evening, seriously?'

'Try not to draw attention to yourself so that you don't distract me from the business in hand. This is a particularly tricky negotiation and I need to concentrate.' He took her hand in his and led her towards the main house just as a car purred into the courtyard.

'It's really that important to you? Any chance that you'll tell me why at some point?'

He didn't answer her question, and when she glanced towards him he was staring down the long driveway at an approaching car. Gone was the lazy, sexy smile that had made him so approachable. Now he just seemed cold and intimidating.

The car came to a halt in a cloud of dust and a man heaved himself awkwardly from the driver's seat, a sheen of sweat visible on his brow as he negotiated the heat and the demands of his own excessive body-weight. Faith guessed him to be in his fifties but it was obvious that he was holding on to his youth with grim determination. His shirt was open at the neck and strained over his thickened waist, his thinning hair artfully arranged to conceal the onset of baldness.

'Vásquez—I hear congratulations are due.'

'Pedro.' His hand outstretched and his tone cool, Raul strode forward and shook the man's hand and Faith watched while the other door opened and a woman slid elegantly out of the passenger seat.

Suddenly Faith understood why the man was so grimly determined not to be parted from his youth. The woman was stunning. She somehow managed to be both slender and curvaceous at the same time and the coal-black hair that hung straight over her bare shoulders shone like polished agate. Apparently undisturbed by the heat, she slowly removed the oversized sunglasses from her exquisite face to reveal almond-shaped eyes of surprising warmth. A friendly smile on her glossy mouth, she walked over to Faith, hands outstretched.

'So Raul finally took the plunge,' she said cheerfully, leaning forward and kissing Faith on both cheeks. Then she linked arms with her, as though they were firm friends, rather than total strangers. 'Half of Argentina is ready to kill you— the female half, of course. The male half are probably incredibly grateful. Finally they can sleep easy in their beds without feeling they need to lock up their wives. I'm Sofia.'

Confused by the other woman's direct approach and unsure how to respond, Faith glanced towards Raul but he was listening to something that Pedro was saying, his dark glossy head tilted because he was so much taller. Realising that he wasn't paying her any attention, Faith turned back to Sofia and froze.

The other woman was staring openly at Raul, a look of naked sexual appreciation in her eyes. Then she looked at Faith and grinned sheepishly. 'Oops, sorry. Caught red-handed.' She gave herself a mock smack on the wrist. 'Naughty me. But you have to admit that he *is* indecently handsome and I don't get to look at men like him very often. I'm sure you're used to women gazing at him. Being with Raul is a bit like owning a very rare and valuable painting—everyone wants to stare at it.'

Shocked and surprised by the hot spurt of jealousy that pumped through her veins, Faith struggled to stay polite. 'And your husband doesn't mind?'

'I can't imagine he'd be thrilled, but he has nothing to worry about. Raul and I were quite unsuited.'

Were?

For a moment Faith thought she had misheard, and then she looked into the other woman's eyes and her entire world shifted.

'You know him well?' *Why was she asking that question when she already knew the answer?*

'Pretty well.' Sofia looked at her. 'Oh dear. Me and my big mouth. Obviously the two of you haven't discussed his past. Very wise. If I was with Raul, I can't say I'd want to know about his past, either. One of the disadvantages of being with an *extremely* rich and handsome man is the knowledge that every other woman wants him too.'

'Sofia…' Raul's voice came from directly behind them and Sofia turned, her eyes dancing with laughter.

'Darling—no need to use that tone. I'm just pleased you finally found someone willing to put up with your domineering, macho ways on a permanent basis. How are you? You're looking good, but there's nothing new in that.'

Before Raul could respond, Pedro approached. Apparently unaware of the byplay, he was mopping his brow. 'Shall we get out of the heat?'

'Of course. We'll have drinks on the terrace.'

Pinned to the spot by shock, Faith looked at Raul in disbelief.

That was it? *That was all he was going to say?*

Tact and sensitivity wasn't his strong suit and she, more than anyone, was well aware of that—but still she couldn't quite believe that he'd intentionally invited his ex-mistress to join them for dinner without at least warning her.

It must have been an unfortunate coincidence.

She desperately wanted to believe that he hadn't known the woman was with Pedro—that any minute now he was going to throw her off his property. Because the alternative to that was to acknowledge that once again her feelings had been bottom of his agenda.

'It's cooler on the terrace,' Raul said smoothly, nothing in his body language suggesting that he considered anything to be amiss.

Faith flinched as though he'd struck her.

So that was it, then.

Clearly he expected her to smile and chat to his ex, while he concentrated on his business deal.

No wonder he hadn't told her what was expected of her.

He'd obviously known that she would have been on the first plane out of Buenos Aires.

Raul strode across the courtyard, Pedro by his side, nothing in his manner betraying the slightest hint of awkwardness.

Deprived of the opportunity to claw his impossibly handsome face, Faith wanted to turn and stalk in the opposite direction, but she was unable to do that either because the other woman tightened her hold on her arm.

'We have a word in Spanish to describe someone like him,' Sofia murmured, her voice like rich honey. '*Guapisimo*. It means "indescribably handsome". I haven't been here for a while,' she confided, as they moved onto the sunny, vine-covered terrace where several staff were poised ready to serve drinks. 'You must show me what Raul has done. This place is the talk of the international polo-circuit.'

Faith didn't bother replying—she was too busy planning ways to kill Raul—but first she turned some serious anger onto herself.

You fool, she chided herself. *You stupid fool.*

He said he wanted the marriage to work and that was all it took for you to run back to him.

He'd hurt her so, so badly but had she learned her lesson? No, she'd come back for more.

Was he being deliberately cruel? Was he reminding her once again that she'd driven him into a marriage, when in fact that wasn't what he'd wanted?

Was he was telling her that marriage wasn't going to stop him living his life the way he wanted to live it?

Was that what was going on here?

A wave of dizziness washed over her and for a terrifying moment she thought she might faint in front of him yet again.

Gritting her teeth with determination, she took several deep breaths and took a glass of champagne from one of Raul's staff. Deciding that it would be kill or cure, she drained it in several gulps.

Dimly aware of Raul's disapproving and slightly startled gaze, she raised the empty glass in his direction. 'To us, darling. And to all those little things you do for me that show just how much you care.'

His eyes narrowed, but whether or not he would have responded to her subtle jibe she had no idea because Pedro dutifully lifted his glass.

'To the pair of you. May you have a long and happy union.'

Faith was deeply regretting the fact that she'd downed the champagne. Her head was swimming again, and now she wasn't sure of the cause.

'So what is it that you do, Faith?' Pedro was blunt and straightforward but Faith was spared the need to reply by his wife's intervention.

'She's married to Raul,' Sofia murmured. 'Which means her time is totally occupied in the pursuit of looking gorgeous.' Her gaze lingered speculatively on Faith's newly cropped hair and Faith flushed.

'I'm a vet. I specialise in horses. Raul has an interesting breeding programme so I chose to come here and work.' *And never left.* But she would now. Any moment. She was going to walk out of the door and not look back.

As soon as she could be sure that her legs would hold her.

'Breeding? Well if there's anyone who could use some advice in that area, then it's Raul.' Sofia laughed. 'Breeding is probably the only area of life in which he has absolutely no experience. I never could quite see him changing a nappy.'

Faith glanced at Raul and found him looking at her. 'Faith is exceptionally talented. Especially with the animals themselves.'

Did he even realise that she was upset?

Deciding that she wasn't going to inflate his ego still further by showing him how much his careless behaviour had upset her, Faith stood her ground.

Apparently unaware of the dangerous shift in the atmosphere, Pedro took a mouthful of his champagne. 'One of my stallions is misbehaving—kicking out his box, biting his groom—the product of an extremely difficult early life, I wouldn't be surprised. He's born vicious.'

'No horse is born vicious.' Faith's years of training made it impossible for her to stay silent. 'It's the way they've been treated that makes them that way. If he's vicious then he obviously feels he needs to defend himself from something.' Her eyes still held Raul's. 'All of us have the potential to be vicious if the provocation is sufficient.'

Raul's eyes narrowed but Pedro simply nodded, his mind clearly still on the problem of his horse.

'You could be right. To be honest, I have no idea what's in his past. My stud groom rescued him from somewhere or other. Thought he had potential. I'm not so sure. I think he needs to be taught who's boss.'

A bubble of laughter rose in Faith's throat. 'In my experience a display of macho domination rarely achieves the desired effect. I've always found that people respond better when you aim for a partnership of trust and respect.'

'People?' Pedro looked at her quizzically. 'I thought we were talking about horses.'

'Horses, people.' Faith shrugged. 'The principles are the same. The foundation of a good relationship is trust and respect.' She emphasised both words and Raul shot her a warning glance, which she interpreted as meaning: *be careful. This deal is important to me.*

And suddenly she wondered if he really did care about anything other than the acquisition of wealth.

Why else would he have chosen to flaunt his previous relationships in front of his wife?

Still apparently oblivious to the undercurrents swirling around them, Pedro drained his champagne. 'You're letting a woman dictate how your horses are handled, Vásquez?'

'I employ the best.'

Pedro frowned. 'I don't think I've ever met a female vet before.'

Faith took a sip of orange juice. 'Well, we're pretty much the same as the male variety, only we're usually a little smaller because our bodies don't have to make room for the ego.'

Sofia laughed with delight. 'I absolutely adore the English sense of humour.'

Pedro reached for a handkerchief and mopped his brow. 'I know it isn't considered politically correct to say so, but I still don't believe that a woman can do everything a man can do.'

'I completely agree.' Faith took another sip of her orange juice. 'No matter how hard I try I simply can't behave in a callous, insensitive fashion. Fortunately that major defect in my character hasn't affected my ability as a vet. Generally animals respond very well to a woman's touch.'

Finally alerted to the fact that the atmosphere wasn't all it should be, Pedro glanced at Raul who displayed a characteristic lack of concern.

'As you can see, my wife is as spirited as the horses she loves so much. Faith is extremely well qualified.'

Pedro's eyebrows shot upwards. 'If she's that well qualified, why doesn't she have her own practice?'

'She met me,' Raul murmured. 'And I derailed her career.'

'Postponed,' Faith corrected him sharply. 'I can return to my career any time I choose to do so.'

Sofia smiled. 'So you fell in love.'

'Who wouldn't love Argentina?' Faith deliberately chose

to misunderstand her. 'It's a fascinating and beautiful country. And the perfect place to practise equine medicine.'

'He's dangerous in the stable.' Pedro was back to the subject of his horse. 'We can't let him out, he'll create havoc.'

'But horses are herd animals,' Faith said. 'They like social contact. Especially the stallions. They are naturally dominant and assertive.'

'Sounds uncannily like Raul,' Sofia drawled. 'Dominant, assertive, a challenge to handle...'

Faith looked at her, startled, because actually the description she'd used *did* sound like Raul.

How many difficult stallions had she handled who'd appeared to give no thought to the effect they had on those around them?

He probably hadn't invited his ex-mistress here with the express purpose of upsetting her. He'd invited her here because he was thoughtless. But did that really make his actions any more acceptable?

How in a million years could she ever be happy with a man this insensitive to her feelings?

Deep in thought, Pedro didn't appear to have heard his wife's comment. 'I might send him over to you, if that is within your realm of experience? Might be a bit much for you.'

Raul frowned. 'There's nothing Faith can't handle. She's very clever.'

'There's nothing clever about it,' Faith said. 'They just need patience and understanding.'

'Now I'm really confused.' A cheeky gleam in her eyes, Sofia laughed. 'Are we talking about Raul or the stallion? Clearly Faith has a special way with difficult men, since she dragged you to the altar.' Sofia slid her arm into Faith's again. 'And now, enough of this. Raul if you don't feed me soon I swear I shall join the horses in your yard. They're better cared for.'

CHAPTER NINE

THEY enjoyed a typical Argentine *asado*—a barbecue cooked over an open fire—and it was dark when Faith and Raul waved their guests off and walked back towards the Beach House.

Furious with him for hurting her and even more furious with herself for caring, Faith stalked ahead, her heels tapping on the path. She didn't trust herself to speak for fear of exploding and she wasn't sure whether she'd produce tears or anger.

'When you're angry, your neck seems longer,' Raul drawled from behind her and she straightened her shoulders and increased her pace. 'And that won't work, either, because my legs are longer than yours and I can walk faster.'

She turned then, like a cornered animal ready to fight. 'Do you really want to have this conversation out here? Think hard, Raul, because you probably won't want an audience for what I'm going to say.'

Apparently unconcerned, he lifted a bronzed hand to his throat and loosened the top button of his shirt. 'I thought we'd had enough conversation for one day.'

'If you want to avoid conversation, *don't* invite your ex-girl-friends to dinner without at least having the courtesy to warn me.'

Raul's eyes narrowed defensively. 'Given that you are the

one wearing the wedding ring, you have absolutely no reason to be jealous.'

'It isn't about being jealous, it's about courtesy.' Faith kept her eyes on his, ignoring the dangerous shimmer in his eyes that warned her of the shift in his mood. 'Let's look at this another way—what would you have done if you discovered that I had invited an ex-boyfriend to dinner?'

'Flattened him,' Raul said in a cool tone. 'But that's entirely different.'

'It is *not* different. I have feelings, Raul. It would be nice if you would remember that.' Shaking so much she could hardly stand, she turned sharply and walked through the door of the Beach House. Dropping her bag as she walked, she went straight through to the bedroom and removed her earrings, dropping them on the bedside table.

'I don't understand your problem.' He stalked into the room like a very angry jungle-cat and she clamped her teeth onto her lower lip to stop herself from crying.

'I know you don't,' she whispered. 'And that *is* the problem, Raul. You don't seem to be able to stop yourself hurting me. You never think about *my* feelings and I promised myself that I wasn't going to allow you to do this to me again.' She kept her back to him, willing herself not to break down and sob.

'That is a totally unfair accusation,' he snarled, 'Given that it was precisely to protect your feelings that I didn't tell you.'

'So in other words, you knew I would be upset.'

She turned and then wished she hadn't because the physical impact of the man almost fused her brain. He was extravagantly, impossibly handsome, his features bold and masculine, his posture one of complete control.

Immediately on the defensive, his fabulous dark eyes narrowed to two dangerous slits. 'I thought you'd behave like a typical woman, and you've just proved me right.'

Faith inhaled sharply. 'She taunted me with your relationship. Waved it under my nose like a red flag. *We have a word
for him in Spanish*—guapisimo.' She mimicked the other
woman perfectly and then glared. 'Well let's see how *guapisimo* you are when I've blacked your eye, Raul.'

'You are behaving in a totally unreasonable fashion.'

'You think it's unreasonable of me to be upset?'

'Frankly? Yes. She's history.'

'She couldn't take her eyes off you!'

'That's her problem, not mine,' Raul replied instantly.
'And not yours, either.'

He didn't have a clue!

'Perhaps I am being silly but she knew a great deal about
you,' she breathed. 'And I couldn't work out whether she was
being friendly or nasty. But I had the distinct impression that
she wished she was the one who was married to you.'

'She wouldn't have been able to handle me in a million
years.' He yanked the tie from his throat with an impatient
hand and Faith swallowed, transfixed by the hint of bronzed
male skin and the tangle of dark hair at the base of his throat.

She wasn't sure *she* could handle him.

'She is very beautiful.'

'Don't do this to yourself,' he warned, dropping the tie and
slowly undoing the buttons on his shirt. 'You're more intelligent than that, Faith. I never pretended not to have a past
and you have no reason to be insecure.'

'Of course I have,' Faith said quietly. 'I know you didn't
want this marriage.'

'Don't do that female thing of dissecting every single
action,' he warned in a throaty voice. 'You'll just hurt yourself.'

'I just spent an evening with a woman who hammered home
just how well she knows you. If I didn't have doubts about sus-
taining this marriage before, then I certainly have them now.'

'Sofia has *nothing* to do with our marriage.'

'You invited your ex-girlfriend into our home without telling me and expected me to be nice to her! That has *everything* to do with our marriage.'

They were circling each other like animals and the atmosphere in the room heated and sparked.

Raul watched her with raw frustration. 'Actually, I invited a business associate into our home in order to negotiate an important deal. Sofia just happens to be his wife. I didn't think that was important, given that she's my *ex*-girlfriend. What possible reason would there be for you to be so upset?'

'Because *I'm your wife*!'

'Precisely,' he drawled in a sardonic voice, his handsome face cold and unsympathetic. *'Cuenta his beneficios.'*

'What does that mean?'

'Count your blessings. *You're* the one wearing my ring. If anyone around here should be upset, it's Sofia, not you.'

Faith was so shocked by his unique interpretation of the facts, that for a moment she couldn't voice a response. 'You can't possibly mean that. Even you can't be *that* arrogant and insensitive.'

The air around them heated to a fierce blaze.

'Don't do this, Faith,' he warned softly, his voice as deadly as the expression in his eyes. *'Don't do this to us.'*

'I'm not the one doing it, Raul,' she spat, but she saw him step towards her and every muscle in her body quivered with tension. 'That's far enough.'

If he came close to her, *if he touched her*…

Terrified that he was going to do just that, she went to stalk past him but he moved so swiftly that she didn't stand a chance. And she knew deep down that she'd never had a chance. With merciless intent one hand locked around her wrist and the other came round her waist.

'No, Raul.' She squirmed and writhed, the silk of her dress sliding against the hard muscle of his thighs. 'Don't you *dare* touch me. After what you did tonight, you're never touching me again!' But they were just words and both of them knew it. The atmosphere was thick with what they were both feeling, and in many ways that made it worse because she so badly wanted to be able to walk away from this man. 'Let me go.'

'Why?' He brought his mouth close to hers and she turned her head to avoid the contact, her eyes closing as she felt the roughness of his jaw scrape the sensitive skin of her cheek. 'Why would I do that?'

'Because we're making each other miserable.'

'Only when we talk, *cariño*,' he murmured softly into her ear, his low masculine voice as sensuous as his touch. 'We hadn't touched each other for weeks and it's been driving both of us mad—'

'No, Raul, that isn't—' She broke off with a gasp as his mouth traced the line of her jaw. 'Don't do that—don't do that.'

But he wasn't listening. 'I haven't paid you enough attention.'

'That isn't what I was saying—' She moaned as his mouth found the tiny pulse at the base of her throat. 'Raul, I'm asking you not to—'

'What? You're asking me not to do what?' His strong fingers slid around her cheek and with firm, relentless pressure he drew her lips back towards his. His mouth hovered a breath away from hers, but he didn't take the kiss. 'Why do you fight this?'

'Because I have to,' she whispered. 'For my sanity and my self-respect.' It was the last desperate plea of someone who was drowning and the words turned to a groan as his mouth finally brushed hers in a suggestive, sensuous kiss.

Flames erupted though her body with explosive force and she felt her insides turn to hot, molten lava.

'You don't want this?' His tone husky and full of dark, sexual promise, he lowered his head and lightly explored the edges of her mouth with his, the erotic slide of his tongue plunging her straight into a whirlpool of excitement. She was sucked downwards, spinning, in sexual free-fall. 'If you don't want to do this, then stop me,' he murmured, his mouth still against hers as he ruthlessly used every skill to drive her wild. 'Walk away, if that's what you want to do.'

Every single part of her was on fire, burning up in the heat of his seduction. 'How can I when you're holding me?'

His dangerously clever mouth curved into a sardonic smile. 'I let go of you five minutes ago, *cariño*. So why are you still pressed up against me?' He gave her less than five seconds for the truth of that statement to sink into her fevered brain and then he brought his mouth down on hers in a bruising, glorious kiss that sent both of them out of control.

This time there was no careful teasing or skilfully orchestrated seduction. There were no tentative touches of his tongue or sly brushes of his firm lips. Instead he claimed her mouth with his, driving out her protests with the force of his kiss.

And she responded because the way he kissed her demanded nothing less.

All the emotion and incredible tension that had been building over the past weeks exploded to the surface and they devoured each other hungrily as their bodies thundered with need.

His mouth didn't leave hers but his hands dropped to her shoulders and he tore ruthlessly through the fabric of her dress. It slithered to the floor of the bedroom and was instantly forgotten by both of them because his hand was on her breast and Faith gave an agonised moan and closed her eyes.

Her head was filled with a kaleidoscope of light, and as his fingers grazed the sensitised peaks of her breasts, sharp arrows of desire shot through her body straight to the very heart of her. She leaned into him, pressing herself against his throbbing, thickened shaft, her response to him every bit as animal and basic as his was to hers.

They had no control. None. And it had always been this way with them.

'Now,' Faith sobbed. 'Now—' And she tore impatiently at his shirt, drew her nails through the dark hair that covered his chest and then moved her hand lower to cover him. His responsive groan echoed her own desperation and when he lifted her, she slipped both arms round his neck because to let him go now would have been unthinkable.

Neither of them was thinking, each of them just responding to a sensual hunger so basic that it bordered on the shocking.

She wanted to touch and taste and he obviously felt the same way because his hand went between her legs and she cried out and arched against him in instant response. When he drew a skilled finger over her silken warmth, she gave a shiver of delicious pleasure, the anticipation exploding inside her.

Somehow she was on her back on the bed and he was above her—bronzed, virile and very much in control. When his mouth found her breast she sobbed with pleasure and when his fingers slid deep, she raked her nails over the hard muscle of his shoulders because his touch was so unerringly skilled and confident that she could do nothing else.

The room was dark except for a shaft of moonlight that sent a spotlight across the floor and she opened her eyes and looked straight into his. Dark locked with green for a fiery, breathless moment and she just feasted on him, savouring the hard, packed muscle of his shoulders and chest and the perfect lines of his bone structure. He was hot, hard, handsome and *hers*—all arrogant, dominant male, the weight of his powerful body pinning her into a position of total submission.

'Mine,' he growled possessively, his hand in the silken curls that guarded the most private part of her. 'You are mine—'

'Yes—' She didn't want to be anyone else's ever and just

to be sure that he knew that she slid her leg over his thigh in a blatant invitation that drew a groan from him.

'Wait.' His breathing erratic, he swore softly in Spanish. There was a brief pause and then he surged into her with all the force of his passion, the power of his silken invasion driving her breath from her body because he was big.

Hard and powerful, he filled her completely and for a moment she struggled to breathe, completely overwhelmed by the feel of him deep inside her. Engulfed by excitement that terrified her in its intensity, she stared up at him in the semi-darkness, completely transported by the exquisite pleasure that their bodies created together. There was nothing but the two of them, their bodies locked in one glorious explosion of excitement as he drove into her with ravenous, fiery intensity. His hand was locked in her hair, her nails were in his shoulders and she urged him on with the thrust of her hips, her legs spread for him, her back pressed against the bed.

'Raul—' She groaned his name and he slid an arm under her hips, strong, virile and demanding as he lifted her into each surging thrust of his powerful body.

It was wild, uninhibited and out of control and when she shot into her first orgasm she took him with her, his body erupting with potent force as her inner muscles tightened around him. Mouths clashed, hearts raced, breathing quickened as every one of their senses was swamped by incredible sensation and they drove each other through wave after wave of pulsing ecstasy. Bodies slick and hot, they kissed their way through the whole incredible experience until the explosion was reduced to flickering, fluttering aftershocks.

Lying on the tangled sheets, weakened by pleasure, Faith wrapped her arms around him tightly and waited for her heartbeat to slow. She was so dazed after her climax that when he slid down her body and deliberately parted her thighs, she was unable to do more than whimper a faint protest.

'I love your body,' he murmured, his lips trailing a path that started at her knee and slowly traced the length of her thigh. 'Do you know how much I love your body? Because if you don't then I'm about to show you…'

Her brain and body still pulsing in the aftermath of her last orgasm, Faith tried to squirm away from him, too weakened to even consider another sensual onslaught.

'No, Raul,' she choked. 'I don't think I can—'

'Then I'll prove you wrong,' he said huskily, guiding her thighs apart with single-minded focus and complete disregard for any modesty on her part. He held her there for a moment, surveying the tangle of bright golden curls with a hungry, sexual gaze that made her squirm self-consciously.

'Don't.'

'I'm admiring.' His mouth curved into a slow, teasing smile. 'How can you be shy? On the surface you can be very English and proper.' He stroked a strong confident finger along the most intimate part of her and she curled her fingers into the sheets because he knew exactly what he was doing, his gentle touch impossibly, agonisingly accurate.

'Raul—?'

'But *below* the surface—' his finger slid deep inside her '—you are wild. All bubbling passion. All mine.' And to prove that point, he lowered his head and slid his tongue over the delicate bud of her womanhood and she cried out in shock because her whole body reacted so dramatically to his touch.

She was consumed by arousal, acutely conscious of every move he made; of the restless flick of his tongue, the flex of muscle as he supported himself on his arms, the roughness of his jaw against the smooth skin of her inner thigh—and it was so agonisingly perfect and he was so skilled that she shot into another climax that he caught with his mouth and fingers.

He slid up her body, fastened his mouth to hers and kissed her deeply, and then he shifted slightly and turned her over.

For a moment Faith just lay on her front, her eyes closed, her body still quivering from the touch of his mouth. Then she felt him move and gasped as his hard fingers captured her hips and lifted her onto her knees.

'Raul—'

'I *love* it this way,' he groaned and before she could wriggle away or protest that she just wasn't ready for more, *that she just couldn't do this again*, he sank into her with a decisive thrust.

Her trembling, sensitised body clamped around his in ecstatic pleasure, apparently ignoring her brain, which was telling her that she just couldn't be doing this again.

He surged deep into her slick heat and it felt so mind-blowingly good that she cried out in shock. In this position he controlled her utterly, his hands holding her bottom, the roughness of the hair on his thighs brushing against her soft flesh. The ache inside her grew and grew with each purposeful thrust of his body and the slow ripples of pleasure spread and built to a crescendo until she was caught in a vortex of excitement so intense that she lost touch with reality.

She was on fire, her senses stormed by an attack of almost excruciating pleasure, her climax so intense that she barely registered the rhythmic thrusts that signalled his own release. For a moment there was nothing but pure, blind ecstasy, a shower of erotic sensations that left her in a state of numb shock and speechless disbelief.

Boneless and exhausted, Faith flopped forwards onto the bed in a weakened, quivering state and Raul sprawled next to her, his lean, powerful body suddenly relaxed, the smile on his face clearly reflecting his belief in his own sexual supremacy.

For a moment Faith just lay there, too shattered to speak. Part of her was afraid to move or draw attention to herself in any way in case he just hauled her against him and tried yet another position. And another part of her—a wicked, wanton part of her that she didn't understand—wanted him to do just that because he was so incredibly gifted and she couldn't get enough of him.

Acknowledging that fact made her turn her face into the sheets with a groan of disbelief and mortification. No matter how she liked to pride herself on her brain, she was a complete pushover when it came to this man.

He only had to touch her and she was his. Every time. Every way. Whenever he wanted.

And just what would her pathetic display of female submission have done to his already over-inflated ego?

Raul already thought he was the best and hadn't she just gone right ahead and proved it?

She raised herself on her elbow but before she could speak or do anything, he rolled her onto her back and flattened her to the bed again, his gaze surprisingly gentle as he studied her from beneath thick, dark lashes.

That long, slumberous look softened everything inside her and her stomach and heart performed a series of acrobatics as she stared up at him.

He *cared*, she knew he did and her own gaze softened in response as she waited for him to say something affectionate. After what they'd shared, how could he fail to?

He stroked her flushed cheek with gentle fingers and lowered his head to kiss her gently on the mouth.

'*Now* talk to me about feeling insecure,' he breathed and then rose from the bed in a fluid movement and strode into the bathroom with long, confident strides.

Faith stared up at the ceiling in stunned, silent disbelief.

That was why he'd made love to her over and over again?
To try and prove that she had no reason to be jealous?

Feeling numb inside, she slid off the bed and followed him on shaking legs into the bathroom.

'Insecure?' She croaked the word from the doorway. 'That

was why you made love to me? Not because you love me or wanted me, but just to prove a point?'

His strong, muscular body already under the shower, he gave a shrug of his shoulders. 'After the last few hours it should be obvious that I'm not thinking of any woman other than you.'

Faith swallowed. 'I wanted you to think about my feelings. A conversation would have done the trick.'

'I've always been more of a practical kind of guy,' he drawled, tilting his head back so that the water cascaded over his glossy dark hair and bronzed shoulders. 'And that is a ridiculous accusation because I have been thinking of nothing *but* your feelings for the past few hours, *cariño*.' Wiping the water from his eyes, he threw her a sexy, suggestive smile.

'Not those sorts of feelings!' This was the wrong place to have this talk, Faith realised numbly. He was gloriously, unashamedly naked, his aggressively masculine body proudly on display in front of her and she just couldn't concentrate because she was agonisingly aware of his broad, powerful shoulders, the burst of dark body hair that shadowed the centre of his chest and the impressive contours of his manhood.

Averting her eyes, she concentrated her attention on the neat pile of towels. 'Tell me something,' she asked shakily. 'Why is it that you think sex solves everything?'

Without answering her question, he stemmed the flow of the water and stepped out of the shower, completely unself-conscious. 'Towel, please?'

She handed him a towel and too late realised her mistake because he closed his fingers around her wrist and hauled her hard against his damp, naked body. 'You want to know why it is that I think sex solves everything?' His mouth hovered above hers and his damp, heated skin brushed her quivering flesh. 'Before, we were arguing and you were angry with me. You were spitting like an angry cat and now you no longer want to spit and you are no longer angry—so you see sex *does* solve problems.' Having driven home his point, he released her and raked wet spears of hair from his eyes with strong, confident fingers while Faith stared at him helplessly.

'I feel more like your mistress than your wife.'

Raul shot her a meaningful look. 'Considering the effect that marriage can have on a couple's sex life, you should be relieved about that.'

'You think you're such a genius in bed, don't you?'

'No.' He hooked the towel round his waist and gave her a slow, dangerous smile. '*You* are the one who makes me think I am a genius in bed. You melt, you sob.' He shrugged. 'You like what I do to you, *cariño*.'

Knowing that it was true, her cheeks coloured. 'I promised myself I wasn't going to let you hurt me again, Raul.'

He frowned. 'I made sure you were protected.'

'I didn't mean that,' she muttered and his eyes narrowed. 'So what then? I was too rough?'

'No!' She was silent for a moment, impossibly aware of his searching gaze. 'It doesn't matter.'

'*Sí*, it matters. If it brings that look into your eyes after we have made love, then it matters.' With an impatient sigh, he took her face in his hands and stroked his thumbs over her cheeks. 'All right, if you want to talk, we will talk. Go on. I'm listening.'

'That isn't enough! You have to do some of the talking, too. This chemistry between us is amazing, we make love and it's like nothing I've ever felt before.' It was difficult for her to be so painfully honest because she was making herself vulnerable and he was so completely *in*vulnerable. 'When we're together like this I feel so close to you but when it's over I realise that I'm not close at all. It's just physical. I don't *know* you at all. We don't talk. Even tonight we didn't talk because the moment I raised a problem, you just turned to sex. I really do feel more like your mistress than your wife.'

'A woman thinks she wants a man to be honest with her but what she is *really* saying is that she wants that man to tell her what she wants to hear.' His tone was cool. 'I'm not like that. I don't lie.'

'All right, fine, don't lie. *But I need you to think about my feelings!*'

He released her and stepped away. 'This business with Pedro is concluded. You won't have to see Sofia again.'

'It isn't just about Sofia. She's just a symptom of what's wrong with our relationship—the fact that we don't *talk*. When we have a problem, I want us to talk about it. I don't just want you to throw me on the bed and have sex with me! I want to *know* you, Raul. And if the truth about how you feel is painful to hear, so be it. At least it's the truth. I want to know you and I want you to know me.'

His dark eyes were shuttered and she almost felt his emotional retreat.

'That is why women have female friends, so that they can chew over issues that are entirely irrelevant to men.' Raul released her and stepped away, his handsome face cold. 'I just gave you a whole lot of messages, all of them positive. If you choose not to read them, then it's up to you.' He strode back into the bedroom leaving her staring after him in exasperation.

Exhausted after her sexual marathon with Raul, Faith slept late and woke to find Raul gone.

Deciding that she needed a distraction, she dressed quickly and walked over to the stables.

As usual they were a hive of activity and Eduardo greeted her with his usual warmth. 'It is good to see you back. Raul is on the polo field, working off his energy with some of the guests.'

Faith spent a few minutes with her favourite horses and

then walked towards the nearest polo field where a game was being played.

People came from all over the world to play polo on Raul's *estancia* but only rarely were they afforded the privilege of playing with the boss himself—but today, it seemed, was one of those prized occasions.

Raul thundered down the field with such an astonishing burst of acceleration that the watching crowd of guests and grooms gave a collective gasp. He rode his pony alongside his opponent's mount, moving him away from the ball so that he could take possession.

'And that's how it's done,' murmured one of the grooms who was watching. 'Just glorious.'

The ponies were drenched in sweat and above them the sun blazed in a perfectly blue sky.

Where did he find the stamina? Faith wondered, watching Raul demonstrate a move to one of the guests and then drive his horse down the field after the ball. He'd had virtually no sleep and yet he was as energetic as ever.

The temperature rocketed and dust flew from the ground as the ponies stampeded over the grass.

Faith watched him, thinking about the parallel Sofia had drawn between Raul and a stallion.

Even the most difficult stallion could be tamed.

But she hadn't tamed Raul, had she?

She'd trapped him. Not intentionally, but if she'd known how he'd felt she never would have gone ahead with the wedding, no matter how much she'd loved him. But the truth was that she'd loved him so much and she'd thought their relationship so perfect, that she hadn't even questioned his proposal. To her it had been a natural progression.

And he hadn't given her the chance to question it.

It was only now, looking back on it, that she realised that from that point until the day of their wedding, he'd been running.

In the middle of delicate negotiations with some company in the Far East, he'd flown to Japan for two weeks and then on to New York.

He hadn't come home and at the time she hadn't thought it particularly odd. Raul set himself a punishing work schedule and his absence hadn't seemed particularly strange. *Until now.*

Faith watched as the horses came off the field and the grooms sprang into action. She'd been so wrapped up in her own emotions she hadn't really thought about his. When he'd immediately proposed marriage, she'd assumed everything was all right.

Naïvely thinking that their love had been sufficient for him to make him rethink his views on marriage, she'd gone ahead without questioning how he really felt.

Arrogance? She'd accused him of arrogance but she'd been the one with arrogance, hadn't she? She'd assumed that she was different from all the other women he'd ever been with. She'd thought that was why he'd been so eager to marry her.

Raul rode over to her and vaulted from his horse. 'You're awake.'

A groom took the horse from him and he walked with her back towards the Beach House. 'You're very quiet. Sofia again?'

'No.' Her voice was small because she was feeling completely and utterly tormented with guilt and Raul gave a driven sigh.

'I have no feelings for her whatsoever. I thought I'd made that clear.'

'Actually I'm not thinking about Sofia,' Faith muttered. 'I'm thinking about us. Our marriage. The baby.' She felt his immediate withdrawal and grabbed his hand in a desperate little movement, as if holding on to him physically might prevent his emotional retreat. 'Don't back off. I *know* this is difficult but will you at least talk?' She watched him, recognising all the signs as he placed himself well and truly on the defensive.

His eyes were hard as diamonds, his thin mouth an uncompromising line in his handsome face. Every muscle in his powerful frame vibrated with tension and his body language screamed 'keep off'. 'I *know* how upset you are about losing the baby. I fail to see what talking achieves unless you simply want to make me feel more guilty.' His raw tone stunned her.

'I—I'm not trying to make you feel guilty.' She shook her head. 'Why would you think that?'

He inhaled deeply and something flickered in the depths of his eyes. 'I suppose because I *do* feel guilty,' he confessed in a husky voice. 'You lost that baby because of me.'

'No—'

'I upset you—'

'*After* I lost the baby,' she said gently. 'And even if it had been before, you wouldn't have been the cause.' She swallowed and gave a painful smile. 'It wasn't anyone's fault, Raul. I think it's normal to feel like that, but it wasn't anyone's fault. Miscarriage is horribly common. A doctor in the hospital told me that—' She broke off for a moment, a rush of emotion catching her by surprise. 'He told me that some babies just don't stick and that is nature's way of saying that something isn't quite right.' Her hand was still on his arm and she felt the flex of muscle under her fingers.

'Fine.' His voice was as tense as his body. 'Good.'

'That wasn't what I wanted to say,' she mumbled quietly. 'I wanted to say that I'm sorry.'

He stilled, and a faint flush spread across his cheekbones, highlighting his striking features. 'So you admit that you became pregnant on purpose?'

'No!' Horrified by his interpretation of her apology, she stared at him. 'No. It was an accident.'

'Then why *are* you saying sorry?'

'Because I never once saw it from your point of view. And I've only just realised that,' Faith admitted wearily. 'I discovered I was pregnant and I was a bit nervous but when you immediately proposed, I assumed you were all right with it. I—I wasn't really thinking. I should have questioned you more closely. There was no way I would have married you if you had doubts.'

He was cold and uncommunicative. 'I didn't have doubts.'

'You didn't want to get married!'

'Once you told me you were pregnant, there was never a choice.'

'So you did the decent thing.' Admitting that was so hard and Faith gave a painful smile and let go of his arm. 'I thought you were marrying me because we had a good relationship,' she admitted. 'Silly me, hmm?' She tried to keep her tone light but the pain cracked her voice and she heard him inhale sharply.

'We *did* have a good relationship,' he snapped impatiently. 'We still do.'

'In the bedroom,' she said dryly and he frowned.

'That isn't true. We talk. You're a very intelligent woman and you have an opinion on everything.'

'We didn't talk about feelings,' Faith muttered. 'And especially we didn't talk about *your* feelings that I was pregnant. So I'm apologising for that. I'm sorry if this marriage wasn't what you wanted and I'm sorry I didn't stop you doing the decent thing.'

'*Nothing* you said or did would have stopped me marrying you,' Raul delivered in a forceful tone. 'So you can tick that problem off your list of things to talk about.'

'Maybe not when I was pregnant, but if I hadn't been pregnant or if I had told you I'd lost the baby before the wedding—' She broke off and he cursed softly, his dark eyes glinting with naked exasperation.

'Last night we were happy! Now you're upset and for no reason! This is why I don't like talking endlessly about issues that can't be changed.'

'Was it Sofia?' The question burst from her and she put a hand on his arm. 'Something must have made you feel this way. Was she the reason that you never wanted marriage or children? *Did she hurt you?*'

He shut down like a nuclear reactor in an emergency. Nothing was going to escape.

'We're married, Faith,' he said coldly. 'Leave it at that.'

And he turned and walked into the Beach House, the set of his shoulders warning her not to follow.

CHAPTER TEN

FAITH curled up on one of the white sofas in the Beach House, horribly conscious of Raul's absence and furious with herself for her lack of tact.

Why had she pushed him?

After their conversation—*the conversation that she'd forced*—he'd changed into a sleek dark suit, apparently cut to display every single one of his assets, and announced that he had business in Buenos Aires.

And she hadn't seen him since. Now she deeply regretted having brought the subject up. She should never have asked him why he didn't want babies and marriage and most particularly she should not have mentioned Sofia's name.

Wishing desperately that she could wind the clock back, Faith took a sip of water.

At some stage Maria had brought her some lunch, but she didn't feel like eating. Her stomach was churning and she felt horribly sick but she knew it was just nerves.

She was totally on edge and unable to relax. She'd tried to understand him and in the process she'd driven him away and now she didn't know how to solve the new problem she'd created. He was very upset, she knew that much. When Raul was cornered, he fought and when he couldn't fight, he retreated.

It reminded her of the day she'd told him about the baby.

He'd immediately proposed, bought her a ring and then proceeded to absent himself on business. At the time she'd just assumed that was normal for him—after all he was a staggeringly successful billionaire with a corporation to run—but now she knew him better she could see that he'd been doing an entirely different sort of running. The sort that left a problem far behind.

And she wasn't much better, was she?

Hadn't she done exactly the same on their wedding day? True, he'd made a grossly insensitive remark but she wished now that she'd stood her ground and forced him to talk about it.

Yes, she'd been devastated about the baby but running hadn't helped.

They were both as bad as each other.

Except that she wasn't running any more. Nor was she going to try and push him to talk to her.

She was handling him all wrong, she could see that now. The more she pushed, the more he resisted. Somehow she needed to persuade him to come to her.

She stared at the food on her plate, deep in thought, her mind once again drifting back to the comment Sofia had made about Raul being like a difficult stallion. In a way she was right. There were similarities. Raul was aggressively masculine, assertive and dominant. And the way to handle that sort of personality was with gentleness and patience. There was no way she was going to force a man like Raul to tell her anything he didn't want to.

She had to earn his trust.

He hated talking about emotions, so she'd stop doing that.

She'd stop dwelling on the past and concentrate on the present—on being happy together. Even *he* had agreed that they'd been happy before she'd become pregnant. All she needed to do was try and recapture that. And as for what was going to happen in the long term—well, she wasn't even going to think about that now.

The sight of the food making her feel ill, she rose to her feet and wandered down to the beach with a book but she couldn't concentrate on that either, so she went to the stables instead, and worked alongside the grooms for the afternoon.

Being with the horses calmed her slightly but still she couldn't stop thinking about Raul and kept one eye on the drive, desperately hoping to hear the throaty roar of his car or the sound of the helicopter which would have announced his return.

Eventually she gave up watching and returned to the Beach House for a shower.

Still he didn't appear and she picked up the phone, intending to call him, and then put it down again instantly, afraid of looking needy—afraid that in his current mood he'd think she was hassling him.

Where was he?

Had she driven him away for good this time?

Exhausted and miserable, she lay down on the bed and turned out the light. What was the point in waiting up for him when he so clearly didn't want her company?

Having spent the day trying to work off his dangerous mood, Raul waited until dark to return to the Beach House, assuming that Faith would be asleep and he'd avoid another bout of female confrontation.

He spoke five languages fluently but never, ever would he understand women.

First she'd been angry with him and now she seemed to think he might need to talk about his feelings.

With an impatient frown, he threw his jacket down on the chair and poured himself a large drink.

Why was it that women thought that spilling their guts was a good thing?

As far as he was concerned it was a pointless exercise, designed to make everyone feel a thousand times worse. In his opinion, the secret of success lay in the ability to stifle and suppress any emotions that threatened one's equilibrium.

And thanks to Faith's persistent probing, his emotions were definitely threatening. She'd opened parts of his mind that he'd kept safely sealed for years.

His hand tightening around the glass, he swallowed the drink in one mouthful, ruthlessly pushing back against the thoughts that were closing in on him, cursing Faith for her desire to know him better.

She didn't want to know *that* part of him, he thought grimly, depositing the empty glass on the table.

Intentionally or not, she was edging him closer to something that he'd avoided for his entire adult life. It loomed in front of him, a dark, deadly swarm of dirty, foul emotions from his past.

Suddenly his phone rang, cutting through the silence, and he gave a soft curse and reached for it, afraid that the sound would wake her.

'It's me.' She stood in the doorway of the bedroom, her voice soft with sleep, the phone in her hand. 'I'm the one ringing you.'

'What for?' Bracing himself for more confrontation, Raul felt every muscle in his body tense to snapping point. 'Why are you ringing me at three in the morning?'

'Because I was worried.'

He scanned her in a single sweep of his gaze. Her feet were bare, her cheeks were flushed from sleep and she wore a tiny, flimsy sheath of silk, apparently designed with the express intention of driving a man out of his mind.

Raul instantly forgot to be angry. In fact his mind emptied itself of everything except thoughts of sex. His body responded with electrifying force, his groin sending urgent signals to his fevered brain. In the grip of an arousal that bordered on the painful, he eyed the sofa.

Hot and fast. Right here. Right now.

On the verge of grabbing her and spreading her flat, he caught the look in her green eyes and saw something that stopped him.

Concern.

She really had been worried about him.

Trying to remember the last time that anyone had worried about him, Raul stifled his instinctive desire to flatten her underneath him, sensing with an unusual degree of insight that this would not be a good move.

On the other hand, not flattening her underneath him didn't seem like a good move either.

'Are you all right? You're so, *so* tense. I can feel it from here.' She was staring anxiously at his face and Raul realised that she had absolutely no idea that she was responsible for the rocketing levels of his tension.

Exasperated with himself for not being able to control himself around her, he scanned his options swiftly.

'I need air,' he ground out, turning and striding out onto the beach in the hope that fresh air and distance might succeed where logic and will power had failed.

What was the matter with him?

Since when had his mind focused on nothing but sex?

He'd always had a high sex-drive, yes, but sex had never before intruded on his every waking moment until the day he'd first met Faith.

He inhaled deeply, searching for some semblance of the control on which he'd always prided himself.

Faced with nothing but the dark expanse of the ocean, the nagging throb in his body eased slightly and some of the tension left his shoulders. But his respite was short lived because he suddenly felt her arms slide around his waist. She leaned her head against his back in an affectionate gesture that took him by surprise.

'I love you.' She spoke the words softly but he heard them nonetheless and her honest declaration knocked the last of the breath from his lungs.

He felt at a loss and he *never* felt like that and when she walked round to stand in front of him, he braced himself for yet another serious disturbance to his emotional well-being.

But she didn't say a word.

Instead she lifted her hands and slowly undid the buttons on his shirt and slid her hands over his chest. Her fingers were warm and gentle and he sucked in a breath as she pushed the shirt from his shoulders. Then she touched her mouth to his flesh and the arousal he'd been fighting returned with twice the intensity.

Driven by the throbbing ache low in his body, Raul followed his instincts and slid his fingers into her hair, holding her still for his kiss. Passion exploded between them and his mouth devoured hers with explicit, erotic intensity. He felt her slender frame quivering against his, her uninhibited response sending his own levels of arousal soaring into the stratosphere.

But before he could follow his instincts and lower her onto the sand, she eased away from his grip and slid her hands over his chest.

'You're an incredible kisser.'

More than happy to demonstrate the full breadth of his skills, Raul reached for her again, but she evaded his grasp and pressed her mouth against his chest, her mouth slowly tracing the line of his body hair.

Then she dropped to her knees in the sand.

Her blonde hair was bright in the moonlight and her green eyes sparkled like jewels as she threw him a look that blew the circuits in his mind. She was pure, lethal seductress and while Raul was still recovering from the shock of that look, she'd apparently finished the task of undressing him because he suddenly discovered that he was naked.

Accustomed to always being the aggressor when it came to sex, Raul's mind was still dragging far behind his body when he felt the scrape of her nails on his thighs and the warm flick of her tongue.

He uttered an oath and her response was to slide her mouth closer to his potent masculine arousal.

'*Don't* talk,' she ordered and Raul was more than happy to comply with that particular request because he no longer had the ability to string a sentence together. The subtle brush of her fingers against his bare flesh was so shockingly good that his abdomen clenched in violent anticipation. His body pulsed and throbbed but instead of doing what he ached for her to do, she teased him, as he had teased her so many times before, with lips, tongue and fingers, seducing and exciting until every bit of his body was pumped up and hard with arousal.

Just when he thought he was going to explode, she took him in her mouth and an earthy groan of disbelief tore from his throat.

His mind went totally blank and his entire world centred on that one, throbbing part of him. Nothing existed for him except the raging, burning heat in his loins and the incredible, unbelievable sensations created by her warm, damp, knowing mouth. That part of him was so shockingly sensitised that he was hyper-aware of every tiny movement she made—the flick of her tongue, the warmth of her breath, the brush of her fingers—and then it all merged and he felt his self-control splinter and crack as he was hurled headlong into the most all-consuming, violent, incredible climax of his life.

Completely unaware of time, Raul stood with his eyes tightly shut and his jaw clenched, waiting for his body and brain to return from that place of blind, sexual ecstasy.

Finally he opened his eyes and found himself staring straight into hers.

He opened his mouth, closed it again and then gave up on speech because this was one occasion when actions would definitely speak louder than words.

He lifted her and tumbled her gently down on the sand, his body covering hers in a decisive, possessive movement but immediately she pushed at his chest.

'I want you on your back,' she breathed. 'I haven't finished.'

Raul rolled away from her immediately, too dazed even to question her. Part of him thought it only fair to warn her that he doubted his capability for more after what he'd just experienced, but already she was straddling him lightly, the smile on her lips pure temptress.

'Are you feeling OK, Raul?'

He was about to attempt some sort of response when she lowered herself onto his throbbing shaft and he discovered with electrifying force that his need for this woman knew no limitations.

She moved her hips slowly and skilfully and his hands closed on the curve of her bottom in an instinctive masculine need to increase the pace.

'No.' She leaned forward and teased his mouth with hers, the new angle of her body creating a wicked, delicious friction that drew another groan from deep within him.

He was on fire again, his entire body pumped up and primed to thrust but she didn't let him. Instead she teased him relentlessly, lowering her body and taking him deep and then staying perfectly still for just long enough for the desperate urgency in his loins to make a partial retreat.

Again and again she prolonged the agony until his body was screaming for completion and her eyes were glittering with her own excitement.

Driven past the point of control, Raul gripped her hips, positioned her as he wanted her and drove into her quivering, shivering, pliant body with an uninhibited wildness that bordered on the shocking. He felt her inner muscles grip him violently and for a moment they were both suspended in the grip of fierce, unbelievable pleasure.

Then she collapsed against him and he closed his arms around her, feeling the softness of her hair brushing against his jaw.

He was the first to break the silence. 'You've never done that before.'

'You've never given me a chance,' she said huskily. 'You just take the initiative every single time. I used to think I was quite a strong woman, and then I met you.'

'That's just because I can't look at you and not want to be inside you,' he groaned, his impossibly frank confession drawing a soft laugh from her.

'You're very dominating, do you know that?'

'Never again,' Raul vowed, stroking her soft hair with a reverential hand. 'It was amazing. *You* were amazing. From now on I'll just lie there and let you do all the work. I'll be passive.'

'Passive?' She lifted her head and her eyes sparkled into his. 'You couldn't be passive if you tried. You and passive are like oil and water, you just don't mix.'

'So why did you choose tonight?'

Her smile faded and there was a sudden shyness in her eyes. 'We had a problem. I didn't know how to get through to you.'

'I thought you said that sex doesn't solve problems.'

'It's always worked for you,' she muttered. 'I thought it was worth a try.'

'It worked.' He gave a groan and cupped her face in his hands, drawing her mouth to his. '*Dios mío*, it definitely worked. Any time you want to be dominating again, just go ahead.'

Faith woke to find Raul sprawled in a chair, a brooding expression on his handsome face as he watched her yawn and stretch.

'It's lunchtime,' he informed her smoothly and her eyes widened in surprise.

'It can't possibly be that late!'

'You just crashed out and you haven't moved since.' His eyes scanned her features with disturbing intensity. 'You are as pale as marble. I am going to ask the doctor to see you.'

'No.' She sat up and rubbed her eyes, embarrassed that she'd just slept for so long. 'There's no need. I'm fine, really. I was just tired. The last few weeks have been stressful.' The moment the words left her mouth she regretted them because she felt the immediate increase in his tension.

'I know, and since this is clearly the time for apologies, I'm willing to accept that some of this is my fault.'

Rendered speechless by that uncharacteristic declaration, Faith stared at him and he frowned.

'Don't look at me like that. Believe it or not, I am capable of apology when the need arises.' His eyes darkened and he looked at her for a moment and a faint smile of self-mockery touched his firm mouth. 'It's just that the need doesn't usually arise.'

She gave a wobbly smile. 'You don't have to apologise. I can see now why you were so upset.'

'You are very forgiving, but I shouldn't have made that comment at the wedding,' he breathed. 'It was insensitive of me and in a way I can understand why you ran away. I gave you no reason to believe our relationship could work, but it can, *cariño*. I *do* care about your feelings and just to prove that I've arranged a very special trip for us.'

'You have?' She sensed the change in him but didn't understand it. *Was this to do with last night?* Whatever had caused it, she wasn't about to question it and risk ruining it in any way.

'You missed out on a honeymoon,' he drawled softly. 'So that's what I've arranged. I'm very aware that when you first came to Argentina you planned to travel around the country and meeting me stopped all that.'

Faith curled up on the bed, butterflies in her stomach as she watched him. He was *so* confident and handsome, so utterly sure of himself, how could any woman ever resist him? Looking at him now, she wasn't surprised that she'd made the decision that she had. 'I don't regret anything, Raul.'

'I'm taking you somewhere really special. You deserve it.'

'When will we go?'

'How soon can you dress?' Raul's glance was faintly mocking. 'My pilot is waiting for us.'

Faith gasped and slipped out of bed. 'Right now?'

'Of course. Why not?'

His response made her smile. With Raul everything had to be right now. His capacity for waiting for anything was severely limited. 'I can be dressed in two minutes,' she assured him, reaching into her wardrobe for something comfortable to wear. 'But I need to pack.'

'That's all been dealt with.' Raul flipped his phone out of his pocket and spoke briefly to his pilot. 'Just bring yourself.'

Faith selected a pair of shoes from the dozens of pairs he'd given her. 'But where exactly are we going?'

'We're going to play tourist.' Taking her hand in a firm grasp, he led her out of the Beach House towards the helipad that was positioned just behind the polo fields.

'But everything will be booked up at this short notice.'

Urging her into the helicopter that bore the logo of his company, he greeted that comment with a glance of shimmering amusement. 'Then my staff will just have to *un*book it.'

And no doubt some ordinary mortal was about to be booted out of the room they'd booked months ago, Faith thought weakly as she sank into her seat and ruefully con-

templated the benefits of being in love with a sexy billionaire. His money wasn't what had attracted her, but she was
intelligent enough to recognise that the aspects of his character that she found so compelling were the same qualities
that drove his success. His astonishingly quick brain, his confidence, his insight and his hard, ruthless ability to outsmart
the competition—all those things made him the man he was.

And she loved him.

Her heart skipped and danced as he sprawled in the seat
next to her and took her hand in his.

'My private jet is waiting for us at the airport.' He stretched
out his legs. 'Get some rest, *cariño*, you're going to need it.'

He took her to Iguazú Falls, on the border with Brazil, and
she gazed in disbelief at the hundreds of cascades that
stretched before her in a horseshoe shape.

'I've only ever seen one waterfall at a time before,' she said
faintly and Raul settled himself behind her and pulled her
against his hard body.

'There are about two hundred and seventy-five different
cascades,' he murmured in her ear. 'We share the falls with
Brazil but two thirds are on the Argentine side.'

She could hear the pride in his voice and Faith laughed and
twisted round so that she could look at him. 'You always have
to be the biggest and the best, don't you?'

His answer was to kiss her and it was another few minutes
before she was able to turn her attention back to the view.

For a moment she just watched, mesmerised by the sheer
volume of water that thundered over the precipitous edge of
the rocky plateau and plunged into the river below, causing
huge clouds of spray.

'It's amazing. Breathtaking.' The falls seemed to glow in
the light and she felt Raul's arms tighten around her.

'*Garganta del Diablo*,' he murmured against her cheek.
'We call it the Devil's Throat. It is the largest cascade. I have

arranged for a boat to take us up the Iguazú River tomorrow. You will love it.'

And she did.

It seemed that everything had been planned for her enjoyment and she felt as though she spent the entire time staring in wonder. And even in their suite in the hotel, she couldn't prise herself away from the balcony.

'I feel as though I have competition,' Raul drawled finally, hauling her back inside the suite and closing the door firmly. 'You're supposed to be looking at *me*, not the view.'

And the truth was, she couldn't stop looking at him. They ate dinner on their private terrace, away from other people and the sheer intimacy of their situation made the nerves jump in her stomach.

'Did you travel as a child?' He waited for the food to be served and dismissed the staff with a single movement of his arrogant dark head. 'Where did you go?'

'Nowhere in particular. Europe.' She selected a piece of fish and tried it. 'This is delicious. We just went on normal family holidays. My parents would have loved it here,' she murmured, her eyes on the view as they lingered over dinner.

'You've told me virtually nothing about your childhood, but it was obviously very happy.'

'Why do you say that?'

He lifted his wine glass, a faint hint of mockery in his eyes. 'You have such a ridiculous faith in love and marriage that your parents must have been happy.'

And his hadn't been? She wanted to ask but she was afraid of spoiling the moment so instead she talked about herself.

'My parents met when they were teenagers and then Mum became pregnant with me.' Faith pulled a face. 'Terrible shock and scandal, because this was *years* ago and things were different then. My grandmother thought she was far too young but my father and mother were adamant that it didn't matter. "We're in love and we were always going to have a family at some point," my dad always said.'

And that, of course had been another reason why she hadn't questioned the motivations behind *their* own hasty marriage. She'd fallen in love with Raul. She couldn't imagine being with anyone else.

At first she'd been panicked that he wouldn't be pleased but when he'd immediately proposed she'd assumed that he'd adjusted to the idea as easily as she had.

'What you've just told me explains a great deal about you.' He sat across from her, his dark eyes fixed on her face, and she had the distinct impression that he was about to tell her something.

She sat still, willing him to offer up the confidence that she sensed hovered on his lips, but after a moment he rose to his feet and walked across to the rail that skirted the balcony.

Having learned not to press him to talk when he didn't want to, Faith resisted the temptation to prompt him and instead folded her napkin neatly and joined him by the rail. 'So where are we going tomorrow?'

He turned to face her, his dark eyes filled with secrets and shadows. Instead of answering her he took her face in his hands and kissed her with hungry, desperate urgency, his mouth hard and demanding on hers.

The kiss went from nothing to out of control in less time than it took him to back her into the suite and kick the door closed behind him. And after that there was no more talking.

CHAPTER ELEVEN

AFTER four glorious days and nights, they flew back to the *estancia* and Faith was feeling more settled.

The pregnancy might have triggered the marriage, but they were happy together, she knew they were.

The only slight blot on the landscape for her was that there were still moments when she didn't feel well physically, and that disappointed her because she could no longer attribute her lack of energy to the stress of their relationship or even lack of sleep. And it wasn't just that she was tired. Occasionally she was overwhelmed by dizziness and sickness and even though the doctor had assured her that such a reaction was quite normal after a head injury, she still felt uneasy.

But she didn't tell Raul because she knew that if she so much as mentioned that she didn't feel well he would fly in an entire team of doctors from all over the world.

So she kept it to herself, hopeful that it would all fade in time.

They were happy together, and that was all that mattered.

'Raul's in a good mood because Pedro sold him the land!' Mateo, a business associate of Raul's, lifted his glass in a toast. 'And Raul is *always* in a good mood when he wins.'

They were dining in the most elegant restaurant in Buenos Aires, surrounded by the city's elite, their table giving them magnificent views over the vibrant city. Candles flickered on the tables and a jazz band played on the terrace outside.

'Raul *always* wins.' Julieta, Mateo's wife, glanced up from her plate. 'I thought you said he wanted to hang on to that land?'

'Apparently he wanted my money more,' Raul drawled, his long, strong fingers curled around the stem of his wine glass. 'I think he was influenced by my wife. Apparently I've become more human since I married her.'

'I wouldn't say so.' Mateo winked at Faith and Julieta chuckled and reached across the table to take her husband's hand.

'Marriage is good for a man. It teaches him to share.' She frowned suddenly. 'You're quiet tonight, Faith. Are you all right? You're very pale. Raul, do you think she's pale?'

'She's English,' Mateo said cheerfully, leaning back as the waiter removed their plates. 'The English are always pale.'

'I'm fine.' Faith managed to smile, horribly aware of Raul's disturbingly intent gaze. The truth was that she felt *exhausted* and she just didn't understand the reason. Normally she was a very energetic person but at the moment she could have happily spent her life in bed. She just wanted to sleep and sleep.

It was probably just living with Raul, she concluded wryly. Too much sex. And she was worrying, of course, about where their relationship was going. Physically he was generous and demonstrative, but emotionally…

Reaching for her water, Faith took a sip. *Emotionally he still locked everything away.*

Julieta lifted her glass in a toast. 'To Emperor Raul, whose land now stretches across most of Argentina.'

Raul lifted an eyebrow. 'You're toasting me with water when there's champagne on offer?'

'Ah.' Julieta's eyes sparkled. 'We have news too, don't we Mateo?'

Mateo's expression softened. 'Julieta is pregnant. We found out yesterday.'

Faith felt as though all the air had been sucked out of the room. The noise and buzz of conversation around her faded to nothing and there was a rhythmic pounding in her ears.

For a moment she was enveloped in a blanket of panic and then she struggled free and realised that they were all looking at her expectantly, waiting for her to speak. 'That's fantastic,' she managed, genuinely pleased for Julieta and horrified by the vicious stab of jealousy that tore through her insides. 'We're so pleased for you, aren't we, Raul?' She answered for him because she didn't want him to say something tactless but deep down she wondered how he felt.

Of course, he wouldn't be as affected as she was, would he?

He didn't want children. She knew that. What she didn't know was why. And she wasn't likely ever to understand that because he didn't talk to her.

Faith struggled against the sudden surge of desolation that threatened to swamp her.

She wasn't going to think about her own situation. Not here. Not now in this public place in front of the man she loved and his friends.

But a thick, dangerous sludge of misery had been stirred inside her and refused to settle down.

She couldn't stop thinking about her own baby. The baby she'd lost.

An incredible sadness oozed through her and the lightness inside her faded away leaving only exhaustion.

In contrast, Julieta's face glowed with health and her eyes sparkled with excitement as she told them about her plans. Every now and then she touched Mateo's hand as if she couldn't quite believe that this was *her* life.

'It will be your turn next, Raul. Given that you've overcome your phobia of marriage, children are a logical next step.'

Worried that Raul might be upset, Faith intervened swiftly. 'It's too soon for that,' she said in a bright voice. 'I'm still hoping to pursue my career and we've barely spent any time together since we married.'

Trying to switch off her emotions, Faith concentrated on smiling, hoping that she looked more convincing than she felt because suddenly she was terrified she was going to break down. Right here. In public. With everyone watching.

What was the matter with her?

Why was she so tearful?

Over the past few weeks, all she seemed to do was sleep and it was completely unlike her.

'I'm delighted by your news, but you'll have to excuse us because Faith is very tired.' It was Raul who spoke and he rose to his feet in a decisive movement. 'It's time I took her home.'

For once Faith was relieved that he was so controlling and she shot the couple an apologetic smile. 'I don't think I'll ever become used to your Argentine hours—dining at eleven o'clock would be considered really odd in London.'

Julieta chuckled. 'That is a perfectly reasonable time in Buenos Aires. Are you seriously driving home? I thought you billionaires used a helicopter or a chauffeur.'

'I'm not good at being driven.' Raul strolled round the table, gently eased Faith to her feet and slid his arm round her waist. 'Great evening. We must do it again soon.'

Impossibly grateful that he'd rescued her, Faith allowed him to guide her from the restaurant and into the low, sexy Ferrari that waited for them outside the door.

Determined not to cry, she slid into the passenger seat and closed her eyes. 'Thank you,' she muttered and heard the engine give a throaty roar as he pulled into the Buenos Aires traffic.

* * *

Raul glanced across at her but her eyes were closed and her face was pale.

Sleeping? Upset?

She definitely *had* been upset and he knew why, of course.

When Julieta had announced her pregnancy, the look on Faith's face had been one of utter desolation before her naturally generous nature had reasserted itself and she'd masked that response.

With a fluent oath, he flattened his foot to the floor, wishing that he *had* chosen to use the helicopter for this particular evening out in the capital.

He didn't like the fact that she was lying still and quiet next to him. He didn't even know if she was really asleep or just pretending. And either activity was completely unlike her. Before their wedding she'd possessed boundless energy and she'd wanted to talk about *everything*.

To his surprise he was fast discovering that her sudden silence disturbed him more than her emotional insights and probing questions.

At least when she'd done that he'd known how to respond.

Now he felt out of his depth and that was an *entirely* new feeling for him.

He was also worried that she was so pale and tired. Had she been pale before Julieta had made her announcement? His mind scanned the past. She'd been tired since her head injury and he frowned suddenly as he recalled the number of times he'd seen her curl up on the bed and fall asleep.

What if there was something wrong with her? *What if she was ill?*

He felt a sudden flash of foreboding.

Increasing his speed, he arrived at the *estancia* in record time but when he pulled into the courtyard, Faith still didn't wake. With a soft curse, Raul sprang from the car and threw his keys to a waiting member of staff. 'Call the doctor. I want him at the Beach House in the next ten minutes.'

'It's two in the morning—'

'I *know* what time it is.' Unaccustomed to having his orders questioned, Raul threw the man a warning glare. 'Just call him.' Then he strode round to the passenger side and scooped Faith into his arms.

Her head flopped against his shoulder and she stirred for a moment but didn't really wake up.

Trying not to think about how slender and impossibly fragile she was, Raul strode along the path into the Beach House and laid her on the bed.

Staring down at her, he hesitated for a moment and then bent down and gently pulled off her shoes. Deciding that the dress didn't look too comfortable either, he slid it down her body with the ease of experience and then wished he hadn't because she wasn't wearing a bra and her pale, rose-tipped breasts seemed to be crying out for his attention.

Teeth gritted, Raul grabbed the cover and pulled it over her semi-naked form, the unfamiliar degree of self-sacrifice leaving his body aching with raw sexual frustration. If this was how it felt to commit an unselfish act, he brooded, then he certainly wouldn't be making a habit of it.

As he tucked her in, Faith stirred and opened her eyes. 'Did I sleep all the way home? Sorry,' she murmured. 'Not very exciting for you.'

'I'm fine,' Raul lied smoothly, relieved to see that her cheeks had a little more colour. Perhaps she wasn't ill. She probably was just tired, he assured himself. After all, he wasn't allowing her much sleep at night, was he? And they were indulging in an unusual degree of physical activity.

And her mind was obviously working along the same lines because she gave him a slow, sleepy smile. 'Aren't you coming to bed?'

For a moment he was sorely tempted and then he remembered that the doctor would be arriving soon. To reduce the temptation to slide under the cover and bring some colour to her cheeks by alternative means, Raul retreated to the chair in the farthest corner of the bedroom. 'I'm not coming to bed yet.'

That statement was so out of character that it should have roused at least a question from Faith, but she simply looked at him. 'All right. Well, don't get too tired.'

Raul looked at her in exasperation.

Was that all she was going to say? What had happened to the probing and the questions? *What had happened to the talking?*

Feeling as though the whole situation was sliding out of his control, Raul decided to just give her the answer she hadn't asked for. 'I'm waiting for the doctor to come.'

'The doctor? Are you ill?' Her eyes widened and she sat up suddenly, her expression anxious.

'Not me,' he ground out, hastily averting his eyes from her breasts. 'You. I've called the doctor for you.'

'Why?'

'Because you're always tired.'

'I'm fine,' she began and he interrupted her with an impatient glance.

'You are *not* fine. You had a head injury and I want to know that these bouts of tiredness are a normal part of the recovery process.'

She looked at him with incredulity. 'It's the middle of the night, Raul!'

'I don't care,' he responded in a driven tone. 'I want a doctor to look at you.'

'I'm fine—'

'Stop saying you're fine. You're *not* fine. For a start you're not behaving like yourself.'

She pulled the covers up to her chin. 'I have no idea what you're talking about.'

Did he have to spell it out? He rose to his feet and ran his fingers through his hair. 'This evening—you were upset. About Julieta.' He saw the sudden wariness in her eyes and his mouth tightened. 'So why aren't you trying to talk about it? You *always* talk if something is upsetting you.'

'I thought I was supposed to phone a girlfriend for that.' Her tone was light and Raul tolerated the gentle dig because he was well aware that he deserved it.

He wasn't good at talking about things.

Even now he didn't want to have this conversation, but he knew he couldn't afford *not* to have it. 'I had no idea Julieta was pregnant,' he confessed in a raw tone. 'Or I would never have invited them to join us.'

'You can't protect me from everyone who is pregnant,' Faith said quietly and he gave a growl of frustration.

'That is *not* an answer. I want to know how you're feeling.'

'No, you don't, you know you don't. You *hate* it when I try and talk about feelings.' She brushed a strand of hair out of her eyes with a shaking hand. 'You just thought you ought to ask or I'll accuse you of not caring.'

His tension levels soaring through the roof, Raul removed his jacket and dropped it over the back of the nearest chair. 'I *do* care. The reason I don't want to know is *not* because I don't care but because I feel guilty,' he confessed and a thick, heavy silence descended on the room.

Now she'd *have* to question him, he thought grimly and he stared at her in silent expectation, waiting for her to spill everything as she always did. Or probe him for how he felt.

She did neither. 'You have nothing to feel guilty about, Raul.'

'How can you say that?'

'Because it's true. As you once told me, you were completely up front about not wanting marriage or children. You're not to blame.'

He was about to respond when there was a knock on the door and two of his staff entered, accompanied by the doctor.

Raul dealt him a glance that would have flattened a man with fragile self-confidence, but the doctor stood his ground and nodded a greeting to Faith.

'I want you to find out what's wrong with her,' Raul commanded. 'And then I expect you to fix it.' Faith was young and supposedly healthy. It wasn't *normal* for anyone to be as tired as she was.

She no longer even had the energy to argue with him.

What if it was something serious?

Facing that terrifying prospect, a sudden chill of fear slid down his spine and he glared at the doctor. 'Well? Aren't you going to examine her or something?'

'I certainly intend to examine her,' the doctor said calmly, walking across to the bed and placing his bag on the floor.

'Well hurry up then.' Raul's voice was hoarse and the doctor sighed.

'If you would leave us alone for a few moments, I'd like to talk to your wife.'

'Leave you alone?'

'Yes.' The doctor opened his bag and removed a stethoscope. 'I insist that all my consultations are private in the first instance. Later, if your wife chooses to have you in the room, we can call you.'

Raul opened his mouth to refuse but then remembered that Faith had completely clammed up with him. He knew her well enough to know she needed to talk to *someone* and since it wasn't him, then it had better be the doctor.

Prepared to make that sacrifice for the greater good of their relationship, Raul turned and left the Beach House in several long, angry strides.

'Your husband seems very tense and worried,' the doctor observed, checking Faith's temperature and her pulse rate. 'He obviously loves you very much.'

If only. Faith decided that it was best not to respond to that statement because she didn't trust herself not to break down and sob. In a state of anxious misery, she lay still while the doctor examined her but all she really wanted to do was run after Raul.

They'd been in the middle of a conversation about Julieta's pregnancy when the doctor had arrived and for some reason he'd been getting more and more exasperated with her.

She'd done her best not to cry on him or talk about the way she felt because she knew he *hated* that, but instead of appearing relieved and grateful for her restraint, he'd actually seemed more agitated.

This whole thing was her fault. If she'd told him that she'd lost the baby before the wedding then he never would have married her. Maybe they wouldn't even be together.

Finding that scenario deeply depressing, Faith closed her eyes tightly and it took her a moment to realise that the doctor was speaking to her.

'Sorry. Did you say something?'

'I asked you when your last period was.'

Faith gave him the date. 'Why are you asking? What does that have to do with my head injury?'

'Because I don't think your symptoms are anything to do with your head injury,' the doctor mused, folding his stethoscope and putting it back into his bag. 'I have a suspicion this is something entirely different.'

'Well it must be something,' Faith muttered. 'Because I'm completely exhausted and that isn't like me.'

'It's definitely something,' the doctor said mildly. 'When was your last period?'

Faith gritted her teeth. 'I haven't had one since the miscarriage.'

'And when was the miscarriage?'

She gave the doctor the date and then turned her head away. 'Do we really have to talk about this?'

'If you're asking whether it's important then the answer is yes, I think it is.' The doctor sat down next to her, his expression thoughtful. 'This miscarriage—describe it.'

So Faith told him what had happened and he gave a slow nod.

'And you didn't see a doctor?'

'No. It was very early on so I didn't see the point. What could anyone have done?' Feeling the emotion bubbling up inside her, she covered her face with her hands. 'Can we stop talking about this? Why is it even relevant?'

'Because I don't think you lost that baby,' the doctor said in a calm, clear voice. 'In fact I'm entirely sure that you're still pregnant.'

His words were so entirely unexpected that Faith lay still, just staring at him. 'S-still pregnant?'

'You had a small bleed at the time that your period was due. It happens. Far more frequently than people imagine, actually. It wasn't a miscarriage. By my calculation you're about three months pregnant.'

Pregnant?

She hadn't lost the baby?

Her hand covered her flat stomach in an instinctively protective gesture and a rush of pure, perfect joy engulfed her.

And then the implications of what the doctor had just told her sank into her brain and she immediately swooped down into a dark pit of despair.

The fact that she hadn't lost the baby was wonderful news, but she realised with a miserable, sinking heart that the doctor's words had sounded the death knell for her relationship with Raul.

* * *

Faith walked onto the beach, bracing herself for the most difficult conversation of her life.

How would Raul respond to the news?

He wouldn't be pleased, she knew that. Suddenly his comment on her wedding day came back to haunt her.

Although it was four in the morning, there was just enough light for her to make out his lean, powerful physique. He stood with his back to her, facing out to sea, and she lifted a hand to touch him and then immediately let it fall again.

What right did she have to touch?

'Raul?' She spoke his name softly and he turned instantly.

The sudden flare of anxiety in his eyes surprised her. 'Well?' He reached out and put his hands on her shoulders, his hard, strong fingers biting into her flesh. *'What did he say?'*

Faith flinched. 'You're squeezing me—'

'Sorry.' He released his grip and took her face in his hands, stroking her cheeks with his thumbs. 'I'm sorry, *cariño*. I've been worried.'

The concern in his tone almost finished her off. 'I'm sorry you were worried.' How was she going to say this? What words could she use to make the whole thing easier on both of them? 'I—Raul—'

'*Dios mío*, you're scaring me,' he said hoarsely. 'Just tell me, quickly, before I chase after that damn doctor and drag him back here. What did he say to you that's made you so scared? You look totally terrified! Whatever it is, we'll fix it, I promise.'

It was such a typical response that in spite of her misery, she almost smiled. 'You can't fix everything, Raul.' Feeling as though she were facing a firing squad, Faith moved her face away from his hands and stepped back from him but still she couldn't bring herself to say what had to be said because she knew that once the words were out there, that would be it.

Their relationship would be over.

Her fingers were trembling, her legs were trembling—she felt physically sick although whether that was down to nerves or her pregnancy she didn't know.

Squeezing her eyes shut she vowed that, whatever he said, she was *not* going to cry. Inside she felt wretched, miserable and just plain desolate.

'Faith,' Raul muttered rawly, turning her to face him. 'If you don't tell me soon—'

She tilted her head back and braced herself. What difference did a few minutes make? She wanted a whole lifetime with him and if she couldn't have that…

'I'm pregnant.' Her voice cracked and she snatched a breath and said it again, just in case he hadn't heard her. 'I didn't lose the baby. I made a mistake about that. I'm still pregnant.'

He stared down at her, his dark eyes glittering in the moonlight and his normally bronzed, healthy skin appeared to have lost some of its colour.

His hands dropped from her arms and he took a step backwards, an expression of stunned disbelief crossing his handsome face.

He didn't say a word.

Not a single word.

The only sound was the soft rush of waves as they broke onto the sand and the frantic pumping of her own heartbeat.

Raul stared down at her for what seemed like endless minutes and then turned sharply and walked away across the sand.

And that, she thought to herself, was that.

No longer bothering to contain the tears that had gathered in her throat, Faith sank down onto the sand and just sobbed.

CHAPTER TWELVE

PACKING was easy because she didn't need to take much.

Just her work gear and a suit that she thought she could use for interviews. The glamorous shoes and dresses she ignored because she just couldn't imagine herself ever wanting to party again.

Closing the small case, she carried it over to the door of the Beach House and then turned to allow herself one last look. Four large, stylish lamps threw shafts of golden light across the room and for one desperately indulgent moment she stood, gazing at the pale wood floors, the filmy white curtains and the soft sofas piled with exotically coloured cushions.

It was just a house, she reminded herself bleakly. *Just a house.*

If she wanted to, she could reproduce it in the next place she lived.

Except that it wasn't just a house, was it?

Everything about the place reminded her of Raul. *It had been their home.*

She turned off three of the lights and was just reaching to do the same with the fourth, when Raul's voice came from behind her.

'If you seriously think I'd let you walk away from me a

second time then you don't know me at all.' His words shimmering with suppressed violence, he spoke from the doorway and Faith turned, her heart rate suddenly doubling.

'I thought you'd—' She stumbled over the words. 'I thought you'd gone.'

'Gone?' Winged dark brows met in a menacing frown. The collar of his shirt was undone and his eyes blazed dark with anger. 'Gone where?'

'I don't know.' Her legs were trembling and her stomach was churning and she gave a helpless little shrug. 'As far away as possible, I suppose.'

The last remaining light illuminated his black, glossy hair and the fierce burn of his eyes. 'I'm not the one who runs in this relationship. Does our marriage really mean so little to you?' His tone grim, he strode forward and took her face in his hands, forcing her to look at him. 'If you're going to cry, you can damn well cry on my shoulder. Not on some stranger in an aeroplane.'

'This isn't the time to be possessive and territorial,' she muttered in a thickened voice. 'Just let me go, Raul.'

His answer to that was to slide an arm around her waist, locking her against him. 'Talk to me, *cariño*. I want to know what you're thinking because at the moment the working of your brain is a complete mystery to me and I'm not used to that. Usually you talk about *everything*. Why would you even consider leaving when we are so good together?'

'Didn't you hear what I told you? I'm pregnant.'

His eyes narrowed warily. '*Sí*, I heard that part. What I didn't hear is why this news would make you miserable. I thought you *wanted* this baby.'

'I did. I do.' She gave a painful little smile. 'But I also wanted you and the two things aren't compatible are they? You don't want babies. *You don't like children!*'

Her passionate statement was met by a long throbbing

silence and then he drew in a long breath and released her, his shoulders tense and his eyes suddenly wary. 'I have never *once* in our relationship told you that I don't like children.'

'No marriage, no babies.' Her tone was flat as she quoted him word for word. 'That's what you told me.'

'Perhaps. I mean—' For some reason his English seemed to lack its usual fluency. 'Yes. I *did* say that but I have never said that I didn't *like* children.' He ran a hand around the back of his neck and his obvious struggle to find the words he wanted puzzled her. She'd never known Raul anything less than stunningly articulate.

'It's fine, Raul. You honestly don't have to explain.'

'*Dios mío*, I am *trying* to tell you something. Usually you are pushing me and pushing me to talk and talk and suddenly when I am trying to talk, you are stopping me!' His fierce glare suggested that he was holding her personally responsible for his difficulties in that area and her eyes widened.

'Because I know you hate talking—'

'I *want* to tell you.'

'Oh.' Her heart thudding, she looked at him expectantly and his eyes darkened angrily.

'I have no idea how to say it,' he snapped at her impatiently. 'I'm not *like* you. I can't just spill out everything I'm feeling. I've never actually said this before so I have no idea how to say it.'

Faith waited patiently and he glared at her again.

'It isn't that I don't *like* children,' he began, but then he stopped, a frown on his face.

Faith decided that she'd better help him. 'I understand. You have this great life, Raul.' She waved an arm in the vague direction of the *estancia*. 'You fly off in your private jet at a moment's notice, you can dine in Paris or New York whenever you like without giving another thought to another person. Why would you want to compromise that lifestyle?'

Raul left a long pause before he answered.

'It wasn't Sofia.'

His driven, emotional statement seemed unrelated to the conversation they were having and for a moment she just stared at him, scanning her mental frequencies for clues. 'What wasn't?'

'Sofia wasn't the reason I'm reluctant to have children,' Raul confessed with raw emphasis. 'It happened long before her.'

Faith stood completely still. 'But it was a woman who hurt you?'

'Yes, but not in the way you're imagining.' He stood for a moment, his breathing slow and steady, as if he were concentrating on that one action. A tiny muscle flickered in his hard jaw and it was several long seconds before he spoke again. 'She took away *everything* that mattered to me, *everything* I loved. She was vicious, selfish and greedy.'

A deafening silence followed his hoarse statement and for a moment Faith was afraid even to move. She *felt* his agony but she suppressed the natural instinct to offer comfort, sensing that if she said the wrong thing now, he'd retreat. So she stood for a moment with her head full of words but her mouth tightly shut.

He glanced towards her and his eyes locked with hers. 'I promised myself, never again. Never would that happen to me.'

Faith had to force herself to ask the question. 'Was she someone that you loved?'

His dark eyes glinted hard and cold and his mouth tightened to a thin line. 'She was my mother.'

His confession was such a shock that for a moment Faith couldn't respond.

Of all the scenarios she'd imagined, that hadn't been one of them.

Clearly he wasn't surprised by her inability to speak,

because he grimaced. 'Not every woman is maternal. She became pregnant to force my father into marriage. No other reason. They divorced when I was nine and it was *extremely* acrimonious. She was determined to take my father for every penny he had and I was the tool she used to do it. And once she'd stripped him bare of everything that mattered, she took me, too.'

'You mean you stayed with your mother?'

His eyes glittered dark and dangerous. 'I mean that she took me from him. Not because she loved me or wanted me, but because she knew how much my father did. I was her trump card.'

Shocked, Faith shook her head in disbelief. 'No.'

'This was my father's land.' Raul turned, looking through the windows of the Beach House towards the *estancia*. 'He was a horseman. A very skilled horseman. There wasn't a horse in South America that my father couldn't work with. He had more patience than any man I've ever met.' He glanced at Faith, his eyes gleaming with self-mockery. 'Needless to say, I have my mother's genes. She was volatile and explosive, given to *major* tantrums.'

'I didn't know your father owned the *estancia*. I thought you bought it.'

'I did. It was sold after the divorce. My father gave my mother the money because he couldn't bear to think that I might suffer. Even though this place had been in my family for generations, he sold it.' Raul was silent for a moment, emotion radiating from every angle of his powerful frame. 'So that's what she did. On the other side of the world.'

'Estancia La Lucia,' she murmured softly. 'I never even asked you about the name. I—'

'Lucia was my great-great-grandmother.'

She'd had no idea. 'Raul—'

'This *estancia* had been our family's heritage for more than a hundred years. It was in my father's blood and in my blood.' Raul's voice was rough. 'He taught me to ride before I could walk. We were going to run this place together.'

Faith stood in silence, absorbing his horrible, horrible story, her insides aching as she imagined the pain of that little boy, longing for his father. 'You couldn't stay with him?'

'A child stays with his mother. That's the tradition isn't it? She told me we were going on holiday.' Each word was another beat of agony. 'It was only when we arrived in Australia that she told me that we wouldn't be coming back.'

Faith licked dry lips. 'You must have missed him so much.' She put her hand on his arm and felt the flex of his strong muscle and the utter chill of his skin.

'At first I refused to accept it. I ran away. I made it as far as the airport and then they rang my mother.' He gave a dark, cynical smile that revealed far more about that encounter than any words could have. 'And she told me to grow up and be a man. And that's what I did. Every day I was in hell, but I kept that hell to myself and just lived it. I was trapped in an alien country with people who were alien to me. I pined for my father, for Argentina, the *estancia*, the horses—everything. I hated the life my mother led and the fact that she didn't even want me. But I learned not to show what I was feeling.'

'And you still don't—'

His beautiful mouth twisted. 'I think I've forgotten how.'

'But you left Australia?'

'I left as soon as I could and came back here only to find that my father had sold the *estancia* to pay for my mother's costs. It was broken up and sold.' His accent grew more pronounced. 'He was trying to make sure that I had a good life. That I didn't suffer. But for me it was never about the money.'

Touched by this surprisingly emotional admission, Faith leaned forward and wrapped her arms around him. 'So you started your own business. What you have achieved is nothing short of amazing.'

'I vowed to buy it back, piece by piece. And I have.'

'The land that Pedro owns…'

'*My* land now.' His possessive declaration vibrated around the room. 'That was the last piece. My father's *estancia* is back in the family again.'

'And your father?' She felt the muscles in his body tighten and suddenly wished she hadn't asked the question.

'After my father sold the *estancia*, he took a job as a *gaucho*—a cowboy—working with horses on other ranches. I know, because I followed his trail. He kept moving on, restless.'

'He didn't make a home anywhere else?'

'He never would have done that because his home was here. He died,' Raul said roughly. 'He died without knowing that I was back. He died before I made my first million and purchased the first thousand acres of land.'

And he'd died without giving his son the chance to tell him how much he loved him.

'You say that there is nothing of your father in you, but I don't think that's true,' Faith said softly. 'You have his strength and his courage, his talent with horses and his love for this land.'

He looked down at her, his eyes fierce. 'What my mother must have put him through—' he said hoarsely. 'I swore that no woman would ever be able to do that to me or to any child of mine.'

For a moment Faith couldn't speak because she couldn't get the words past the lump in her throat. 'So it isn't that you don't like or don't want,' she said softly. 'It's that you're afraid of loving and losing. Now I understand why you married me. You were determined to do everything possible to exert your rights over the baby.'

'Faith—'

'And I don't blame you for that. If I'd been through what you have, I'd feel the same way, I'm sure.' Faith stood still, thinking about what he'd said. 'I wish you'd told me this, instead of just proposing. I would have understood.'

'You would have run a mile, taking my baby with you.' It was the most painfully honest conversation they'd ever had. 'And you did run, Faith. Just hours after you married me, you ran. That's what women do when things go wrong. That's what my mother did.'

She bit her lip, understanding why her actions had triggered such a depth of emotion in him. 'That's true,' she admitted, 'I did. But you have to look at it from my point of view. When I told you I lost the baby you were *relieved*.'

'I hadn't expected to have to confront the issue of pregnancy at all. For me it was simpler if it just wasn't there.'

'I see that now, Raul, but at the time you hadn't shared any of this with me. All I saw was a man who was so fixated on his own desire to stay single that he didn't care about my feelings. You thought I'd become pregnant on purpose.'

'Which was exactly what my mother did. And I wasn't thinking about your feelings. I was thinking about mine,' he grated. 'Panicking. I know I hurt you and I regret that more than you know. I was a total bastard, but it wasn't anything to do with you—I was protecting myself.'

'Because you thought I'd hurt you?'

'You have to understand that none of my relationships up until now have ever been based on anything other than sex,' he confessed and she looked up at him, her heart executing a dangerously fast rhythm.

'And now?'

'You really need to ask that? It's true that I'm totally out of control when I'm with you, *cariño*, but believe me when I tell you it isn't just about the sex. I love the fact that you're so bright and clever, I love the fact that everything in your head comes out of your mouth because it makes you so easy to understand.'

Faith was astonished. 'You hate the fact that I want to talk!'

'*Not* true,' he asserted, bending his head and stealing a quick kiss. 'In fact since you stopped talking, it's driven me mad because I'm wasting so much time guessing what's in your head.'

Her legs wobbling, Faith sank down onto the nearest sofa. 'This is—' She broke off and breathed in and out. 'This isn't the way I thought this conversation would go. When you walked away from me—I assumed you were horrified that I was still pregnant.'

'I went to talk to the doctor. I'd managed to convince myself that there was something really wrong with you. You were so pale and tired—I wanted to make sure he'd taken a really good look at you,' Raul confessed. 'I'm not great at trusting other people with important issues. I virtually pinned him to the wall and made him recite everything he'd told you.'

Knowing Raul as she did, Faith had no problems imagining it. 'And how did he respond to that?'

'He wasn't that impressed,' Raul admitted wryly. 'But he told me he was making allowances for a guy who was seriously in love.'

His words drove the air from her lungs. 'He did? And did you tell him you don't believe in love?'

'No, because that wouldn't have been true.' He reached for her hands and pulled her back to her feet. 'I *didn't* believe in love, until I met you. And even then I didn't recognise it. But apparently the signs are all over the place if you know what you're looking for.'

Her heart pounding, Faith looked up at him. 'Is that right?'

'Of course.' His usual confidence apparently restored, Raul curved his arms around her in an unmistakably possessive gesture. 'I can't let you out of my sight, I worry if you're even half a shade paler than you usually are and when you stop wanting to talk about everything I get really, *really* worried.'

'You *hate* talking.'

'Given a choice between conversation and sex, I'm going to pick sex every time,' Raul admitted, with typical male frankness. 'But I'm prepared to concede that a certain degree of emotional honesty has its place.'

'Does it?'

'Yes.' He smoothed her hair away from her face. 'I should have talked to you sooner, but you have to understand that I've never talked to *anyone* about this. I don't even let myself think about it.'

'I don't blame you, but I'm glad I know because now I can understand why you feel the way you do. And I have something to say that's important.' Faith took a deep breath. 'You don't have to stay with me just because you're afraid of losing your child, Raul. I would never take your child from you, ever. If you're saying this because of the baby, then we can work something out. You own ten-thousand acres—you can build me a house to live in.'

'I am not building you a house to live in. The only place you're living is here with me,' he growled and Faith bit her lip.

'I'm worried, Raul,' she said quietly. 'I'm worried that you're only saying this because of the baby. I mean, it's not as if you had a choice about this.'

'Come with me!' Having delivered that command, he took her hand and led her up the staircase to the upper floor.

'Where are we going? We never come up here—' Exasperated, she tugged at his hand. 'Raul, we were *talking*—'

'And talking is fine,' he purred, turning to her with his most charismatic smile. 'But there are times when actions speak louder than words, *cariño*.'

Mesmerised by that incredibly sexy smile, Faith felt her insides tumble and flip and gave a moan of disbelief. No, no, no! She wasn't going to respond like this, not now! They were discussing an important issue. *Surely* he wasn't going to try and solve this problem with sex? Not after the discussion they'd just had. 'Raul, this just isn't—'

'Trust me.' With his usual confidence, he threw open a door and stepped aside for her to pass him. 'Go in. Tell me what you see.'

Puzzled, Faith stepped inside the room and her heart tumbled over in her chest.

It was a nursery.

A beautifully decorated, sunny nursery complete with an old-fashioned rocking chair, an antique cot and pretty curtains.

For a moment Faith couldn't speak at all and then when she finally tried to say something, nothing came out of her mouth.

His hands curved over her shoulders. 'What do you see?'

'I see—' Her voice cracked. 'I see a nursery.'

'No.' He gently turned her and cupped her face in his hands. 'You see a man in love.'

'But—'

Raul was watching her reaction with a self-satisfied smile on his handsome face. '*Now* try telling me I'm insensitive,' he drawled softly, pulling her against him and bringing his mouth down on hers. 'I had this decorated when we were on our honeymoon.'

'Our honeymoon?'

'That was when I realised that I couldn't imagine a life without you in it. I didn't know you were still pregnant, Faith. But this was how I saw our future. As a family.'

She felt tears prick her eyes. 'You—you'd already done this?'

His eyes gleamed with sardonic humour. 'You think I shot up here with a paint brush five minutes after the doctor left?'

'No. Yes.' Tears filled her eyes and his smile faded.

'Don't cry. *Te amo, cariño.* I love you. Do you understand me?' He took her face in his hands and kissed her gently. 'Do you? Answer me, because if you don't then I will have to solve the problem the way you suspected I was going to solve it.'

She sniffed and made a sound that was half sob, half laugh. 'I thought—'

'I know what you thought and perhaps that would have been a better option.' He frowned. 'Given that talking just seems to make you cry.'

'I thought I was going to lose you. I know you only married me because I was pregnant.'

'I married you because you were pregnant,' Raul agreed in a husky tone. 'But I'm *staying* married to you because I love you.'

She squeezed her eyes shut but the tears fell anyway because she just adored him so much and suddenly everything had gone from being wrong to being very, very right. 'I love you, too. So much. You have *no* idea.'

'I think I have.' His voice was soft and he brushed the tears away from her cheek with the back of his hand. 'I behaved so badly to you. I was cruel and thoughtless and yet you are still here. You have to be in love to have put up with me. Stop crying!'

'I can't,' she croaked. 'And it's your fault. It's all the things you're saying.'

'Which just goes to prove that talking has its limitations,' he drawled, a dangerous gleam in his eyes as he lowered his head to hers. 'So now it's time to solve this problem in a very different way. Do you agree?'

'Yes,' Faith whispered against his mouth. 'Oh yes.'

the Buenos Aires Marriage Deal

MAGGIE COX

The day **Maggie Cox** saw the film version of *Wuthering Heights*, with a beautiful Merle Oberon and a very handsome Laurence Olivier, was the day she became hooked on romance. From that day onwards she spent a lot of time dreaming up her own romances, secretly hoping that one day she might become published and get paid for doing what she loved most! Now that her dream is being realised, she wakes up every morning and counts her blessings. She is married to a gorgeous man and is the mother of two wonderful sons. Her two other great passions in life—besides her family and reading/writing—are music and films.

To Trish
May your love and appreciation of beauty continue
to lift your spirits and give you wings to fly!

CHAPTER ONE

RETURNING from his morning hack beneath the dazzling Palermo sunshine, Pascual Dominguez cantered into the relative cool and shade of the stables and dismounted. Patting his steed on the rump as a groom promptly materialised, he ordered the young man to turn the pony out into the field after he had seen to him.

He was in good spirits. After a family party last night in honour of his forthcoming marriage he was looking forward to having his fiancée Briana to himself again in a couple of hours, after she had finished work.

There had been far too many people there last evening for them to grab even one moment together, but tonight they would be having dinner at his favourite restaurant, and afterwards he fully intended that she would be spending the night with him, prior to enjoying a few days together before the wedding.

Time alone away from no doubt well-meaning family and friends…just the two of them.

Briana had turned Pascual's well-ordered world upside down and that was a fact! Never having dreamed that such a powerful instant connection with a woman would ever come his way, every day he woke and counted his blessings.

From practically the moment he had set eyes on the young English nanny his friends Marisa and Diego de la Cruz had hired to take care of their baby girl, Briana Douglas had become the sole focus of all his hopes and dreams. She had consented to become his wife, and now he found himself counting the days to their wedding.

Whistling softly beneath his breath, he found his housekeeper waiting for him as he strode through the opened double doors of the main house. A frown puckered the friendly, still smooth olive-skinned features that belied her years.

'What is it, Sofia?' Pascual arched a dark brow, an inexplicable dart of apprehension shooting through him and making him feel suddenly cold.

'Señorita Douglas came by while you were out riding…' the older woman began.

'Where is she?' he interrupted, gazing impatiently round the stunning marble vestibule.

'She did not stay, señor.'

The housekeeper was delving inside the pocket of

her long black skirt for something. In the next instant she handed Pascual a slim white envelope. *The cold feeling inside him deepened to ice.*

'She told me to give you this letter.'

'Gracias.' He all but snatched it from her hand and headed towards the grand winding staircase, taking the steps two at a time before she'd barely finished speaking.

In his personal suite of rooms, he started to rip open the envelope, now frankly *hating* the presentiment of doom that seemed to be clutching his vitals in a vice. *What was wrong with him?* Was he coming down with something? With his wedding only days away, he sincerely hoped not. Standing by the opened balcony doors of his sitting room, he felt a gentle welcome breeze that carried the enticing scents of jasmine and honeysuckle ripple across the single page of cream vellum notepaper that his hand clutched so avidly.

As he started to read, the icy sensation that had gripped him sickeningly intensified.

Dear Pascual

Where do I start? This is so hard for me to tell you, but I have decided that I can't go through with our marriage after all. It's not because I have fallen out of love with you or anything like that. My feelings are still as strong as ever.

But I have increasingly begun to realise that a marriage between us could never really work. The reason is that our backgrounds and who we are as people are just too different. I've tried discussing this with you, but you always tell me there is nothing to worry about and I am just inventing problems where there are none.

I'm afraid you're wrong. Ultimately our vast differences can only impinge negatively on our relationship. Already there have been repercussions within your family because you want to marry an outsider. They mean the world to you, I can see that, and I don't want to come between you and for you to gradually grow to resent me because of it. So, rather than cause any worse heartache by staying and watching what we have slowly disintegrate, I have made the decision to go back to England and resume my life there.

I realise this news will come as a tremendous shock to you, and I am so sorry for any hurt or grief I may cause, but I believe that ultimately this is the right decision for both of us. You have been so good to me and I will never forget you, Pascual, no matter what you might think as you read this letter. I'm also sorry that you have to be the one to tell everyone that the wedding will not be taking place after all—

but, having come to know your family a little, I am certain that this news will only confirm their beliefs that I was totally unsuitable for you in the first place.

Please don't try to contact me again. That's all I ask. It would only prolong the pain for both of us, and I think it's best if we just make a completely new start. Take care of yourself, and I wish you only good things—now and always.

All my love

Briana.

'Dios mio!'

As wave after merciless wave of disbelief, hurt and disappointment submerged him, Pascual scanned the letter again, hardly able to take on board the devastating contents that had been so cruelly revealed to him. *She had left him...* Briana—the woman of his heart—the beautiful girl he had fallen so hard for almost on sight and had been going to marry—had left and gone back to England, without even having the guts to tell him to his face the unbelievable decision she had made.

Last night at the party she had seemed so happy. *Hadn't she?* Now he remembered that later on during the evening at his parents' house she had been looking a little tired and strained, and he had longed to get her alone and find out what was troubling her.

In the end—because his friends had not wanted him to desert the party too early—he had conceded to stay and had got his chauffeur to drive Briana home, thinking he would see her tonight and get to the bottom of her disquiet then.

It was too cruel to realise that his intention would now never materialise because she had elected to leave rather than wait and talk to him. *Why had he not listened to what she had tried to tell him before?* he asked himself, anguished. Clearly Briana had believed there definitely *were* problems, even if he had not. But how dared she assume that she knew what was 'ultimately best' for both of them? She was merely speaking for herself...not for him!

Suddenly feeling that the generously sized room had become a stifling prison, the growing need inside him to escape and breathe some fresher air galvanised him into unhappy action. Throwing the letter down on a nearby bureau, he once again went outside. A violent expletive left his lips as he strode purposefully out into the hot mid-morning sun, the heels of his hand-crafted, made-to-measure calf leather riding boots ringing out clearly on the bleached white cobblestones before him.

For the second time in his thirty-six years he had been brought starkly face to face with what loss meant and it had left him reeling. The year he had turned thirty his best friend Fidel had lost his life in a horrific car crash, leaving behind a wife and child.

Pascual had been brutally awakened to the fact that life was short—and what was the use of having great wealth at his fingertips if he had nobody significant to share it with? Soberly he had reflected on the future and realised that he craved a wife and family of his own. But in his hopeful search for a mate it had unfortunately transpired that he had given his heart to a woman who had clearly thought so little of his feelings that she imagined it was nothing to him for her to simply walk out without warning or giving him proper explanation.

Again it hit Pascual that Briana had left and such was his agony of spirit that for a moment despair almost brought him to his knees. Why had she not trusted him enough to talk to him about her doubts for their future—if doubts were what she had had? As far as he was concerned right now, her actions put her beneath his contempt! His only consolation was that he hoped she would come to bitterly regret her hasty desertion of him and suffer accordingly.

Because he would not go after her... Not for a second time would he invite her rejection of him— no matter how desperate he might become to see her again in the following few days, weeks, years. *And if he ever happened to discover that she had left him because of the unthinkable...because she had fallen in love with somebody else...then he would honestly curse her to the very end of his days...*

Five years later, London, England.

'Was that the postman, love?'

'Yes, Mum.'

Staring down at the slim brown envelope that she'd retrieved from the mat, Briana felt her heart drop like a lead weight inside her chest. If she wasn't mistaken it was another missive from the bank, and this time maybe the threat of a court summons that had been hanging over her head for weeks now had become a horrible reality.

Just eighteen months ago the hospitality business she had set up, providing administrative and organisational services for visiting business people from abroad, had been flourishing almost beyond her wildest dreams. But since the threatening global recession had taken a grip the way Briana's thriving business had started to plummet was no joke. People were not so eager to use less well-established businesses like hers when other, more long-standing companies could risk undercutting their fledgling competitors and charge less for the same services.

She had a son to raise and rent to pay—and how was she going to do either of those things when there was barely enough money coming in to feed them, let alone pay bills?

'Briana? Are you going to come in and have some

breakfast with me and Adán before you leave for your weekend away?'

'Of course. Just give me a minute, will you?'

Stuffing the offending envelope unopened into her bag, Briana sighed heavily. She had no intention of sharing with her mother the news that she had received yet another worrying letter regarding her debt. Frances Douglas would sell the clothes from off her back if it would help her daughter and grandson make ends meet, and she had already threatened to take a second mortgage out on her own house to help them. *She had done enough.* Without her help Briana wouldn't have been able to set the business up in the first place. Now it was up to her to get them out of the hole they were in.

Pushing her fingers resignedly through the mane of silky brown hair that seemed to have a mind of its own, she returned to the kitchen with a deliberately cheerful smile on her face. Her young son was seated up at the breakfast bar on a high stool, eating his cereal, and his grandmother was busy slotting two slices of wholemeal bread into the toaster.

The child beamed when he saw Briana. 'Mummy, this is my second bowl!' he happily announced, milk glistening on his small dimpled chin.

'Is it, my angel? No wonder you're getting so big!' Lovingly dropping an affectionate kiss on the top of his silky dark head, Briana started moving away towards the boiling kettle on the marble-effect worktop. 'Cup of tea, Mum?'

'Why don't you sit down with Adán and let me do it? And you're not going out of this house this morning until you eat at least a couple of slices of toast, either! All this worry is making you thin and pale—and how is it going to help anybody if you fall ill?'

'It's not that I'm not eating.' Curling her hair behind her ears, Briana sighed and dropped teabags into the two waiting mugs, 'I've just been a bit distracted, that's all. This weekend simply *has* to go well, Mum. I've got three entrepreneurs entertaining some billionaire from abroad, and I've got to help take care of them in a Tudor mansion I haven't even had a chance to familiarise myself with yet. I have to get there early and get my act together to greet them or I'll be for the high jump! Thank God Tina went there yesterday, to do some groundwork for me! If I impress, it's been hinted that there might be some more work coming my way from that direction—so keep your fingers crossed for me, won't you?'

'You shouldn't need me to keep my fingers crossed!' Frances Douglas announced, her smoothly powdered features gently chastising. 'You are the very best at what you do, Briana Douglas, and don't you forget it! Your trusting nature brought you that bad debt that's got the business into trouble…not your lack of ability!'

'Thanks, Mum. I needed a boost this morning. You're an angel!'

'And don't fret about Adán either. I have a lovely weekend for us both lined up. I just want you to go to work and concentrate on what has to be done without worrying about us.'

'I promise I won't let you down.'

The older woman's light grey eyes glistened. 'You've never let me down in the whole of your twenty-seven years, child, so don't even think such a thing!'

Her own eyes moist, Briana sniffed and gave her mother a brief hard hug. *She was so lucky.* She had the most wonderful mother a girl could wish for, and a darling little boy who was the light of her life. All things considered—financial problems aside—she wasn't doing badly. *So why, then, just at the moment when she had determinedly decided to look on the bright side, did a disturbing vision of her child's father slide across the cinema screen of her mind and clamp her heart hard enough and painfully enough to take her breath away?*

The house was startlingly impressive. Set in the napped velvet green of the gently undulating Warwickshire landscape, in what was known as Shakespeare country, it was a genuine beautiful relic from England's tumultuous Tudor past that anyone with half an interest in history would relish.

Pascual had stood outside for several minutes after the chauffeur had opened the door of the Rolls-Royce that had brought him from the airport—simply to admire its black and white three storeyed wattle and daub façade and the small arched windows with their leaded panes. The grounds were stunning too. On the way in they had driven past an imposing gatehouse and parkland, as well as some trees that looked as durable as any fascinating ancient monument he had ever seen. As if to doubly remind him that he was in the English countryside now, and far from the vibrancy, colour and heat of Buenos Aires, rain had started to fall—softly at first, then hard enough to make him immediately dash for cover.

As he did so he literally bumped into a young slim blonde who announced that her name was Tina and that she was working for the businessmen who were hosting Pascual's stay this weekend. After showing him to his suite of rooms she said she would bring him some coffee and refreshments—then her colleague would take him to meet his hosts.

Welcoming the opportunity to shower and take stock of his surroundings before partaking of any re-freshments and putting on his 'business head,' Pascual took his time getting ready for his meeting. All the while the steadily falling rain drilled against the diamond-patterned leaded windows of his bedroom and, glancing outside, seeing the boughs of the surrounding trees bend almost to the ground, he realised that the wind was whipping up quite a storm too. But inside it was cosy and warm, and the kind of peace and quiet that he almost *never* experienced at home descended like a soft down blanket, cocooning him from the rest of the world.

His ensuing sigh was almost contented. *After all...what had he to worry about?* However long he made his hosts wait, the last thing they would do would be to voice a complaint. They were getting the chance to buy the most sought-after thoroughbred polo ponies in the business—the elite of the elite—and so they would stem their impatience and relax for however long it took before Pascual finally sought them out.

Absorbed with fastening the small diamond cufflinks on his tailored deep blue Savile Row shirt, he frowned at the sudden knock on the door. No doubt it was the little blonde, returning with his refreshments, he thought lazily. Good. He could do with some strong black coffee.

Outside the panelled oak door in the long, low-ceilinged corridor, Briana was schooling herself to try and breathe more slowly. She'd arrived late, despite all her best efforts, and had just got there in the nick of time to take the tray of coffee from Tina and bring it up to their VIP guest's room. Patting down her hair, she hoped her motorway dash and her lack of time to retouch her make-up would not detract from the warmth and professionalism that was usually her byword. She hadn't even had the presence of mind to ask Tina what their important guest's name was! *Never mind.* Perhaps he'd just be so grateful for the coffee he wouldn't notice that she didn't address him by his name.

The silver coffee pot, patterned cup and saucer and little white jug on the elegant silver tray rattled a little between her hands as Briana held it, and she made herself take another steadying breath.

'Good timing! I was just—*Dios mio!*'

Hooded eyes the intensity and colour of luxurious cocoa set in a handsome strong-boned face with high cheekbones and the most sensuous masculine mouth imaginable stared back at her, as though its owner hardly believed the validity of his own eyesight.

'What in God's name are *you* doing here?'

Just in time Briana held onto the already precariously rattling tray. *Was she dreaming?* As her heart pounded out a shocked tattoo, she had to struggle to maintain her balance. *Pascual was the VIP guest?* How could she not have known that? Suddenly her equilibrium and professionalism fled altogether, and she was left feeling so painfully vulnerable, exposed and inadequate that tears were a mere breath away.

'Did you hear what I said?'

For a moment his accent sounded heavier than

she remembered. The naturally sensuous timbre of that arresting voice still had the power to turn her limbs to the fluidity of water Briana discovered disturbingly. 'I'm working…and I've brought you your coffee,' she managed through numbed lips, giving him a nervous lopsided smile. 'Do you mind if I put the tray down? I'm afraid I might drop it.'

Holding the door wide so that she could enter, Pascual allowed his dark, accusing gaze to follow her like sharpened daggers as she crossed the room to deposit the tray on a small carved oak side-table.

'What is the meaning of this?'

He was studying her as if she were a nasty trick being played on him…a trick he abhorred and detested.

'I told you…I'm here working. Your hosts hired my company to provide hospitality services for your stay. I didn't realise that you were the VIP guest. I'm sorry, Pascual…'

Biting her lip, she felt herself blush hard at the old familiar use of his name and instantly regretted voicing it. Especially when his handsome face demonstrated no pleasure whatsoever in seeing her again…in fact the exact opposite!

'This is probably the last thing you need. Seeing me again, I mean,' she murmured. Her confidence drained away as his eyes tracked slowly and devastatingly up and down her body, in a simple but professional black A-line skirt and jacket, as if checking her out for flaws.

What was he going to do? If he dismissed her and she couldn't carry out her job it would be the last straw as far as her finances and her reputation went. Briana prayed he wouldn't go as far as that. And at the same time as she worried about losing this job— *and laying the hurt of the past aside*—her hungry eyes wanted to weep with joy at the flesh-and-blood evidence of the man she had loved and had secretly dreamed of one day seeing again.

He looked wonderful. 'A sight for sore eyes', as her mum would say. And he'd hardly changed at all—though his stature seemed more imposing than ever. His physique was still leanly muscular, and underneath the sublimely tailored clothes he wore no doubt still in tip-top, enviable condition. And with that arrestingly gorgeous face Pascual Dominguez was not the kind of man who appeared on a girl's radar every day. At least not where Briana came from.

Right from the start she had been smitten, and in no time at all had found herself blissfully and madly in love with him. When she'd discovered that he felt the same way about her she had hardly been able to believe her luck. *But that had been five years ago— five years in which she'd had to come to terms with being a single mother, because Pascual had no clue that he had fathered a child with her when she left.* Not a day went by when the dreadful guilt of that reality didn't weigh her down…

When he still didn't speak, but continued to stare at her as if not knowing whether to shake her senseless or verbally rip into her until her ears rang, Briana twisted the suddenly chilled fingers of her slim hands together and glanced back at the ornate little table where she had put down the tray she had brought. 'Shall I pour you some coffee?'

'Forget the damn coffee! What do you think you're playing at?'

His bitter, chastising tone shocked her blood to ice. 'I'm not playing at anything. This situation is as unexpected and shocking for me as it is for you.'

'But you *did* play me for a fool—didn't you Briana?' His dark eyes narrowed furiously beneath their long-lashed hooded lids. 'I still find it hard to believe you did what you did...even after all this time!'

'It was never my intention to make you feel like a fool.'

Feeling her lips tremble, Briana desperately sought to hold it together—not to break down in front of him and confess all. What would it serve to fully explain now why she had left him? Five years had passed by. He hadn't wanted to listen to her then, so why should he listen now? Anyway...right then she was hardly prepared or willing to rake over old coals and engage in a row—which was no doubt what would happen. As for Adán's existence—she *couldn't* tell him about that just yet. She needed more time...

'I'm really sorry things turned out the way they did, but perhaps it was for the best?'

It was a *stupid* thing to say, and it sounded totally banal.

'For the *best*?'

The words reverberated round the room on a savage breath, and Briana registered the emotion Pascual was feeling like a punch. Confusion, anger, frustration…it was all there.

Scraping his fingers agitatedly through silken layers of rich dark hair, he moved his head from side to side, staring at her hard. 'I can get over being made a fool of in front of my friends and family, but what I *cannot* come to terms with or forgive is that you gave me no indication that your professed feelings for me could be broken off so easily. Or that you would leave without even giving me a chance to hear why from your own lips instead of reading it in some cold, unemotional letter! You must be a consummate actress, Briana… You seemed happy and in love and I believed you. What an idiot I was!'

CHAPTER TWO

HIS heart was thundering as hard and as fast as any express train. It was difficult to take in the fact that the woman he had once loved, who had so callously deserted him mere days before their wedding, was standing there in front of him.

Pascual discovered that his memory of her had not served him as well as he'd thought. In the flesh Briana Douglas was far more beautiful than any mental picture he could call up. Right then she reminded him of an exotic intense port wine, and even though he deplored what she had done he still wanted to drink in every inch of her until he was intoxicated. She had always had a figure to make his pulse race, and in the slim pencil skirt and smart tailored jacket she wore he saw that it was Marilyn Monroe hourglass perfect. Her very presence exuded an earthy sexiness that heated his blood. Would heat *any* man's blood! *But it was her face that arrested his attention the most.*

With her almost feline smoky-grey eyes, apple cheeks and lush enticing mouth, she was a woman to entertain the most sensual private fantasies about. With that face and body she would stop rush-hour traffic in any major city of the world in a heartbeat. Suddenly Pascual was intensely excruciatingly jealous at the idea of her with somebody else—the idea that she might have left him because she preferred another man to him. It took him a moment to get his bearings as well as his sudden inconvenient and shocking desire under strict control.

'There must have been some other reason you left me besides the one that you stated in your letter. Did you leave me for another man? Is that it?' However controlled he strove to be, he still had to voice the question that had been burning in his mind all these years. She flinched, and his gaze clung to hers, fear of her answer making him as tense as a string on a harp.

'Of course I didn't! I'm sorry if you thought that, but there was no one else…there still is no one else.'

Exhaling a long, relieved breath, he was still infuriated by her apparent calmness when inside everything in him was churning as turbulently as the Atlantic in a squall.

'And what about you?' she ventured tentatively. 'Did you get back with your ex?'

'My ex?'

For disturbing seconds Pascual recalled something that had happened the night before Briana had left. The Brazilian model he had briefly dated before he had met her had unexpectedly turned up at the family party, on the arm of his cousin Rafa. His mother, being the perfect hostess, had not turned her away. During the evening Claudia had drunk a little too much cachaca, and when Briana had been out on the terrace talking to Marisa and Diego she had pulled a stupid stunt on him. She'd circled his neck with her arms, pressed her body hard against his and kissed him full on the mouth…

Pascual's blood ran briefly cold as he remembered the incident with renewed distaste and anger. He wasn't remotely interested in taking up with Claudia again…either then or now. It was Briana he had loved. But clearly she had not loved *him*. Why else had it been so easy for her to walk away? The idea pierced his very soul. No man liked to think the loving relationship he believed to be real was based on a lie. A lie that meant his sweetheart did not feel as strongly for him, her lover, as she had insisted she had. Renewed hurt and fury coursed through his bloodstream that the woman in front of him had treated him so abominably.

Raising her bewitching gaze to his, she attempted a smile of sorts. She wasn't quite successful, and he saw the worry and concern reflected clearly in her eyes. *Good.* He was glad he had unsettled her. God knows, she had unsettled him!

'When she showed up at that party…I just thought that you and she—'

'Well, you were wrong. She was dating my cousin and he brought her with him. End of story!'

'Well, then…I'd better just leave you to have your coffee,' she remarked. 'Your hosts are waiting for you in the drawing room downstairs. Shall I tell them you'll be ready in about twenty minutes or so? I can meet you in the lobby and take you to them.'

'I will be ready when I am ready, and not before!' Pascual snapped, turning his back on her and moving towards the tray of coffee.

Choosing to remain silent for a few moments, he poured some of the hot aromatic beverage into the porcelain cup and took a sip. Definitely particular about the type of coffee he drank, he found he could not fault whoever had chosen this particular blend on his behalf.

Facing Briana again, he observed the slight pink flush across her cheekbones. 'You are here the entire weekend?' he asked, knowing this conversation they had started had only just begun.

'Yes…my job dictates it.'

'And how long have you been working for this company that provides "hospitality services"?'

'About three years. It's my own company.'

'So you are a businesswoman now? You have managed to surprise me again!'

Unable to keep the cynicism from his voice, Pascual was actually genuinely taken aback by the revelation. The Briana he had known had never given any indication of being remotely interested in starting up her own business. Back then she had vowed she was only happy working with children and animals. On her arrival in Buenos Aires she had found work as a professional dog-walker, then as a children's nanny. But he had learned to his cost that she had not been entirely frank with him about many things, and her dishonesty still cut him to the quick.

'I'll leave you to enjoy your coffee in peace and go and wait downstairs.'

Moving towards the door, Briana could not disguise her eagerness to get away, and it incensed Pascual that she should want to effect distance between them again.

'Before you run away I want you to tell me something of these businessmen I am meeting with. No doubt you have some information that might be useful?' Staring at her pointedly, he knew a sudden desire to test her out and see if she was at all competent at the business she had chosen for herself. If he himself had been in this line of work the first thing he would want to know was about the kind of people who were employing his services.

'What do you want to know?' she asked, clearly discomfited that she could not escape as easily as that.

'I want to know the things they have *not* revealed in their bid to buy my horses. You know the kind of information I am getting at? It is important that my ponies go to the very best homes. As I am sure you are aware, I do not make these transactions just for money.'

'All their credentials are first class, but if you want to ask me about specifics fire away. I can assure you that I've done my homework in that regard.'

'Really? But you clearly did not know that it was *me* that was the VIP guest this weekend, did you? Is that not somewhat remiss of you?'

A scarlet brand seared even hotter colour into her cheeks. 'It wasn't a mistake I would ever make normally, I can assure you! It's just that I've had a lot on my mind lately, and I—'

'Your personal concerns should never impinge on your ability to do your job well.'

'In a perfect world that might be so, but in case you hadn't noticed this world *isn't* perfect, and from time to time people *do* have worries that cannot help but disturb them.'

'What kind of worries do you have nowadays, Briana?' Pascual shot back, no small amount of bitterness edging his tone. 'I thought you must be perfectly happy and content. After all…you escaped from a man and a marriage you clearly did not want, did you not? I imagined that you must have got *exactly* what you wanted when you walked out on me.'

'Can we *not* do this? It's painful enough that we should meet up again like this without us sniping at each other. We're both here for more important reasons than what's between us personally. I know we need to talk, but this is hardly the right time.'

Wanting to, but hardly able to refute her argument right then, Pascual took another sip of his coffee, then placed the cup and saucer back on the tray. 'Give me five minutes and then I will meet you downstairs,' he responded tersely. 'No doubt we will indeed have an opportunity to discuss our personal issues over the weekend. If it looks like we will not—then we will have to make sure we create an opportunity. I can assure you of one thing: you are not leaving this establishment until I hear the full account of why you ran away from our marriage. And even then I will not let you go until I am satisfied that you have told me the truth!'

After her encounter with Pascual, Briana was still inwardly shaking as she attempted to chat to Tina in the lobby, and she knew her colleague saw that she was unusually distracted. Priding herself on her ability to remain unflappable in most situations— especially when it came to her work—she feared she was going to have to dig deep for resources she wasn't even sure she had to get her through the rest of *this* weekend.

When Pascual descended the thickly carpeted staircase, only moments later, her breath all but got locked inside her throat. If he'd meant to make a statement that there was no question it was *he* who was the VIP guest this weekend, then he had more than succeeded. He had teamed the most exquisite bespoke black jacket with beautifully tailored trousers and a deep blue shirt, and Briana's knees almost gave way beneath her at the sight of him. He had always looked amazing in a suit—elegant in a way that most very masculine men couldn't attempt to carry off, as well as effortlessly stylish, fit, and sexy enough to make a woman forget what she was thinking about the second she clapped eyes on him. No matter what her age or marital status!

It was no surprise when Tina leaned over to her and whispered, 'My God! He's the most *gorgeous* man I've ever seen. How lucky are we that he's the VIP client!'

Lucky? That wasn't exactly how Briana would describe what she was feeling as Pascual turned his disdainful dark gaze her way and silently warned her that he was not finished with her yet…not by a long chalk.

'Señor—Mr Dominguez…your meeting is this way. Please come with me.'

As she led him into the elegant drawing room where the three businessmen were waiting to meet him, they rose in unison from their pin-tucked armchairs round the fireplace. Her voice had a slight tremor in it as she made the formal introductions. There was no doubt in her mind that the men were relieved that Pascual had finally appeared, and straight away she sensed how deferential they were towards him. Her ex-fiancé had always seemed to elicit that kind of response from other people. There was something almost *aristocratic* about him that, along with his sensational looks, guaranteed he commanded instant attention wherever he went.

After five years of not seeing him the impact he made when he walked into a room had not lessened one iota, Briana discovered, and she wondered what Tina would say if she ever found out that this 'gorgeous man', a wealthy Argentinian, was the father of her little boy Adán. Surveying him now, she could hardly believe it herself. Their whirlwind romance seemed such a long time ago. A long, *lonely* time ago, she thought with a sudden profound ache in her heart.

'Can we get some more coffee in here—and maybe some brandy, sweetheart?' Steve Nichols, MD of an advertising agency in Soho and lately co-owner with his two colleagues of highly desirable stables in Windsor, took Briana aside.

Glancing into his pale blue eyes and looking at his slightly shiny pallor, she couldn't help shivering with distaste. Unfortunately she knew his type. He might be on a business trip, but he would consider any reasonably attractive female between the ages of sixteen and forty fair game. Briana knew she would have to keep her wits about her around him. His business credentials might be impeccable, but that didn't mean his manners or his behaviour towards women followed suit.

To Pascual—a fellow entrepreneur, with a commodity to sell that he very much desired—he would be sycophantic and deferential to a tee. But to her and Tina he could potentially be a nuisance.

'Of course… Was there anything else?' Glancing deliberately over at the other men she waited until they all agreed that coffee and brandy was just perfect for now.

As she turned to leave Steve Nichols leaned over to her and whispered conspiratorially, 'Hurry back, sweetheart,' and winked. At that very moment she sensed Pascual's deeply disapproving gaze come to rest on her, and then on the man beside her. Briana's face flamed again. She hoped to God he didn't think she was *encouraging* him!

The meeting went on for at least three hours, and by then it was nearly dinnertime. The hosts had requested that dinner be provided and catered for by a local well-known Michelin-starred restaurant, and while Briana and Tina dealt with the staff from there, who had arrived with their supplies and were currently ensconced in the house's ample kitchen, the three businessmen retired to their respective rooms to get ready.

To be honest, Briana was glad of the breathing space in which to busy herself with the practicalities of her job and stem the tide of anxiety and emotion that had swept over her since she'd seen Pascual again. *But she knew she couldn't avoid him for ever.* Sooner or later he would confront her about the events of the past and the unexpected and abrupt manner in which she had left Argentina.

He would demand a fuller account of *why* she had left.

The plain fact of the matter was that her reasons for leaving had not become any easier to come to terms with over the years. In fact, some days she worried that they would be with her, spoiling her chance of happiness with a man, for ever... Not that she even *wanted* any other man. After all that had happened, Pascual's trust in her was obviously going to be in very short supply. Would he even believe her when she *did* finally explain things?

About halfway through the evening Tina emerged from the private dining room that overlooked the beautiful gardens which now, as darkness fell, were hidden from view by the heavy velvet drapes at the windows. Briana rose up from the padded love-seat in the lobby and asked, 'How's it going in there? Everybody happy?'

'The food looks amazing! Everyone is tucking in, but our gorgeous Argentinian looks bored, frankly— as if he'd much rather be somewhere else than here.'

Briana's stomach sank. Their personal business was one thing, but if Pascual was looking bored then the businessmen who had hired her company's services would not be so thrilled, and she felt responsible for that. Somehow she had to rescue the situation.

'I was thinking everyone might like to go out somewhere afterwards. There's a private members' club with a casino in town. I've already been on the phone to them and they would be more than happy to have our party visit.'

'Great idea! Why don't you go in and tell them?' Tina replied, with a wink of her plum-coloured eyelid. 'They'll probably appreciate the suggestion more coming from you… I've noticed how they've all hardly been able to take their eyes off of you— *especially* the heavenly Mr Dominguez!'

'You're imagining things.'

'All I know is if I had even *half* the sex appeal you've got, Briana Douglas, then I'd be milking it for all I was worth! Every one of those men in that dining room is a multimillionaire, and Mr Dominguez— who's by far the yummiest of the lot—is apparently a *billionaire*! Haven't you ever fantasised about some outrageously rich and gorgeous man sweeping you off your feet and marrying you?'

Briana would have laughed out loud if the irony of her colleague's words hadn't been quite so acutely painful. Touching her fingers briefly to her burning cheek, she dismissed the younger girl's comments with a deliberately distracted air, and gave the black velvet waistcoat she wore over a white silk blouse a little tug to bring it better into alignment with the waistband of her matching fitted skirt.

'I'll go in and talk to them... In the meantime, Tina, could you get me a cup of coffee and a sandwich from the kitchen? I don't think I could face a meal tonight. Do you mind?'

'You're mad, turning down the chance to try some of that fantastic food that's been brought in! They brought enough for us with them, you know.'

'Then why don't *you* have my share?'

Heading down the rich maroon carpet of the hallway that led to the dining room, Briana thought she'd be hard pressed even to eat the sandwich she'd requested, let alone a full meal. Her stomach was deluged with butterflies at just the thought of having a private conversation with Pascual, as she knew she must. She felt doubly unsettled when she thought about her little son...the child he had no idea that he'd fathered when she'd left Argentina in such an unseemly hurry. Following on from that came the realisation that someone with the wealth and status *he* had at his fingertips could all too easily take Adán from her if he had a mind and a will to…

'A casino? What an inspired idea—if you don't mind my saying so, Miss Douglas!' Steve Nichols leant back in the rather grand Tudor dining chair he occupied as his colleagues readily concurred, and gave Briana another one of his irritating winks.

Compressing her lips in mild irritation, she quickly glanced round the rest of the table and endeavoured to engage the other diners with her pleased smile. But the gesture faded prematurely when her anxious gaze inevitably collided with Pascual's. He did not simply look bored, as Tina had suggested. Quite clearly he was more annoyed than anything else! Was that because she had walked in and soured his mood?

Once upon a time his face had lit up whenever she came into a room where he happened to be, and again Briana's heart couldn't help but yearn for those happier times. To be young and in love with the man of her dreams, living in a vibrant and amazing city like Buenos Aires, had been *more* than in- credible! Sometimes she had to pinch herself to remember that it had ever happened at all… Perhaps it was something she'd dreamt up, because of her loneliness now? But she only had to glance at her son's sweet dark-eyed face to see the startling resemblance to his charismatic father, and she told herself to simply count her blessings. Having Adán reminded her that she hadn't lost everything, after all. She had her precious child.

'What about you Mr Dominguez?' she forced herself to ask. 'Would you like to go the casino?'

'Only if you will agree to accompany me, Miss Douglas,' he answered smoothly, with an arch of his eyebrow. 'I always like to have a beautiful girl on my arm when I go to a casino…for *luck*, you understand…'

'I…I'm afraid I have work to do.'

All eyes were upon her, and Briana wanted the floor to open up and swallow her. *What was Pascual playing at, inviting her to go with them?* He must know it was completely inappropriate and would put her in a most awkward position.

'Come, come, Miss Douglas,' coaxed Mike Daniels, one of the other businessmen. 'Mr Dominguez is our guest tonight. He's come all the way from Argentina for our meeting—the least we can do is grant him this one request, don't you think? Think of it as one of the perks of the job. Myself and my colleagues will gladly foot the bill.'

Still doubtful, Briana easily guessed that Pascual was taking the utmost pleasure in her obvious discomfort and embarrassment. She wanted to tell Mike Daniels that acting as escort to his VIP guest on a visit to a casino was definitely *not* part of the services

her company provided. But she sensed her ex-
fiancé's potential to make life very difficult all round
for everyone if she refused.

Her grey eyes beseeching, she gazed back into the
compellingly handsome face that still lazily studied
her, and disturbingly saw that a small mocking smile
was playing around his lips.

'I haven't brought anything suitable with me to
wear to a casino.'

'What you have on is absolutely fine.' Her tormen-
tor's smile widened, and his dark eyes lit with
mischief as he deliberately swept his gaze up and
down her figure, letting it linger in particular on the
lush curve of her breasts outlined by the snug black
velvet waistcoat.

His aim was obviously to embarrass and belittle
her as much as he could, Briana saw, and she would
have had no bones about demonstrating her fury with
his behaviour if only they had been alone. As things
stood, she couldn't do that. Not without making a
scene and besmirching her hard-won reputation as a
professional businesswoman.

'Very well, then. I'll go and ring the casino and
let them know how many of us are coming.'

CHAPTER THREE

THE private members club was situated in an elegant Georgian house tucked away down a quiet country lane, and it welcomed them with open arms. Used to his name and his wealth opening doors Pascual hovered conveniently close to Briana's slim back as they were shown into the private casino that was set aside for VIPs only.

If he was announcing to all who cared to observe them that *he* was the one who was her escort for the evening then he did not stop to examine why he should be acting so possessively over a woman who had treated him with such disdain. All Pascual knew was that not only did he need to be close to Briana, but he would take a secret sardonic delight in her discomfort too. She had hurt him badly. He knew it was pure animal instinct, but he wanted to find a way of getting back at her for the deed…of ensuring that she would think twice before ever behaving like that again.

Asked what his favourite game was by the club manager, he had no hesitation in replying, 'American Roulette.' Once seated at a circular mahogany table, with a roulette wheel at the centre, and having given their drinks order to a pretty auburn-haired waitress in a short satin lilac dress, he made sure Briana sat next to him on the padded red-velvet seat. His thigh deliberately pressed up against hers. The distinct quiver that shuddered through her made him smile with satisfaction. The sweetly seductive scent of her light perfume and the warmth of her body elicited a similar response inside Pascual. *Dios mio!* He could hardly credit why he should still be so violently attracted to her after all this time.

Something about the combustible mix of chemistry they produced when they were together, obviously.

Seeing the jealous flare in Steve Nichols' pale watchful gaze as he surveyed the brunette with Pascual, the Argentinian ironically found himself musing that all was fair in love and war, and deliberately leaned closer to Briana, so that she gazed up at him with those smoky alluring eyes of hers and coloured hotly.

'You choose the numbers for me tonight,' he instructed softly as the smartly dressed croupier dealt the chips.

'I'm not sure I agree with gambling,' she breathed. 'What if you lose everything because of me?'

As if realising what she had said might also refer to the way their relationship had ended, she let her even white teeth come down hard on her tender lower lip and couldn't hide her intense discomfort.

'I'm sorry,' she murmured.

For a moment Pascual forgot they were in company, in a public albeit supposedly discreet venue that was used to visiting VIPs with a need for privacy, and warred with an almost insatiable urge to savagely claim her mouth and passionately kiss her.

Maybe that could come later? he considered, willing his heartbeat to slow down, unable to tear his heated gaze from hers. A quiet but pervasive excitement took root inside him at the idea.

'Place your bets,' the dealer invited, and Pascual raised an eyebrow at his female companion. 'What will it be?'

Clearly reluctant to participate, but knowing she could hardly refuse, Briana frowned. 'Red six,' she replied.

'Why six?'

'It's always been lucky for me.'

As the little hard white ball hopped and skipped round the moving wheel, every glance round the table seemed hypnotised by it. The other patrons had bet too. Hardly caring whether he won or lost, Pascual felt his heart nearly miss a beat when the ball landed squarely on red six. He had just won thirty-five times his stake, and his had been the only coloured chip on that number.

His hosts and the other two couples round the table politely applauded. When the croupier paid him out in the appropriate chips, he turned and put them on the table in front of Briana.

'Play again,' he urged smoothly, smiling at the shock on her face. 'Perhaps you have other lucky numbers at your disposal? Whatever you win…you keep.'

'I'd rather not, if you don't mind.' Appearing distressed, she pushed to her feet. Her cheeks reddening, she halted a passing cocktail waitress. 'Can you tell me where the ladies' cloakroom is, please?' she asked.

In faint concern, Pascual also got to his feet. He caught Briana's elbow as she started to move away. 'What is the matter? Are you unwell?'

'I shouldn't have come here!' she hissed, her silvery eyes shimmering beneath the twinkling lights of the opulent chandelier sparkling above them. 'I came against my better judgement, and now I wish I hadn't!'

'Why? Are you so averse to winning money?'

'I'm not winning anything, Pascual! It's *your* money that you're so recklessly throwing away to chance, and I want nothing more to do with it.'

'Such principles you have! What a shame they were not in such evidence when you ran away from me in Buenos Aires five years ago, without even giving me a good reason why you'd suddenly decided I was not good enough to be your husband!'

'I saw you kissing another woman!' Jealousy and hurt slashed through Briana's insides like a blade, with no lessening of the pain she had suffered at the time of the incident five years ago.

Remembering where she was, she quickly glanced behind her and realised that they had an audience. She moved her head in anguish. She hadn't meant to just come out with it like that, but the memory had been dragging at her heart from the moment she'd set eyes on Pascual again and she could stem the tide of hurt no longer. Pulling her arm free from his hold, she tried to regain control of her briefly lost equilibrium and restore her dignity.

He considered her with a stunned look. 'Who?' he demanded. 'Who was this woman you saw me kissing?'

'You know very well who!' Her lip trembling, Briana kept her voice low.

'I imagine you are referring to Claudia at the party that night? A very *drunk* Claudia, who barely even knew what she was doing!'

'Oh, she *knew* what she was doing Pascual... And so did you, by the looks of things.'

'Why didn't you tell me you saw this? Was that the real reason you left? *Dios mio!*'

'We'd better not have a scene here, in front of everyone. Think how it will look to your hosts—and it might reflect badly on my business too.'

'Yet you clearly did not care how it looked to my family and friends when you heartlessly deserted me just a week before our wedding!'

Pascual's heart was pounding again, and he almost did not care whether he made a scene or not. The memory of Briana's renunciation of both him and their marriage still cut him to the bone. *And now to discover that she had witnessed that distasteful incident with Claudia, to learn that that was the reason she had left!* Inside he was reeling from the knowledge. Why hadn't she immediately said something to him? Demanded an explanation and given him the chance to tell her that his ex had been drunk and he had frankly been appalled by her throwing herself at him?

Mindful that they were not alone, he had no intention of providing entertainment for the night for all and sundry who might be watching. A more personal discussion of events would have to wait. Giving Briana a stiff little bow, he barely disguised his impatience and annoyance.

'Go to the ladies' cloakroom. When you return I will instruct our driver to take us back to the house. I have suddenly lost my interest in gambling any further tonight!'

* * *

Taking her brush out of her compact leather handbag, Briana made a half-hearted attempt at tidying her hair. The bank of sparkling mirrors in the luxurious ladies' powder room left her with no place to hide her distress. *She should have controlled her emotions better just now in the gaming room!* But it had been so hard, when the reality of Pascual had just kept overwhelming her. And then when he had so carelessly and tauntingly put that little pile of coloured chips in front of her, each one reflecting a sum that would easily pay three months' rent on her house, it had all been too much. Here she was, worrying herself sick over her business and facing potential bankruptcy, and Pascual was acting as if money was nothing to him! But of course with the vast wealth he had at his disposal the value of those coloured chips was even less than a drop in the ocean. If Briana was really honest it was not her financial worries that were causing her the most concern right then. Her little son's beautiful face was constantly in her mind—a face that was a perfect miniature version of his father's—and she wondered how on earth she could break the earth-shattering news of his existence to a man who would probably despise her even more than he did already when he heard it. She had kept Adán from him, and Pascual had every right to deride her.

But she had been utterly devastated when she had seen him with Claudia in his arms that night.

Briana's motives in doing what she had done had only been to try to protect herself and her son from possible future hurt… Not for the first time fear that her decision had been the wrong one clutched deep in her vitals. Claudia had been drunk, he had said. Was he telling her the truth?

Drawing the flat of her hand across her jittery stomach, she resignedly moved away from the uncomfortably candid bank of mirrors and returned to the gaming room. When she did, true to his word Pascual was waiting for her, his dark elegant suit and disturbingly handsome face easily singling him out from all the other men in the room.

'Are you ready to leave?' he asked, his sable eyes flicking over her from head to toe.

'What about the others?' she returned anxiously, glancing back at the roulette table and the three men they had arrived with.

'I will instruct the chauffeur to return for them. Do not fret—we will not leave them stranded!'

Almost complete silence reigned on the journey back to the house. Both parties were painfully, acutely aware of the shattered past that lay between them, and they barely knew how to raise the topic again— a topic that was akin to negotiating a bed of jagged broken glass in their bare feet.

Inevitably, the growing tension gathered uncomfortable strength in the small luxurious space that was the passenger seat of the Rolls...like a small but lethal storm about to break. *There had already been evidence of thunder and lightning.* Thinking back to the scene in the gaming room earlier, when Pascual had let his temper and impatience with her spill over, Briana knew a major confrontation was definitely brewing.

Protectively, she folded her arms over her middle, the too intimate scent of his aftershave and his disturbing body heat unsettling her even more. Everything about the imposing man beside her seemed to emphatically illustrate the marked differences between them. He was wealthy, beautiful and powerful—and as out of reach as he had always been. Oh, he might have professed to love her but he had always held something back...something that had fuelled Briana's already damaging belief that she really *wasn't* quite good enough for him after all. *When she'd seen him kissing his elegant model ex-girlfriend at that tension-filled family party it had inevitably highlighted all her very worst fears that their union wouldn't last— that she wasn't just 'not good enough' but not enough...period!* Now she turned her face away to try and prevent herself from weeping.

Back inside the house, she prayed hard that the confrontation that was definitely imminent would not be tonight. Briana knew she was only putting off the inevitable, but somehow she was feeling far too vulnerable to get into another painful argument with Pascual now—with both of them aiming accusations at each other like lethal missiles and scoring devastating hits. A good night's sleep might help strengthen her besieged resources, so she could face him tomorrow instead.

They were standing at the foot of the impressive Tudor staircase, and she tentatively touched the carved oak handrail, as if to signify her intention to retire. But Pascual's glance was thoughtfully brooding, and it confirmed to her that she would not be allowed to dismiss him or say goodnight as easily as that.

'When I set out from Buenos Aires I had a feeling that something disturbing was going to happen,' he remarked, low-voiced.

As if feeling a chill, Briana rubbed her hands up and down her arms in the thin silk sleeves of her blouse. 'I don't want to ruin your trip, Pascual... honestly, I don't. I know the hurt and resentment you must feel towards me probably still runs deep, but—'

'You are right about that!' His dark eyes flashed, as though his emotions were simmering fire contained behind a mere thin veil. Any moment now the heated sparks would flare into an inferno and incinerate the veil to nothing.

'Look,' she went on, praying he would hear her out and agree, 'tomorrow, after the polo match that's been lined up for you to go to, there'll be time to please yourself what you do next. I'll be here overseeing the arrangements for dinner if you want to come back and talk to me then. I promise I'll give you as long as you like and I won't cut our meeting short. Please, Pascual… It's been a long day and I'm tired tonight.'

'You always *did* manage to get your own way whenever you looked at me like that.'

'Like what?'

'Like a sad, lost little girl.' His lips were twisting wryly, but perhaps with a hint of bitterness in them too, Pascual reached out and touched his fingertips to Briana's soft cheek. 'You could wrap me round your little finger when we were together, and that is the truth!'

'Is it?' Hardly daring to breathe, Briana felt the blood thicken and slow in her veins. There was a tight, coiled feeling in her womb.

'More fool you if you did not know it!' His countenance was unremittingly harsh for a second, but in the next instant it visibly softened and became almost too beguiling for words. Certainly too beguiling for her to resist. 'I will let you go to bed if you give me a kiss,' he intoned huskily. 'For old times' sake.'

Briana was not given time to give Pascual an answer, because suddenly his mouth was on hers, his velvet tongue sliding commandingly between her already partially opened soft lips and dancing with hers in hot, erotic foreplay that heated her blood to fire and stole all the strength from her limbs as though her legs had been violently swept away at the knees.

His hands possessively cupped her hips, impelling them hungrily towards him, and he briefly withdrew his mouth from her lips and suckled the sensitive skin at the side of her neck. When she felt his teeth graze the surface hard enough to sting, Briana gasped out loud. *She was drowning in an erotic sea in which she barely had enough strength left with which to swim.* If she didn't stop this intoxicating insanity right now then she had no doubt she would *not* be spending the night in her room's stately four-poster bed alone.

The thought both shocked and terrified her. As far as she was concerned Pascual Dominguez was a force of nature she could never resist—yet how could she contemplate sleeping with him again when he was not even aware that they had a son together? Her sin, if sin it was, would be compounded way beyond repair.

'You must stop!' Her breathing ragged, she pushed her hands with as much force as she could muster against a chest that was like the hardest steel wall.

'Why?' A silky lock of sable hair flopped sexily across his tanned brow and his expression was mockingly defiant. 'Because you are afraid I will keep you up all night doing all the things I used to do to you that you professed drove you wild, *carino mio*?'

Capturing the handrail for much-needed support, Briana couldn't do one thing about the scarlet flush that she knew seared her face. There wasn't a single inch on her entire body that wasn't burning up with heat at the images Pascual's taunting words so vividly conjured up. When it came to making love, the passion and fire in him had always taken her breath away and made her half crazy with loving him and wanting him, she remembered, aching with sudden renewed longing. But she *had* to be strong!

'I'm here to work…not to provide night-time entertainment for my clients!' she told him indignantly.

'I'm glad to hear it. Because I have no doubt given the chance the admiring Mr Nichols would be at the head of the queue, *amante*!'

Briana shuddered. 'Even if that were true, I can assure you I'm not remotely interested in the man.'

'Good.'

'You don't like him?'

'I have not seen much to make me particularly warm to him as yet,' Pascual confessed candidly. 'This is by no means a done deal, you may be surprised to learn. Like I said before…it is not just about money. I have to be certain that my ponies are going to genuine horse-lovers and will be taken care of as excellently and as well as their pedigree and training dictates they should be.'

'The stables that they own at Windsor certainly have an impressive reputation, so I hear.'

'That may be so… But it is a very recent acquisition for our three businessmen friends, having only lately discovered their passion for polo… That is no guarantee that they know how to run a stable successfully *or* take care of the ponies.'

'Surely there are people there who will know how to do that for them?'

'Even so…' Pascual shrugged. 'But that is enough talk of business for tonight.'

Moving closer, he let his long hands with their surprisingly artistic fingers come to rest either side of Briana's slender upper arms. 'I am sure you are aware that I am much more interested in getting you to agree to spend just one more night with me than in discussing anything else.'

'Why?' Her gaze was steady and direct, even though her heart was racing. 'For old times' sake? Or just to prove you can? Let me save you any doubt if doubt—is what you are suffering from, Pascual. Yes, I still find you attractive, and, yes, I could probably quite easily let you seduce me. But we both know in our hearts it wouldn't be the best of ideas, and it probably wouldn't leave either of us feeling very good. Not physically…but *mentally,* psychologically, I mean. What we had was in the past and, however badly it ended, I really think that that's where it should stay.'

'And leave things as unsatisfactorily unfinished between us as ever?' His expression was scornful. 'That may suit *you*, Briana but it does *not* suit me. I have already had to wait five years to hear from your own lips a full explanation as to why you left, and learning that you saw my ex kissing me at that party is only the tip of the iceberg, I am sure!'

'I promised I would talk to you tomorrow, didn't I?'

'Yes, you did. But, as I am already aware to my detriment that your promises are hardly the *lasting* kind, you can see why I have my doubts.'

Swallowing hard, Briana felt guilt, regret and dread wash through her with equal force. *If her capacity for being honest was in dispute right now, how was Pascual going to react tomorrow when she told him about the son whose existence she had deliberately kept from him?* Her legs felt so weak she wondered how on earth she remained standing.

'Very well.' It seemed he had reluctantly come to a decision. 'We will continue this discussion tomorrow, after I return from the polo match. Now…I am going to go and help myself to a nightcap, then sit in the drawing room for a while and imagine you all alone in your bed to see what fantasies I can conjure up about what you will be wearing. I know you always resisted sleeping naked…is that still the case?'

Remembering how he'd used to tease her about

her 'charming modesty', Briana gripped the stair-rail a little harder as she also recollected that—no matter whether she'd worn something in bed or not—Pascual had always ensured that she ended up naked.

'Goodnight, Pascual,' she murmured, electing to ignore the tantalising question altogether.

'*Buenas noches*, Briana.'

Turning abruptly away with a little half-smile, he made the long walk down the carpeted oak floor to the drawing room. All the while Briana's anxious gaze cleaved to his tall, straight back—until he went inside the door and disappeared from view. The intoxicating taste of him was still clinging to her mouth like some kind of drugging nectar, making her perversely wish for a very different ending to their evening together indeed…

CHAPTER FOUR

IT SOUNDED as if someone was trying to break down the door. Her heart beating like a loud bass drum, Briana let her gaze adjust to the dark for a second, before leaning over to the bedside lamp and switching it on. As soon as light flooded the room she was out of bed in a flash, hurrying to see who her urgent-sounding caller was. Her mind was wild with fear that something unthinkable might have happened to her son.

The figure that loomed up before her out of the semi-darkened corridor was Pascual, and he was glaring at her like a man holding onto the last vestiges of his self-control. His furious, contemptuous gaze seared her to the spot with its ferocity.

'You heartless, selfish little bitch!' he spat out.

'What's wrong?' she asked weakly, her hand nervously going to the V of her short cotton nightie. She was afraid she knew the answer.

Kicking the door shut behind him with the heel of his shoe, he moved towards Briana in head-to-toe black clothing, like some deadly feral panther alighting on his kill, and she honestly thought she might pass out in shock. She was almost tripping over her own feet in her anxious bid to get away, but nonetheless Pascual easily caught her and impelled her towards him, his hard chest acting like an impenetrable wall to confound her escape.

'You have a *son*! A four-year old son! He's mine, isn't he? He *must* be mine! Even *you* would not have deceived me with another man when we were together...not when I made sure that practically every night you were kept occupied in my bed!'

For long, excruciating seconds every possibility of speech deserted Briana. Staring up into the sea of pain and accusation bearing down on her in Pascual's scorching livid gaze, she felt her stomach clench sickeningly with fear and regret.

'How did—?' she began brokenly, hardly even feeling the immovable band of his fingers that was tightly circling her small-boned wrist. 'How did you find out?'

'Your colleague Tina was most illuminating about a lot of things,' he answered scathingly. 'I found her alone in the drawing room, reading, and I suggested she share a nightcap with me. Sitting by a cosy fire, it did not take long for alcohol to loosen her already willing tongue. Before I knew it she was practically telling me your life story!'

'She—she wouldn't!'

Throwing Briana's arm away, as if her touch was nothing less than poison, Pascual snorted. 'How little you seem to know about human nature… No wonder your business is failing! Did you not know that *anyone* can be bought for a price? In your colleague's case just a small sherry was enough for her to spill all your guilty secrets at my feet…like a treasure trove!'

Lost for words for a second time, Briana threaded her fingers through her tousled hair in deepening anguish. If only Tina had not been so free with her conversation, or had made the decision to retire to bed the same time as her boss instead of sitting up to be dazzled by Pascual's undoubted charm! But what troubled her the most was the fact that he had discovered the existence of his son *not* from his mother but from a gossipy colleague! No wonder he was enraged. Nothing would prevent her from taking the full brunt of the blame, even though she still believed she had had good reason to leave him.

'Yes…Adán is your son.' Her mouth was almost too dry to get the words out. Wincing, she lifted her gaze to meet the blistering reply of the man whose sheer charismatic presence seemed to fill up the room, making her feel as if she was relegated to just a small corner of it.

'Adán?' His voice grated, as if he too were having trouble with words. 'You had the temerity to call him by a Spanish name and not even let me—his *father*—know of his existence…why?'

Moving his head from side to side, Pascual couldn't hide his torment and Briana's heart went out to him—even though she knew he would likely despise and detest any compassion she demonstrated.

'Why did I give him a Spanish name?'

'No! Why did you keep the fact that you were pregnant from me and disregard my feelings as though they were of no account whatsoever? I thought that you could not hurt me any worse than you did when you left…without giving me even the smallest indication that you were planning such an unbelievable act. But now I have discovered that you are capable of *far* worse crimes. I was wrong to think that I knew you, Briana… Your behaviour is beyond my understanding and makes you an utter stranger to me!'

Staring at her, Pascual saw a myriad of emotions cross her pale just-stirred-from-sleep face. But he wished he could see *more* than just the evidence of feelings there. He wished he had a mental microscope to probe deep inside her heart and see if he could understand what had motivated her to deal him such a cruel and yet perversely *wondrous* blow all at the same time?

The news that he was a father had turned his

whole world upside down, and it was by far the most momentous thing he had ever heard. But right now rage and despair were the prevalent emotions crashing through him, battering him like a violent cyclone at the thought that he had already missed out on four years of his child's life because of the woman that stood in front of him.

Had he somehow treated her so badly that she would act in such a vicious way towards him? He did not think so. From the first he had always treated her with the utmost care and respect...*hadn't he*? Because of the immense gravity of what she'd done to him, there was a painful glimmer of doubt in Pascual's mind. Had he missed out something important? Searching his memory with rapier-like honesty, he could recall nothing that he'd done or said to wound her in any way. Apart from that unfortunate scene at the party that his inebriated ex had instigated—*the incident which he had tried to explain had been genuinely nothing to do with him...* No, he concluded. That could not be the *only* reason she had kept him in the dark about his child. This was all about what had been going on with Briana personally, and he vowed he would let nothing stand in the way of his getting to the bottom of it.

Looking distressed, she brushed back her hair with a trembling hand, and Pascual's attention was helplessly drawn to the short pastel blue night garment she wore that resembled an oversized T-shirt—probably a chainstore item that had not been designed to be alluring in any way, he guessed. Her lack of sophistication and guile-free attitude towards things like that had once totally charmed him. And even now, in the midst of his disbelief and despair at what she had done, his libido was unequivocally and treacherously aroused by the sight of her body in the plain, nondescript nightwear...the firm rounded breasts that pressed against the thin material, nipples provocatively erect, the perfect Botticelli angel-like curve of her hips and her long shapely bare thighs.

'I've anguished so long about talking to you about things. Then it turned out you're the VIP guest this weekend and—and it was such a shock. I wasn't deliberately trying to avoid discussing what happened between us earlier... I just needed time to get my bearings.'

'So now you have had *plenty* of time to deal with the fact that I am here—and you owe me an explanation...to put it mildly!'

'Why don't you sit down?' Moving gracefully towards the striped pink and cream slipper chair that she'd laid her robe across, she gathered up the flimsy blue garment and slipped it on over the matching oversized T-shirt, leaving the chair empty.

Barely knowing how to contain his impatience and frustration at what he perceived to be deliberate delaying tactics, Pascual threw up his hands in temper. 'Do not tell me what to do!' A string of Spanish invective escaped him, and he saw the frisson of fear that flickered across the darkened grey irises, but just then he refused to concern himself with the fact she might be intimidated by him. 'All I want is a truthful explanation of your actions. After that…'

'After that…what?'

'*Dios mio!* Just stop wasting time and *tell* me!'

'All right. I—I wanted to tell you not long after you'd proposed… There's no easy way to soften this, but the truth is I'd begun to seriously realise that I was only kidding myself that a marriage between us could ever work.'

The sense of rejection and pain that had never left him since Briana had walked out coiled like a band of steel round Pascual's chest and squeezed as tight as a deadly cobra, intent on crushing it.

'You only have to start with our backgrounds,' she continued, unable to disguise her apprehension. 'You were born into the most extraordinary wealth and privilege, with all the expectations that go along with that, and I came from much more… shall we say ordinary beginnings? I was never going to fit into the incredibly elite lifestyle you were used to, Pascual! Your family made me quite aware of that very early on. They saw me as a drifter. Someone with no purpose or direction because I had taken time off from my usual routine to travel and work at not very prestigious jobs to keep myself.'

'Why bring my family into this? You are just using them as a convenient excuse. You clearly did not feel the same way for me as I felt for you, and were simply too cowardly to just come out and say it!'

'No! That's not how it was at all.'

'Then why did you not tell me that you were pregnant? How could you have left, knowing that you were carrying my baby? What kind of man do you think I am that I would not be interested in such an incredible piece of information? Did you not think that I would want to know my *own* child and have some say in how he was raised? You must either have taken temporary leave of your senses or you are even more heartless than I thought!'

The lovely face before him crumpled a little, but quickly she appeared to gather herself and determinedly returned her gaze to Pascual's. As he studied her, his heart was thundering as fast as a racehorse galloping for the finishing line. Years of turmoil and anguish over her desertion had just reached a crescendo, and he had no intention of reigning in his emotions now. *Especially* since he had so shockingly discovered that Briana had had his baby and had deliberately kept him in ignorance of the fact.

She pressed her hand to her chest. 'I didn't *know*

I was pregnant when I left. I only found out a couple of weeks after I got home… The thing is, Pascual…'

For a moment the depth of pain that glimmered in her ethereal grey eyes and the small catch in her voice unexpectedly got through the armour he had erected and pierced him.

'This is the truth. I had personal experience of what it was like, coming from parents from two different worlds, and it made for a very schizophrenic upbringing…a painful one too. My mother was from an ordinary working class background but my father went to public school and when they met was training to be a barrister. Unlike you and I—' heated colour swept into her face '—they *did* marry… But somehow their initial strong attraction for each other couldn't bridge the social and educational divide between them and the relationship quickly got into trouble. They rowed a lot, and my mum says that my father started to put her down by making fun of where she'd come from and her lack of education. But even when he was cruel to her she still loved him, she said. Then he went and made things even worse by having an affair…the first of many.'

Pushing some of her tousled hair away from her flushed cheek, Briana gazed into the distance for a moment, clearly haunted by what had happened.

'When I was just five years old they broke up. I grew up spending two weekends a month with my father, in his ancestral family home in Dorset, and the rest of the time with my mother in a tiny mid-terrace house in Camberwell. When I was with my father he got his housekeeper to take care of me. He used to call me his "regrettable mistake". After the divorce he quickly remarried…someone from his *own* class. None of his family ever welcomed me or made me feel at home, and after every painful visit I couldn't wait to get back to my mum's! We no longer keep in touch, in case you're wondering.'

A heavy sigh fell on the air.

'When I met you, Pascual, I really wanted to believe that where we both came from wouldn't sabotage our future together. But then I started to have the most terrible doubts…doubts that just wouldn't go away. The dinner parties and polo matches you took me to with your wealthy friends, the disdain I saw in your family's eyes because I was not from the same background… Well…it finally got to me. And because of the way I'd seen things play out between my own parents I knew I was only kidding myself that our relationship could work. Then I saw you with your ex that night, and suddenly I knew the hell my mother must have gone through when the man she loved had an affair. I knew then that I could never be with someone who might have the capacity to be unfaithful…that it would likely destroy me.'

'*Dios mio!* I *told* you what really happened!' Pascual interjected with frustration. 'She had had too much to drink—the woman was just making mischief. She was jealous because it was you I wanted to marry and not her. I thought I showed you in so many ways that I genuinely loved you and wanted no other. And yet you judged me so quickly over that stupid incident, and did not even give me the chance to defend myself before you chose to walk out!'

'I saw what I saw and I was devastated. Given my background, surely you can understand that now? I just couldn't take the risk that once we were married you might quickly grow tired of me and have affairs. You see, I didn't want what we had to turn into something ugly and painful. Nor did I want to be someone else's regrettable mistake either! As for Adán... When I found myself pregnant with him, I anguished for a long time about what to do for the best. Obviously I had to make some decisions about his future. I found myself asking how, in all practicality, he could go to and from Argentina every month to visit you. The situation would have been impossible. All a parent wants for their child is for them to grow up feeling loved and secure, and I finally came to the conclusion that I could only do that for him if he stayed with me. In the cold light of day I know it sounds utterly despicable to have made that decision without involving you. But, having walked out on you, I simply *had* to make it.'

'You keep referring to the child as *your* baby, but *I* had a part in making him too—did I not?' Emotion locked inside Pascual's throat and he struggled to speak past it. 'Why did you not tell me all this about your background before? You should never have just left without speaking to me first. To have a note thrust into my hand the day after a party that had been meant to celebrate our upcoming marriage and read that you had left was unbelievable. I thought I was having a nightmare!'

Staring briefly down at the floor, Pascual recalled the devastation that had for a time driven him to the very pits of despair and shook his head.

'I—it was hard to think straight at the time,' said Briana. 'Preparations were going ahead for the wedding, and every day I got more and more scared that I was making a dreadful mistake… Then that incident with your ex happened.'

'And you could not talk to me about any of these things? I was not some uncaring stranger…I was supposedly the man that you loved!'

'You *were*! I mean, you—'

His glance was withering. 'I fear your explanations have come far too late, *carino mio*. You should know that nothing you can say to me now could ever regain you my trust or respect. Any feelings I might once have had for you have been crushed to dust by what you have done!'

Moving across the room, Pascual tried hard to clear his head. The rain outside thudded with force against the old-fashioned leaded windowpanes, echoing the sensation of pressure building up inside him. So many thoughts, regrets and painful feelings were crowding his mind and his heart that he almost could not stand it. But out of all the turmoil, one thought gripped him more than any other. *He had a son.*

Recalling how passionately his friend Fidel had felt about *his* only son, he was deluged by the strongest determination to make things right in that quarter at least. He might have not been present in the first four years of his child's life, but by God he would be *more* than present in the rest of it!

Turning back to survey the lone slender figure standing in the centre of the room, he ruthlessly stamped out any fleeting feelings of sympathy that arose inside him. It was true what he had told Briana…her explanations *had* come too late. *Whatever happened next…she had brought it all upon herself.*

'I do not want to discuss this any further tonight. I need time to think. It has come as the greatest shock to me to learn what I have learned…that I have a son. A son whose *cold* and selfish mother decided that I did not have the *right* to know about him! We will talk again tomorrow, after the polo match… By which time I will have come to some important decisions where both you and he are concerned.'

'Any decisions about the future are not just up to you, Pascual!'

'If I were you, Briana,' he said, his furious glance utterly scathing, 'I would not risk saying anything more on that subject tonight. You have already had everything your way for far too long. You should know that I do not intend to let that situation continue...*believe* me.'

Striding to the door, realising that a serious explosion of temper was imminent if he stayed in the same room with her for even a second longer, Pascual let himself out into the narrow dimly lit corridor and did not look back...

'Rough night?' Tina's relentlessly cheerful tone almost made Briana snap when she joined her for breakfast in the kitchen the next morning. Her nerves were on edge as she poured herself coffee from the generous-sized cafetière on the ornate sideboard, and she threw the other woman a wry glance. 'You could say that.'

Carrying her cup across to the sturdy oak table, she pulled out a chair and sat down. Reaching for the milk jug and sugar bowl, she absently added some of the contents of each to her drink. It was clear the dark shadows beneath her eyes must reveal she'd hardly slept a wink—but what woman could possibly sleep after that distressingly painful scene when Pascual had woken her from sleep in the middle of the night? And exactly *what* important decisions had he reached about her and Adán after he had left her? she wondered anxiously.

Last night he had been *beyond* furious, and a big part of her acknowledged that she deserved his condemnation. She should never have kept Adán a secret from him, no matter how scared she was of her future life repeating her mother's. The tragedy was that she had loved this man so much—with all her being, in fact—and seeing him again she had shockingly realised that her love had not died. It had merely been lying dormant.

There had been a few moments during their unhappy confrontation last night when Briana had wanted to reach out to Pascual and beg his forgiveness…to ask him how she could start to make amends. But so fearful was she of what he might demand that she hadn't been able to bring herself to do it. Now she anguished over whether he might seriously contest her for custody of their son, and the icy tentacles of fear that were running in the back of her mind and in the pit of her stomach clutched at her even more. With his incredible wealth and powerful family Pascual had all the means necessary to take Adán from her, and there would be *nothing* Briana could do about it. In the light of this most worrying crisis of all going to court for an outstanding business debt couldn't be *less* important!

Hardly knowing what to do about anything right then, she gazed despondently into the beverage, watching the curling wisps of steam from the delicate porcelain cup in front of her as if she was staring into a dark tunnel with little prospect of ever finding a source of light at the end. If only her father had not been so incapable of staying faithful to her mother—had put her and his daughter's welfare above the snob value of class and money he had grown up with—then maybe Briana wouldn't have found herself in the heart-rending situation she was in now with Pascual.

'What's the matter, Bri?'

As she dropped down into the seat opposite, there was genuine concern on Tina's pretty face. Mindful of what the girl had unknowingly revealed to Pascual last night, Briana felt naturally reluctant to discuss anything personal. Her young colleague hadn't meant any harm, she was sure, but she shouldn't have been quite so free with her conversation.

'I'm fine. I just didn't sleep very well, that's all.'

'Our gorgeous Mr Dominguez was asking me about you last night. In fact every time I tried to turn the conversation around to something else he turned it back to you! I think he really likes you, Bri.'

'It's neither here nor there whether the man likes me or not. I'm just here to do my job and that's all. And in future I'd be very grateful if you wouldn't tell all and sundry about my personal circumstances. *Especially* not people I've been hired to work for.'

Appearing genuinely shocked at her boss's uncharacteristic burst of temper, Tina shrugged apologetically. 'I'm really sorry. It was just that he was being so charming, and before I knew it he'd got things out of me that I normally wouldn't tell anyone under pain of death! About the business being in difficulty, I mean, and you being a single mum…'

'I accept your apology. But trust me…if you want to get on in this business as well as in life, Tina, you need to learn to be a lot more discreet! Now, I'm going to finish my coffee and then we've both got things to get on with. And if Mr Dominguez asks you any more questions about me just tell him to come and ask me himself, will you?'

CHAPTER FIVE

HE'D sat up nearly all night mulling over events, thinking what to do. Finally, needing some air, he walked out of the still sleeping house and headed off—hands deep in the pockets of his trenchcoat—down one of the winding country lanes that led away from the house. Dawn was just breaking, and a silvery mist was draped over the trees and hedgerows like a diaphanous cloak. The air contained just enough frost in it to make Pascual shiver. The English countryside in the autumn was a sight to stir the heart, he silently acknowledged, his shoes flattening damp golden leaves deep into the gravelled lane as he walked, and he experienced the first real pleasure he had had since arriving.

Back home in Buenos Aires the temperature would be a predictable twenty-two degrees, warm and sunny. But strangely at that moment he felt no particular longing for the place of his birth. Where he was right now was perfect because that was where his son was, he realized—that was enough to make Pascual content to be there. *What did he look like, this boy of his?* Did any of his features resemble his father's? What characteristics might they share? Feeling his throat tighten almost unbearably, he muttered something impatient into the frigid air.

How could she have done it? How could Briana have deliberately kept his child from him? Even if he had cheated on her with Claudia—which he most definitely had *not*—was he deserving of such unbelievable treatment? And just because her faithless father had had affairs, did it naturally follow that Pascual would do the same? He was a different kind of man entirely…an honourable, *loyal* man. If only she had seen that. And he was even less likely to have an affair knowing he had a child to think of! How was it possible that he had once loved such an untrusting woman—a woman who had preferred to leave him rather than stay and hear his side of the story?

Preferring to focus on solutions rather than regrets, and for the moment determinedly putting the past aside, he concentrated on some of the decisions he'd reached last night about the future. *When he returned to Buenos Aires in a couple of days he would be taking the boy back with him.* No question about it. 'When you become a father,' his friend Fidel had once told him, 'everything changes. In a way the path becomes much clearer. You are less concerned with your own needs and ambitions. Instead almost every waking moment is given over to this precious child you have helped bring into the world…'

Sadly, his friend had not lived to see his own child grow up. Having already missed out on Adán's infant years, Pascual was determined that from now on it would be a very different story for *him*. And if Briana made it difficult in any way, then he would not hesitate to take a legal route to claiming what was his. *But he hoped it would not come to that.* Much better that she saw she had done both him and his son a grave injustice in keeping them apart, was ready to right a wrong rather than make that wrong even worse by obstructing him.

Taking a moment to expel a long, troubled breath, he continued on his journey up the winding lane. He almost stumbled when he remembered the kiss he had stolen last night—*before* he had found out about his son. Heat coiled in his belly with a fierce demand that shocked him. *How could it be that she could still arouse such lust and need in him even after five years of being apart?* Feeling betrayed by his own body, Pascual impatiently lengthened his stride. He would walk hard for a while and burn up some of the nervous heightened energy that throbbed through him, he concluded grimly. His treacherous and inconvenient desire would give him no peace if he did not.

And there was something else he had made a decision about. The planned visit to a polo match at one of Britain's most elite sports grounds today no longer held any appeal for him, he realised—end of the season or no. No… He had far more important upcoming events commanding his thoughts—the first one entailed putting Briana in the picture about his plans, and the next was visiting his son…

Dumbfounded, Briana stared at her fresh-faced colleague. 'What do you mean he's decided not to go to the polo match? The others are all waiting outside in the car for him! What reason did he give you?'

Looking uncomfortable, as well as bewildered, Tina frowned. 'He just said that he'd changed his mind…that something more important had come up and to send his apologies. He'll meet the others at dinner tonight, he said. In the meantime…'

The younger girl hesitated, and Briana's heartbeat quickened with apprehension. 'In the meantime…what?' she demanded, fear making her tone impatient.

'In the meantime Mr Dominguez said he'd like to talk to you in private…in his room.'

The blonde's curious glance spoke volumes, and inwardly Briana groaned. That was *all* she needed. Tina speculating that there was something going on between the gorgeous Argentinian and her boss!

Then she remembered the slightly pink abrasion at the side of her neck—the parting gift that Pascual had left her with last evening—and her face and body briefly burned with self-conscious and guilty heat. Automatically she lifted her hand to tug the silk collar of her blouse closer to the skin there.

'Well, then...you'll have to go outside and repeat what you've just told me to our clients... Needless to say *not* the part about Pas—Mr Dominguez wanting to see me in his room!'

Feeling her face flame at inadvertently almost exposing herself even more, Briana turned abruptly away and reluctantly—feeling as though she had *lead* in her shoes—ascended the staircase to the landing where Pascual's suite was situated.

Nibbling worriedly on her lip, she rapped smartly on the oak door.

'Come in!'

Giving her a briefly cold look, his sensual mouth bracketed by distinct displeasure, Pascual held the door wide to invite her in. Clothed from head to toe in stylish black once again, his indomitable maleness projected the arresting package of a man used to giving orders and being in charge—and heaven help anyone who dared to obstruct him.

Briana's anxiety went up several notches merely at the intimidating sight of him. Closing the door behind them, he followed her into the centre of the

room. The maid had put fresh flowers into a huge
white vase on the polished chiffonier, and the scent
of lilies in particular lay on the air like an exotic and
drugging perfume. It only took one glance into the
disturbing midnight gaze before her and she knew
she was in trouble.

Just the same she ventured, 'Why—why don't
you want to go to the polo match?'

'Because my priorities have changed...as I am
sure you are well aware.'

Saying nothing in return, she sensed the atmosphere spark as dangerously as a flickering flame
near a bale of straw.

'You may well be silent!' A muscle jerked briefly
in the shadowed hard jaw. 'Because I warn you that
nothing you can say can alter the path I have resolved
to take. When I leave for Buenos Aires in two days'
time you and my son are coming with me for an
extended holiday—a holiday during which time a
marriage between us will take place. The marriage
that should have taken place five years ago!'

'What?'

'You heard me. And when you return to the UK
it will only be for the purposes of winding up your
business and closing it down.'

'Closing it down?'

'*Sí*. It is in trouble anyway, is it not? It can only be
a relief to put it behind you. Once you are back in

Buenos Aires, instead of running a business you will have to get used to fulfilling the role of my wife instead. Do not worry, Briana…' Pascual's dark-eyed gleam was deliberately provocative '…there will be plenty to keep you occupied as far as *that* position is concerned. And that includes sharing my bed, mothering our son, playing hostess at any dinner parties I may give and being my *unimpeachable* escort at any social functions we may attend as I attempt to integrate you into my world. The world you clearly despise so much you could not bear to entertain being a part of it! You can quickly forget any ideas you may have had about remaining a single mother and raising our child on your own in England. That was in the past. Today is a new day, and from now on things are going to look very different for you. You can count on it!'

Feeling as if a storm had just ripped off the roof of her house, Briana found the power of speech had temporarily eluded her. It was as though what she'd just heard had rendered her mute with shock.

'Have you nothing to say?' Pascual thrust his implacable jaw forward in annoyance.

'Yes…I do.' Her returning glance was wary. 'I have plenty to say. But whether you'll listen to it or not is another thing.'

'I will listen. It does not mean that I will concur or change my mind.'

'I understand that you want to be in Adán's life,

and that is your right as his father. But you can't really be serious about us going back to Buenos Aires with you and the two of us getting married. We surely don't have to go *that* far? And anyway…I can't believe that you'd even *want* to marry me after what's happened between us. It just doesn't make any sense.'

He scowled. 'Well, it is certainly not because I have found I cannot live without you, or anything as ludicrous as that! No. I am doing this purely for the benefit of my son. The son you have denied me for the past four years. You are his mother, and even though you have not shown me the least respect in any way I will accord *you* respect and not let him down. No…I intend to become the father to Adán that I should have been right from the beginning—and if that entails marrying his treacherous mother, then—'

'Treacherous?' Briana's grey eyes rounded in protest. 'I never cheated on you…*ever*! If anyone showed any tendency to be attracted to other people, it was you!'

'You are still holding a grudge about that ridiculous scene with Claudia?' Pascual sighed with impatience. 'What can I say that will convince you of the truth? I swear to you that she was drunk. Because I had broken up with her and she was mad at me, she wanted to make me look bad in front of you. I had not even realised you saw what happened! If I had you can be sure I would have talked to you about it and explained. But you never gave me the chance to do that, did you?'

'I was too upset and shocked!'

'And apparently you believed that I was just like your father! The reason I call you treacherous is that you made me a promise that you would become my wife, Briana. You did not keep that promise. Instead you left and made me look like a fool in front of everyone I cared about, and then kept the fact that you were pregnant with my son a secret up until now. Disloyal, duplicitous, untrustworthy… Treacherous is as good a word as any in your English vocabulary to describe your actions…would you not agree?'

'Even if you think that, you can't really expect me to go along with your plans without protest and simply do everything you command, Pascual. We're not living in the Middle Ages, here, and I'm not going to agree with everything you say simply because I feel bad about what happened between us five years ago!'

'So you feel bad, do you? At last! Some indication of regret!'

'Of course I feel bad about what happened. Every day…watching Adán grow…I've thought about what he's missing by not having his father in his life. I truly regret what I did as regards to that. But I wasn't being vindictive or cruel by not contacting you about him. At the time…considering the strain I was under…I just did what I thought was right.'

'It is my view that you did not employ any *thinking* at all in the matter! You purely reacted! I knew you could be impulsive and I liked that about you...but I did not guess in a million years that that impulsive nature of yours would lead you to take the drastic steps that you took five years ago.' His blistering glance narrowed. 'I have a question. Did you *ever* plan to contact me about Adán at all? What if business had *not* brought me to the UK this week? What if you had *not* been providing hospitality services at the same venue where my meeting was being held? Would you have let more time go by? Perhaps not getting in touch until our son was a grown man? Maybe not even then?'

It was a terrible thought. And one that made Briana feel as if she had committed a crime that carried a life sentence. It was not the first time that the gravity of the decision she'd made in leaving Buenos Aires five years ago hit her so hard. But never before had it swept over her leaving such destroying hurt and regret in its wake. Faced with the flesh-and-blood reality of the handsome, vital man in front of her, she began to see exactly what she had done to him. Because of her he had suffered humiliation and torment—and he was suffering doubly now. Instead of going through with the marriage and committing herself to the man she had truly loved she had let fear and doubt rule the day—and this scene that was akin to torture was the result.

Again she wished that she'd had a better example of a man than her deceitful, cruel father... Whatever way she reflected on it, her actions had resulted in denying Pascual the opportunity of having a relationship with his own son. Even if he potentially *might* have strayed in their marriage—and Briana had to recall the devastation she had endured when she'd seen him in the arms of his ex in Buenos Aires and believed the worst—he surely didn't deserve that? Breathing out a troubled breath, she moved a few paces towards him. With all her heart she wished she knew a way to make everything right again, but she realised that was like wishing she could turn back time. It was simply beyond human capability.

'You were always there at the back of my mind, Pascual. I suppose I just got caught up in the day-to-day demands of trying to run a business and support myself and Adán,' she explained. 'And because so much time had gone by without us speaking I worried that if I *did* contact you, you'd either slam down the phone or...if I went to Buenos Aires...shut the door in my face!'

'Knowing that I had a son? You really believed I would do that?' With even more disbelief, Pascual dropped his hands to the lean, masculine hips encased in black corded trousers. 'It makes me realise even more that you do not know what kind of man I am Briana. Words desert me at the idea that you thought I would not be interested in the fact that I had fathered a son with you!'

Disturbed by the thought that clearly she *hadn't* really known Pascual as well as she'd thought she had, and feeling a sense of shame wash over her, Briana lifted her shoulders uneasily. 'What can I do to help make things right?'

Levelling his black velvet gaze right at her, Pascual did not hesitate to illustrate. 'Apart from doing as I outlined and coming back to Buenos Aires with me? You can arrange for a car to drive us to where you live so that I may at last become acquainted with my son!'

'But that's three hours away and another three back... You won't make dinner tonight with our clients if we do that.'

When she saw how Pascual received *that* particular piece of information, Briana instantly regretted speaking her thoughts out loud. But she hadn't *only* been thinking of what her clients would say if he did not meet them for dinner as arranged. She was genuinely concerned for her son, and how he would cope if she suddenly arrived home with a man he'd never seen before and declared that he was his father!

'Do you think I *care* about attending a business dinner over seeing my child for the first time?' Pascual uttered furiously. 'Tell them I will meet them in London tomorrow instead...they can name the venue. You can say that something of the utmost importance has called me away. Why not?' The formidably broad shoulders beneath the perfectly fitted black shirt lifted in a dismissive shrug. 'It is the truth.'

'First I'll have to ring my mother to tell her we're coming. She's been looking after Adán for me while I've been away this weekend.'

'Do that—and then arrange for a car. I am anxious to get going as soon as possible.'

'I have my own car here. I can drive us.'

'Good. Then go and make your phone call and let us not waste any more time, hmm?'

Clearly dismissing her, Pascual turned away to reach for the water jug and glass on the coffee table to pour a drink. Feeling as if her limbs had turned as fluid as the water in the jug, Briana moved towards the door and silently exited the room.

Once outside, in the monastic quiet of the corridor, she briefly leant against the panelled wall, trying hard to stem the sudden onrush of fear and doubt that had overtaken her about the impending visit home. *How would it be*, she wondered, *when father and son came face to face for the very first time?* Her little son could be shy and uncommunicative even with people he knew—let alone strangers. How would Pascual react if his child appeared to reject him?

Feeling for them both, she felt hot tears well helplessly behind her eyes and spill over onto her cheeks.

Impatiently scrubbing at them with the heel of her hand, she pushed away from the wall and returned to her room to make the phone call...

The house was situated down a pleasant tree-lined street in one of London's less busy boroughs. It was a neat terraced property, painted white, and next to the other less bright edifices on either side of it easily stood out. As Pascual followed a definitely subdued Briana up the short path that led to the front door, with its pretty stained glass panelling, adrenaline shot through him like rapids at the prospect of meeting his little son.

He'd quizzed her on the way about him, but she'd seemed almost reluctant to give him answers—just as if she was preserving the right to hold onto that information...as if she feared that if Pascual knew too much he would make it even harder for her to keep the boy to herself. It infuriated him that Briana was still reluctant to let him into their lives when all he wanted was the chance to be a proper father. *Every bit of trust between them was gone.* It had all been smashed into the dirt five years ago. And now they stood on either side of the ground they were both determined to capture—like warring factions in a soul-destroying battle instead of the passionate lovers they had once been.

As Briana let herself into the narrow hallway with

her key, along with his great anticipation at meeting his son Pascual sensed the full extent of her betrayal of his heart as he had never sensed it before—and right then his soul had never felt bleaker...

CHAPTER SIX

HER mother was the first person to greet them. Her usually calm and attractive features looking strained, Frances Douglas glanced behind her daughter at the tall, startlingly good-looking man behind her and frowned. When Briana had told her that she was unexpectedly returning home early, and bringing Adán's father back with her to visit, her ensuing soft intake of breath had spoken volumes.

Whilst knowing that her mother wouldn't unfairly judge any decision she made—and indeed had *never* judged her for leaving Buenos Aires so abruptly, calling off her planned marriage and returning home pregnant—Briana realised that this impromptu visit by Pascual would naturally fill her with anxiety about her daughter and grandson's future…as it did Briana herself. But right this minute her heart was thumping like a full-blown percussion band inside her chest at the knowledge that Adán might run out into the hallway at any moment to set eyes on his father for the very first time…

'Hi, Mum.' Her gaze was quizzical as she kissed the older woman's scented, powdered cheek. 'Where's Adán?'

'Asleep on the couch. I took him swimming. They had all the inflatable toys out in the pool, and he was tired by the time I got him home. He's been out for the count for about half an hour or so.' Warily, Frances glanced up at the dark-haired Adonis who was currently making Briana's tiny hallway resemble the entrance to a doll's house instead of a normal-sized dwelling. 'I presume this must be—'

'Pascual Dominguez.' Standing aside to make the awkward introductions, Briana somehow made her lips form a smile. 'Adán's father. Pascual—this is my mother, Frances.'

Catching the instantly disturbing drift of his expensive cologne as he extended his hand past her to greet her mother, Briana sensed his disapproval of her informality.

Her intuition was proved right when he announced, 'Mrs Douglas…it is good to meet you at last.'

'As I'm sure you heard me tell Briana just now,' her mother replied, 'Adán is asleep and may not stir for a while.'

'It does not matter. I have waited a long time already to see my son. I will wait as long as I have to until he wakes.' This time Pascual made no bones about casting his meaningful gaze at Briana directly, so that she couldn't mistake his displeasure with her.

'Well…shall we go into the living room, then? That's where he'll be if he's asleep on the couch.'

'And in the meantime…shall I make some tea for us all?' Frances suggested, her even-voiced tone acting as temporary balm to the tension that had enveloped them all.

'A cup of coffee would be most welcome…black, no sugar…*gracias.*'

'And you, darling?' Briana's mother started to move towards the long galley kitchen at the end of the hallway, with its cheerful red and white checked curtains.

Hardly able to think straight for the emotion that was tightening her chest, Briana answered distractedly. 'Tea would be great—thanks.'

'After you.' Observing her glance towards the living room door, Pascual gestured that she precede him.

In the small square room with its pine bookshelves crammed with books and CDs, its small television, compact music system and carpeted floor strewn with various children's toys, her small son was lying asleep on the smaller of the two dark gold couches. His slumbering form was covered warmly with a cheerful patchwork rug Briana had made last winter. On the pillow his curly dark hair framed a sweetly heart-shaped face that wouldn't shame an angel, she thought lovingly, her heart constricting with a surge of strong emotion as she gazed down at him.

Sensing Pascual move next to her, she glanced up, her pulse racing hard at the realisation that his handsome face was equally affected. He was moved by what he saw. Adán was an exceptionally beautiful child, and people often stopped her in the street to tell her so. *But then how could he not be beautiful when he had a father who looked like Pascual?* Briana concluded.

Straight away she knew that he could see that the boy was his. At least there would be no degrading speculation about paternity to deal with, on top of all the other accusations that he'd levelled her way, she mused with relief.

'He looks not unlike myself as a small boy,' he commented quietly beside her, the warmth in his voice replacing its previous chill.

'He's often mistaken for a girl with those lustrous curls!' Briana smiled back. 'But I can't bring myself to cut his hair short yet.'

'My mother would feel the same if she saw him. She had the same dilemma with me.'

'Did she?'

Almost afraid to say anything, in case she broke the suddenly intimate spell that seemed to enfold them, Briana crossed her arms over her silk shirt and

chewed apprehensively down on her lip. She remembered Paloma Dominguez well. The woman was as
tall and striking-looking as her son, and could be
equally intimidating. Once upon a time she had been
one of the world's most famous fashion models. It
was hard to imagine her as a relaxed young mum,
making a fuss of her beautiful little boy…

'How long will he sleep, do you think?' Crouching
down beside the couch, Pascual leaned forward to
brush back some of the wayward silky curls from the
child's creamy smooth forehead.

Watching, Briana almost held her breath. Knowing from experience how tender as well as passionate this man's touch could be, she knew a spon-
taneous longing for him to touch *her* as gently and
reverently. All the things she had loved about him
were coming back to her in a beguiling wave of
powerful memory, and every defence was suddenly
terrifyingly open and vulnerable to him. Seeing him
with their child, Briana felt even more exposed.

'He should wake very soon. He'll be hungry,'
she answered.

Rising to his feet, Pascual studied her deeply.
'How could you have kept him from me?'

Her gaze locked with the heartbreak in his unguarded ebony eyes, and regret and sadness almost
made her stumble. 'I see now that it was wrong of
me,' she said, her voice dropping to almost a whisper.

'Yes…it *was*. Whatever you think I did to you…I did *not* deserve this!'

'Mummy?'

At that very moment Adán stirred, and both adults' attention was immediately diverted.

Hurriedly wiping at her moist eyes, Briana dropped down onto the edge of the couch and drew the small sleepy form into her arms. 'Hello, my angel. Grandma told me she took you swimming… did you have a lovely time?'

'Yes…' Adán's voice was still husky from sleep. He leant his curly dark head against his mother's chest, then glanced up warily at the tall dark man looking down at him.

Bestowing a kiss at the side of his soft cheek, Briana tightened her arms a little round his pliant warm frame. 'Sweetheart…I've brought someone home to meet you. His name is Pascual, and he's—'

'A friend.'

To her complete surprise, Pascual dropped down onto his haunches and took one of Adán's small chubby hands in his own. 'I have heard a lot about you from your mother, Adán and I have been looking forward so much to meeting you. I hope you do not mind?'

Her heartbeat regaining a more normal cadence, Briana threw him a grateful glance. His sensitivity in not immediately declaring who he was to their son completely took her aback, and she gazed at him as if confirming what he had said a while ago—she *hadn't* really known him at all, all those years ago. Instead she'd allowed her fears of being rejected to consume her and colour her judgement of him completely.

To her surprise, Adán was smiling at Pascual as if he was far from a stranger, and he was struggling to sit up straight so that he could more easily talk to the man who still held his hand in his. 'I've got lots of cars!' he declared. 'Would you like to see them?'

'Of course. I would *love* to see them.'

Smiling, Pascual quickly stood up, moving swiftly to the side as the small whirlwind on Briana's lap jettisoned itself off the couch and flew across the room to drop down beside a large blue plastic box in front of the television. Several small model cars were plunked onto the floor and pushed towards Pascual as Adán retrieved them one by one from the box.

'Look!' he said, eyes shining. 'I've got a Ferrari!'

'I've got one of those too.' His face perfectly serious as he knelt beside him on the carpet, Pascual held up the toy car to examine it interestedly.

'What colour?' Adán demanded.

'Silver.'

'I like this black one best.'

'You are right. It is a much better colour than silver.' Adán beamed.

Briana's mother returned with the tea and coffee. As she straightened from leaving the tray on a small side-table, she glanced pointedly at her daughter. 'Is everything all right, darling? Do you want me to stay, or shall I leave you all alone for a while?'

Now she glanced over at Pascual, seated on the floor with her small grandson. He looked as at home with him as if he'd been a father to the boy from day one.

Gazing back at her, Pascual formed his lips into the most disarming of smiles. 'Do not worry, Mrs Douglas…I am only here visiting with Adán. I do not intend to make a scene…you have my word on that.'

'She's done a good job in raising him…you'll soon find that out.' An emotional catch in her voice, Frances quickly withdrew her glance from Pascual's and returned it to Briana. 'Are you staying here tonight, or do you have to go back?'

'We are going back,' Pascual said clearly. The expression in his eyes was hard to decipher, momentarily duelling with Briana's. 'Unfortunately I have one more meeting that I need to attend. But I will come and see Adán again tomorrow.'

'Do you mind staying over with Adán tonight, as planned?' Briana asked, her mind whirling at the implications of returning to Warwickshire with Pascual. And yet she felt an undeniable sense of relief sweeping through her at not having to let down her clients after all.

A very special dinner had been arranged for tonight, in Pascual's honour, and a lot of hard work and organisation had gone into getting it exactly right. He might believe that her business was failing, and that she should be relieved to put it behind her, but she still felt committed to seeing it through right to the end and giving the service her clients had hired her to provide. It was a matter of pride, if nothing else.

'Of course I don't mind! You know I *love* taking care of him. Shall I come back in, say…' she glanced down at her watch '…one hour?'

'That would be great. Thanks, Mum.'

'I'll see you then.'

'She lives just down the road,' she explained as the door shut behind her.

'That must be a big help to you.'

His observation of her had not lingered over-long. Pascual had returned his attention once again to his son, who was busy delving deep into the large box to eagerly display the full extent of his impressive collection of toy cars.

'It is.'

Reaching for her mug of tea, Briana carefully sipped at the steaming hot liquid and wondered how long this apparent peace between them would last before Pascual once again demonstrated his disappointment and disapproval of her. But then, quickly becoming engaged by the only ever before imagined scene of father and son together, she determinedly put her fears aside and willed herself at least to try and relax for the moment.

* * *

He fixed his tie—then pulled the knot apart and fixed it all over again. He seemed to be all fingers and thumbs this evening, and it was not like him. *But then how was he supposed to function normally when he had just spent the afternoon with his son for the very first time?* The boy was incredible—beautiful—his own flesh and blood.

He had changed everything for Pascual. His life would no longer be the same now that he knew Adán existed. His emotions ranged from wanting to shout out his joy on discovering he was a father to complete strangers, to feeling devastated that he had missed four precious years of his child's life and would never get them back.

Pausing in front of the mahogany cheval dressing mirror, he saw the fevered glint of excitement mingled with regret in his eyes and realised the last thing he felt like doing tonight was attending a tedious business dinner—no matter how sublime the menu or how beautiful the house. Making conversation with three men he had barely anything in common with, apart from a love of playing polo, was hardly a big draw, he reflected soberly. And he was still not certain whether he wanted to sell his precious ponies to them after all.

But then Briana would be there—attending to their every need, no doubt, keen to impress her clients and do a good job, potentially rescue her failing business. Even though he was mad as hell with her for keeping Adán a secret from him, Pascual didn't doubt her lush curves and flawlessly beautiful features would compensate for having to talk business when he would much rather have spent the evening with his small son, trying to get to know him a little.

At some point during those two precious hours spent with her and their child Pascual had suddenly woken up to the reality of the fact that her business was what allowed Briana to pay the rent and put food on the table. Knowing that, he could not allow himself to deliberately make her turn her back on tonight's event. Even though it might be the last of its kind—seeing as he intended to take her and Adán back to Buenos Aires with him...

Leaving the others to their cigars and a third or fourth glass of wine at the table, Pascual excused himself and went in search of Briana. The last time she had appeared before them had been about an hour ago, and with the business part of their dinner over—he had finally decided to go through with the sale of the ponies after all—he was anxious to see her again. Her perfume had lingered in the air long after she had left them, and all through dinner it had subtly taunted him, reactivating that tight, coiled feeling deep in his belly.

Putting his head round the door of the large Tudor

kitchen where once again staff from the Michelin starred restaurant were busy packing away, he spied Tina sipping a cup of coffee and munching on a biscuit.

Her face lit up with genuine pleasure when she saw him, and she hurried across the stone-flagged floor to greet him. 'Hello. How did the dinner go?' she asked in a rush, her cheeks pinkening a little.

In return Pascual's smile was polite, but restrained. 'It was very good. The duck in particular was excellent. Please give my compliments to the chef.'

'Of course I will. Are you looking for Briana?'

'Yes…as a matter of fact, I am.'

'She had a bit of a headache, to tell you the truth, and went up to her room for a while. If there's anything you need…perhaps *I* can help?'

Feeling the tight, coiled sensation become even more intense at the memory of Briana in the classic black jersey dress with a slightly plunging neckline she had been wearing that evening, Pascual smiled again—with just a hint of wry humour. 'Thank you, but no. It is Miss Douglas I need to speak with. Goodnight, Tina.'

'Goodnight, Mr Dominguez.'

At the knock on the door, Briana sprang guiltily up from the bed, thinking immediately that it must be Tina. She had not intended to leave the younger woman on her own to cope for long, but she had needed a few moments to lie down and try and get rid of the tension headache that had plagued her ever since she and Pascual had arrived back at the house from their trip to London.

She didn't doubt it had manifested itself because of the stresses and strains of the day. The whole time Pascual had been with her and Adán she had veered between worrying about their future and being flooded with joy that at last her son and his father were together...*whatever the consequences*.

Her heart knocked wildly against her ribs when she found the man she'd been thinking about on the other side of the door, still dressed in his immaculate tuxedo, looking as if he could give James Bond himself a run for his money and then some.

'Is anything the matter?' she asked, catching her breath as his dark brooding gaze dropped to her cleavage and for a disturbing moment lingered there.

'Your colleague told me you had a headache. Can I come in?'

A wise woman would probably have told him no. But right then Briana did not feel equipped to be particularly wise *or* strong where Pascual was concerned. Not when he stood there looking like the living embodiment of her most heartfelt fantasy and greatest desire...

'I'm not up to talking very much,' she answered, lightly touching her forehead.

'That is fine with me,' he came back, the look on

his strong-boned face inscrutable. 'I do not particularly want to talk either.' The panelled door shut firmly behind him.

'Then why are you—?'

The rest of her question was cut off by the feeling of the most intensely melting pressure from Pascual's commandingly erotic mouth on hers. Then his tongue thrust deep, and Briana groaned her pleasure hungrily and out loud. His hands were firmly at the side of her ribs. His touch seemed to have the shocking capacity to burn right through the jersey material of her dress and sear the skin underneath. She *ached* for them to be everywhere at once, such was the torrent of desire that engulfed her.

Her whole body was held hostage to the heartfelt sensation of sensual aliveness that Pascual's bold passionate caresses elicited, and Briana realised she wanted even *more*. It was true she didn't feel like talking—the day's events had emotionally drained her to the marrow—but she felt even less like thinking, or offering up excuses for her recklessly wild behaviour now. In truth, thinking straight around this man had always been difficult.

Before she even knew what she was doing, she was running her fingers through the silky strands of his gleaming dark hair and arching her back, so that he could slide his hungry seeking hands into the low neckline of her dress to cup and stroke her breasts, to pinch her tight-puckered nipples inside her bra until she whimpered.

Bending his head, once again he suckled and then nipped the sensitive skin at the side of her neck with his teeth. Erotic heat sizzled through Briana's insides like a flaming thunderbolt. Temporarily losing her balance as she sagged with pleasure against his taut hard frame, she was hardly surprised when he tipped her up into his arms and carried her across the carpeted room to the bed without so much as speaking a word. She heard him relinquish his shoes and leave them by the side of the bed. Then, before she could quite get her bearings, he caught handfuls of her soft jersey dress and tugged the whole garment up over her head. Discarding it, he shrugged off his immaculate tuxedo, then his tie, closely followed by his perfectly tailored Savile Row shirt.

As Briana gazed at his tanned broad chest, with its awesome display of toned musculature and the finest dark hair swirling round his flat male nipples, she almost wanted to cry at the epitome of staggering masculine beauty that was before her.

For a moment Pascual tipped up her chin and gazed deep into her eyes. She had no clue what he was thinking. Then, once more in the grip of urgent passionate heat, and just before he attended to the zip fastener on his trousers, he hauled Briana hard against that heavenly chest of his and claimed her lips in the longest, deepest, most devastating kiss she had ever known. As his addictively spellbinding taste poured over her, like the most drugging and sensual wine she could ever imagine tasting, Briana knew right then that she had no intention of calling a halt to what was about to happen.

She caught her breath as he slid his hands round her back and unhooked her bra. On his lips was the most lascivious heart-pounding smile Briana had ever seen, and he filled his hands with the full, soft weight of her aching breasts at last. Her relief and pleasure were indescribable.

'Do you want me, Briana?' His voice was low and resonant, with a husky catch in it. 'Do you want me as much as I want *you*? It has been a long, long time…no?'

Moving his hands down to the sultry curve of her hips, Pascual removed the remainder of her clothing and then, placing his warm palm in the centre of her chest, pushed her gently back onto the plump silk pillows behind her.

Immediately she was on her back, and his mouth claimed her tight, engorged nipples in turn, suckling and laving them, his hot tongue stroking over her aching flesh like the only balm that could ever bring true ease. Sliding a hand down over her ribcage onto her flat stomach, he dipped even lower into the triangle of silky hair between her thighs. Urging them apart, he slid one finger into Briana's moist heat, then two. Such was the intensity of pressure and pleasure this act bestowed that she wondered for one starry moment how she hadn't shot right through the ceiling. Hungrily, as he moved inside her, she reached out to curve her hand round his hard velvet shaft. Memory flooded her, of the many nights just like this one when she had shared his bed and been driven half out of her mind with the joy and ecstasy his magnificent body passionately delivered to hers.

Pascual moved her hand and replaced his fingers with that most intimate part of himself, and as he thrust upwards and deep inside her Briana cried out, gripped his lean masculine hips with her thighs, wrapping the rest of her long slender legs possessively round his back.

'Kiss me!' he entreated, his dark gaze burning down into hers.

Eagerly complying, Briana hardly knew who devoured who as their lips met and melded into one. All she knew was that the sensations and feelings the contact wrought was *wonderful* and she didn't want it to stop. Just as Pascual's thrusts became more demanding and focused she felt herself start to unravel helplessly. It had been just as he had said…a long, *long* time…and her emotions were so heightened round him that she couldn't hold back either her desire or her need. Stunned, she fluttered her eyelids closed as each pulsing wave of pleasure seemed to intensify even more than the last.

Just as she was returning to earth he held himself rigid above her. His disturbing glance was as serious as Briana had ever seen it.

'Maybe now we make another baby…*sí*?'

CHAPTER SEVEN

BRIANA'S hands tightened in shock round his smooth hard biceps. 'You can't be serious?' Right up until that moment she had barely given birth control a thought, she was ashamed to admit. The realisation made her aware of just *how* reckless she could be around this man—how swept away by forces she definitely wasn't in control of. 'No! You *can't*. We *mustn't*!'

But he was moving inside her again, and the sensation of his hard, strong body joined to hers was hurtling every thought that arose crashing against rocks.

'I should have been there at my son's birth! I should have been there for him for the last four years!' Suddenly growing still, Pascual withdrew from her just before it was too late. He sat back on his heels, breathing hard.

Startled and hurt by what he had exclaimed, Briana lay there, her breath laboured, watching him as he suddenly moved further down the bed—as if he wanted to put as much distance as possible between them.

Dropping his head into his hands, he murmured some words in Spanish she didn't comprehend.

'Pascual? Pascual, are you all right?'

Pulling the silk counterpane up to her chest, she moved towards him to lay her hand on the strong broad bank of his shoulder. He flinched as though struck.

'No…I am *not* all right! It was crazy of me to come here to you. Next time I will try and show a little more restraint!'

Grabbing up his silk boxers from the end of the bed, he quickly pulled them on and then did the same with his trousers. Sliding his bare feet into his shoes, he reached for the rest of his clothing and then turned solemn-faced to survey her. His expression told her that he was in a dark haunted place where she could not reach him and it made Briana shudder.

'I feel nothing for you…*nothing*!' he declared savagely. 'Do you know that? Your body may still arouse me, but in every other respect you leave me cold. You kept me from my own son and that I can never forgive. Tomorrow I will make arrangements for our return to Buenos Aires, and from then on Adán will have the life he was meant to. As for you…you will just have to learn to make the best of what you find when you get there. It is really no concern of mine whether you will be happy or not when we marry. I will provide every material comfort you could want...but as for companionship and friendship?' His lips thinned disparagingly, 'Maybe that is something you will just have to learn to live without...just as I have had to live without it these past five years. I will see you in the morning.'

As he left, strangely *not* slamming the door as she'd expected, but closing it as if the temper that had arisen like an electrical storm on a sunny day had suddenly dissipated as abruptly as it had appeared, Briana sank back down on the bed, feeling stunned and cold. Drawing the rich purple counterpane round her now shivering shoulders, she heard Pascual's heated words echo round and round inside her head once again, bringing home to her just how deeply and irrevocably she had hurt him by keeping Adán from him.

Up until now she had resisted the whole idea of returning to Buenos Aires and the three of them making a life together there. But even though he had warned her she would have to forgo companionship and friendship as far as he was concerned, Briana wondered if she didn't *owe* it to him to give the unconventional arrangement he was demanding a try? There might be genuine fears about not fitting into his world, just as before, but it was her fears which had driven her from Pascual in the first place and brought about the situation with Adán. *What had she got to lose?* she thought unhappily. Unless she could clear her debt her business was probably going to fold anyway—and what prospects would she have staying in the UK as a single mother, trying to raise her son all on her own and relying far too much on her own mother for help?

If Adán had his father in his life and grew up feeling safe, secure and well-loved by *both* parents, what did it signify if Briana had to sacrifice her own longing for love and companionship on the way? *She had already spent too many years alone and she should be used to it by now.* But tonight— tonight when Pascual had held her once again and for a while responded with all the passionate intensity of the most ardent lover—had rekindled that need inside her to be loved and desired and cared for by this man—a man she would willingly go to the ends of the earth for because she still felt the same way about him.

Hardly even realising that tears were spilling down her cheeks, she sighed as though her heart would crack, and felt like dying as she recalled Pascual's recent scathing words. *You leave me cold!* he had declared. That harsh announcement had made Briana feel as if she was being sliced in two.

Hardly able to bear thinking about it, she pushed aside the warm counterpane and got determinedly to her feet. Her heart might indeed be breaking, but she still had a job to do and she would do it to the very best of her ability—even if it were for the last time. As for Pascual—she had already made up her mind to tell him in the morning that she would agree to return to Buenos Aires with him. As long as his demands were reasonable and he took her views into consideration then she would not be putting any obstacles in his way.

He did not sleep well. But then he had hardly expected to after that unfortunate scene in Briana's bedroom. Sexual frustration made for a most uncomfortable bedfellow, Pascual discovered anew. And after leaving his lover's warm bed much earlier than he'd anticipated, because his anger and hurt had finally got the better of him, it was his legacy. But the truth was that for a few moments there, when the possibility had arisen for him to become a father for the second time, he had had a heartrending vision of a baby being put into his arms—something that Briana had cruelly denied him with Adán. He had longed for such a scene to become a reality.

Five years ago she had *willingly* agreed to become his bride. Now she might not be as willing, but Pascual vowed to harden his heart against that. This marriage of convenience he was determined to go ahead with might not be the romantic idyll he had foolishly once envisaged their partnership would be, but it would ensure that she would not be free to fall in love with someone else—share her body with someone else and desert him and their son.

It had been the most incredible experience to see Adán for the first time. One glance at the boy and Pascual had known straight away, with the most profound inner certainty, that he would gladly lay down his life to protect him and keep him safe. Fidel had been right about how having a child became the most important concern of a man's life—driving away all other ambition that had previously seemed so significant. *That was why he would take Briana to Buenos Aires and marry her...even if the love between them was gone for ever.*

Rubbing his chest to try and relieve some of the emotion that for a moment made it hard to breathe, he went to the window, drew back the sumptuous lined drapes and gazed out on yet another cold and frosty morning. Contemplating the scene without the pleasure he had experienced during his early-morning walk yesterday, he felt his longing to be back home in warmer climes was suddenly close to overwhelming.

On their way back to London the following morning, Briana glanced at her so far silent passenger and tightened her hands apprehensively on the steering wheel. Since bidding farewell to her clients as they got into the waiting Rolls-Royce that would take them home to their various destinations, Pascual had only spoken to her when he had absolutely *had* to. Such as when he had informed her that he was going back with her to 'sort things out', and then on to the hotel he was staying at for the duration of his stay in Park Lane.

Despondent that he was still mad at her, Briana wondered how they would sort *anything* out if he continued to be furious with her and maintain a sullen silence.

As they joined the stream of motorway traffic heading for London, a long-suffering sigh escaped her and Pascual's head immediately snapped round.

'What is wrong?' he demanded.

Ruefully shrugging her shoulders, she stole a brief glance sideways at him. 'Do you want a list?'

'If you expect me to apologise for what happened last night, then—'

'I don't,' she cut in, grimacing, 'I hurt you by not telling you about Adán, and whether you believe me or not I'm truly sorry. I also want you to know that when we get home I'll be telling him who you *really* are...that you're his father and not...not my friend.'

'Good. I see no reason in denying him the truth any longer.'

'And as for going back to Buenos Aires...' She

sensed his brooding gaze suddenly cleave even more intensely to her profile—as she kept her eyes firmly on the road ahead. 'I'll agree to go back with you for a while at least, to give us time to come to some arrangement about the future. But I can't stay away too long because I've had a court summons regarding my business debt and I'll be in serious trouble if I'm not there to answer it.'

'That is nothing to worry about.'

'To *you* it might not be, but it certainly *is* something to worry about as far as I'm concerned!'

'I mean that *I* will pay the debt on your behalf. Since I am to be your husband, then naturally I will take responsibility for it.'

'Now, wait a minute I—'

'Watch the road!'

In the blink of an eye Briana suddenly found that they were far too close to the rear bumper of the car in front of her. Guiltily, her stomach turning over in fright, she eased down on her speed. 'Sorry.'

'As I said…' Pascual continued, without so much as a hint of warmth or conciliation in his accented voice. 'I will pay this debt for you and then you can forget about your business.'

'Do you think what I do is so unimportant I can just cast it aside as if it was nothing? Besides…I can hardly forget about it when I have an employee to think of. What will Tina do if she doesn't work for me?'

'This was the only job you've had on your books for some time, so I gather?'

'What are you saying? How did you—?' Her shoulders hunching in resignation, Briana sighed. '*Tina*. I should have guessed.'

'She has already told me that she temps from time to time in between jobs. She seems a resourceful girl to me…she will be okay. And you will have other important occupations to think of when we go back to Argentina.'

'All right… That aside…if you pay this debt for me—and I will only agree to let you do so because of Adán—then you know I will have to insist on paying you back, Pascual?'

'Now you are being foolish.'

'I won't accept your help unless you agree to let me pay you back. I mean it!'

Sighing, as if she was taxing him to the very limits of his patience, the man beside her reluctantly nodded. 'Okay, okay! Just concentrate on the road, will you? Or we will find ourselves in the hospital instead of at your house!'

'My driving's not *that* bad!'

To Briana's complete disconcertion he chuckled, and her skin broke out into tingling gooseflesh at the sound. 'Not as bad as *some* I know, I will agree.'

'I suppose you're referring to women in particular?'

Unable to prevent the sharp slash of jealousy that ripped through her at the thought of Pascual with another beautiful model like Claudia, or worse Claudia herself, her mood grew even more despondent.

'Are you jealous, *carina*?' he drawled softly.

'Let's change the subject, shall we?'

'So…today we will put your business affairs in order, and tomorrow I will organise our travel arrangements. I will also ring home and instruct Sofia to make ready a room near us for Adán.'

'Sofia is still with you?'

The older Spanish woman who was Pascual's housekeeper had always been so sweet to Briana, and she had never forgotten her kindness. Of all the people she had met when she'd stayed in Palermo, she was the one who had truly accepted her for herself and had never given her the slightest inkling that she disparaged where she came from. She'd been totally happy with Briana because Pascual—whom she revered—loved her.

'Of course!'

For a moment Pascual sounded nonplussed, as if he could hardly fathom why anyone he employed would even *think* of leaving him to work for someone else. And of course he was right. As far as Briana had been able to observe he was a fair and generous employer, and Sofia clearly *idolised* him.

'And *you*, of course,' he continued, his magnetic

voice lowering, 'will not need a room of your own—because you will be sharing *my* quarters.'

The possessive intent with which he shared this last piece of information made her hair bristle, but she held onto her indignation…*just*.

'Perhaps in the light of what happened yesterday, it might be best if we kept our relationship purely platonic?' she ventured.

'I was mad at you yesterday…but my anger at you will not interfere with the physical side of our relationship in future, I promise you.'

'Well, I—'

'There is one thing I assure you our marriage will *not* be, Briana, and that is platonic!'

'Even though I leave you cold?' The small nugget of hurt inside her chest was like a sharp stone as she remembered the insult. She sensed his glance intensify again.

'I did not say your body left me cold…far from it!'

'But—'

'Call me arrogant, if you will…but I *know* that my body does not leave *you* cold either. If nothing else we can at least take consolation in our mutual desire for each other and in being good parents.'

Biting her lip on a despondent retort, Briana concentrated all her attention on the road ahead for the rest of the trip. The only time she allowed her thoughts to wander was when she tried to imagine how Adán was going to receive the news that the man she had introduced to him yesterday as a friend was really his father…

'Do you really think this is the right thing to do, Briana?'

Standing in her daughter's kitchen, Frances Douglas cupped her hands round her recently made mug of coffee and frowned in concern.

'I honestly don't know. We'll just have to wait and see how things pan out, won't we? I feel so *torn*, Mum. It was very wrong of me to keep Adán from Pascual…I know that now. And I owe it to him to at least give this marriage he's suggesting a try. Can you imagine how he's feeling right now, learning that he's been a father for the past four years and didn't even know it?'

Pushing her hair away from her eyes, Briana leant back against the kitchen worktop and folded her arms.

'He's in the living room with Adán, down on the floor playing cars, and already they look like they're crazy about each other! Adán was so pleased to learn Pascual was his dad… His little face lit up as if he could hardly believe it. I didn't expect that. You know how reticent he can be about meeting new people, don't you? It's as though the natural bond between them was just waiting for the chance to be forged. Okay, so there's the not so small matter of Pascual living in Argentina, but it's only natural that he wants his son to be with him there. Adán can have a good life there, and we won't have to struggle any more. There are lots of pluses.'

'Adán can have a good life, you said? What about *you*, Briana?' her mother asked thoughtfully. 'Can you live with a man you've already told me can't possibly love you, who bears resentment towards you because you kept his son from him?'

'Pascual's not like Dad, Mum. I don't mean to upset you, but he wouldn't be deliberately cruel to me...I know that.'

Frances's light grey eyes—so like her daughter's—narrowed. 'Withholding love from someone has got to be about the *cruellest* thing there is in my book,' she said softly, and Briana shivered as though someone had just walked over her grave...

Buenos Aires...three days later

The heat was like a sultry tropical kiss as soon as they stepped out of the plane. Even though they were only in the airport terminal, the sense that they were somewhere much more exotic and different from home was palpable immediately. Breathing in the myriad scents and the atmosphere of being back in the city that she had embraced with such excitement and hope when she'd first arrived there five years ago, for a beguiling moment Briana felt her fears and doubts replaced by unexpected optimism.

A short time later, in the chauffeur-driven Mercedes that had been waiting to pick them up, she had a chance to view their location more closely through discreetly tinted windows, her hands in her lap and her gaze soaking up everything she saw just like a child…just as if she were seeing it all for the very first time. Someone had described the city as the 'Paris of South America', and with its sweeping boulevards and grand architecture, she could easily understand why. But Briana also knew that every *barrio* or district had its own distinct features that reflected the multiplicity of cultures that resided there. Some were not grand at all, but intimate, lively and colourful.

Next to her, Adán had fallen asleep, his curly dark head against Pascual's suited shoulder, the child's sweeping long lashes and hair the same intense sable of his father's. Glancing at them both, she felt her breath catch. That bond they seemed to have instantly forged on sight was growing ever stronger, she intuited, and would continue to deepen the more time they spent together.

'How are you feeling?' His disturbing gaze touching hers, Pascual raised an enquiring brow.

'Fine. Hardly tired at all after the journey.'

Having imagined that the trip to Argentina would raise all kinds of challenges and concerns—not least because of the tension between herself and Pascual—Briana had figured without the effortless reassurance of first-class luxury travel. Her husband-to-be had only to click his fingers, it seemed, and the attentive flight staff would bring them anything they desired… from a four-course gourmet meal to champagne on ice.

Taking Pascual at his word when he had urged her to 'rest and relax' while he chatted to their son, to her complete surprise Briana had soon found herself dozing comfortably in her luxurious seat in the blissfully quiet first-class cabin, and in no time at all it seemed they had arrived in Argentina.

'I meant how do you feel about being back in Buenos Aires?'

Nervous, apprehensive, scared you'll keep on punishing me and I won't be able to stand it… Clutching her slender hands tighter in her lap, Briana bravely met Pascual's penetrating unsmiling glance, then sighed. 'I can't tell you that yet. It's a bit like a dream right now.'

'Not a nightmare?'

For a startling moment Briana saw a flash of what she thought was genuine apprehension on Pascual's arresting face, but he seemed to recover quickly and revert to complete control of his emotions—as though that possible moment of doubt and fear had never transpired.

'Not a nightmare…no. I—'

'I have been in touch with Marisa and Diego…remember them?' he cut in, his tone lighter.

'Of course I remember them!' A burst of warmth infiltrated Briana's tense insides as she recalled the affluent couple she had worked for once upon a time—the couple in whose house she had first met Pascual.

'Sabrina…their little girl…she must be—what? Nearly six now?'

'That's right. They are looking forward to seeing you again—and to meeting Adán of course.'

'You told them—you told them about Adán?'

She saw his jaw briefly harden. 'Did you think I would *not* tell my closest friends about the fact that I have a son?'

Putting her hands briefly up to her face, Briana shook her head. 'I didn't mean it like that. I was…I suppose I'm just a bit nervous about meeting people who knew me before. People who knew me when I was with you.'

'Because you fear their judgement? Marisa and Diego have too much innate good sense and class to be influenced by what others say.'

This announcement hardly reassured Briana. She was too busy wondering what kind of reception she would receive from Pascual's family when she finally met them again, and fearing the encounter would merely confirm their worst thoughts about her. That she had proved to them she wasn't worthy of marrying Pascual five years ago, and she was even *less* worthy now!

CHAPTER EIGHT

HEADING north, they soon arrived in Palermo, where Pascual's impossibly grand and palatial house was situated. Remembering the first time she had seen it, having already been bowled over by the size and beauty of Marisa and Diego's spectacular residence, just a few lanes away, Briana could still recall her jaw dropping at her first glimpse of the dazzling white mansion with its secluded drive lined with acacia and tipuana trees.

It looked no less beautiful and imposing now, resplendent in the late-afternoon sunshine, and not for the first time she was seized with nerves at seriously contemplating living there for good. The parallels with her experience of living two weekends out of four with her father in his large house in Dorset—far less grand than this—still hovered painfully in her mind. She hadn't *ever* fitted in there, nor been made welcome, and she wondered how she would fare now in Pascual's palatial home. Trepidation was gathering inside her at the prospect of seeing his family again…especially his mother Paloma, who had disliked Briana on sight.

Drawing her attention firmly back to the present, Adán stirred, suddenly wide awake and alert. His big eyes wide, he sat up and stared curiously through the tinted windows of the car at the huge mansion looming up in front of them. He had never travelled on a plane before, nor been abroad, so this was a day of firsts he would probably always remember.

Affectionately, Briana gave his small shoulders a squeeze. 'We're here, darling.' She smiled.

'You mean this is Daddy's house?' he asked, dark eyes round as saucers.

'*Sí, hijo*… This is my house—and yours too.' The small boy between them was not the only one who had excitement and pride reflected in his gaze. In fact, if Briana wasn't mistaken, there was a definite glint of moisture in Pascual's eyes as well. This was a momentous occasion for him, she realized—and not just because his son had just referred to him as 'Daddy' for the first time. He was a proud man—proud of his family, his country and his lineage. To bring his son home at last meant *everything* to him.

'And what about Mummy?' Adán demanded, a momentary frown on his clear smooth brow. 'Is it her house too?'

Her heart racing, she found herself under Pascual's disturbing intense scrutiny once again. Briana swore she could hear the sound of her own blood rushing through her veins.

'*Sí,* Adán… This will be your mother's home as well from now on. We will all live here together.'

Their glances met and held, and a frisson of electricity buzzed through her whole system, radiating from deep inside her womb and making her more intimately aware of him than was frankly comfortable or desirable, given the circumstances.

How did she do that? Pascual wondered, feeling dazed. Look at him with such a relatively innocent glance and make him immediately long to be alone with her, so that he could tear off her clothing with barely restrained urgency and join his aching needy body to hers…so that he could breathe her breath and taste her beguiling flavours until he was intoxicated—drunk on sensuality and desire so that he barely knew his own name any more. No woman before or since had ever made him feel like that. How he had walked out on her the other night he did not know. Except that fury and pain had overcome him and he had not been able to contain it. That would not happen the next time he found himself in bed with her! he vowed.

As the car drew up in front of the wide gleaming

steps that led to the double-doored entrance, Pascual forced himself to attend to the present as his chauffeur smartly came round to open the car doors. Taking Adán with him as he left the vehicle, he scooped the little boy up high into his arms against his chest. Waiting a moment or two for Briana to join them, and admiring the tantalising glimpse of slender thigh as her blue silk skirt revealingly rode up as she left the passenger seat, he even managed a smile in her direction before leading the way into the house.

And if at that moment he felt proud, possessive and protective of his newly acquired family—then let no man *dare* to question or blame him! Right then he did not even want to question his *own* need to include Briana as family.

'Señor Dominguez!'

Sofia—brimming with happiness and comfortingly familiar in gleaming white blouse and black-tiered skirt—greeted him as he stepped inside onto the black and white marble floor, Adán in his arms and Briana hanging back a little as though shy. Totally spontaneously he reached for her hand and pulled her to his side, pleasure exploding inside him like a firecracker at the impossibly soft touch of her skin.

'*Holà*, Sofia!' Grinning at the barely contained joy that radiated from the older woman's face, noting her eager glance dart from Adán to himself and then Briana, as if all her Christmases and birthdays had come at once, he wasn't surprised when she got out a lacy white handkerchief and dabbed at her eyes.

'I am so, *so* happy to see you all back safe!' she declared, in clear, well-spoken English. 'And to see the little one…your *son*…I can hardly believe it!' Jamming the dainty white square back into the fulsome pocket of her skirt, she slid her hands round Adán's startled face and proceeded to kiss him soundly on both cheeks. '*Holà*, Adán…I am Sofia, and I am honoured to meet you.'

'He is a little shy,' Pascual said tenderly as he set Adán on his feet and slid a reassuring arm round his shoulders. Glancing round at Briana, he gripped her hand more tightly for a moment, surprised to feel her tremble. 'And you remember Briana, Sofia?'

'*Sí*…of *course* I remember her!'

Without preamble, the housekeeper pulled Briana towards her for an enthusiastic hug, and after observing the younger woman's initial stiffness in the other woman's arms Pascual sensed his own breath ease out when he saw her slender shoulders drop a little. She hugged Sofia back.

'It's lovely to see you again, Sofia. Are you well?' she asked, stepping back to Pascual's side, her previously apprehensive expression transformed by a smile.

'*Sí, señorita*…I am *very* well…*estupendo* now that you are all here!'

'Sofia?' Addressing his housekeeper and speaking

in their native Spanish, Pascual told her they would
all like to go to their rooms and freshen up a little
before dinner. He was sure that Adán *especially*
would like to see the room that would be his. He also
asked her to instruct his chauffeur to bring in their
luggage and ask Carlo—his groundsman and
gardener—if he would kindly transport it upstairs.
That done, Pascual turned to Briana, one hand still
firmly holding onto his son's. 'I have told Sofia that
we would like to go up to our rooms. Shall we?'

Having inspected his own very large bedroom—
Briana was sure the ground floor of her whole *house*
would have fitted into the square footage it commanded!—Adán was now busy running from the huge
en-suite marble bathroom in his father and Briana's
room back into the bedroom, and then through the
opened patio doors onto the generous-sized balcony,
examining everything just as though he had been let
loose in Hamleys toy store in Regent Street.

'Slow down!' she called out to him as he exited
the balcony and ran back again into the bathroom.
'You'll wear yourself out!'

'He is happy…no?'

Suddenly Pascual was in front of her, his dark
gaze travelling at leisure down the front of her scoop-
necked white T-shirt and pastel skirt. An unexpectedly warm smile touched his lips as Briana tried

desperately *not* to look at the huge canopied empress bed to the side of her. Heat prickled all the way down her spine as she studied him.

'You promised him an adventure and he's certainly got it! He'll sleep like a top tonight after all the excitement.'

Self-consciously she folded her arms across her chest. Reaching out, Pascual tugged them free. His hand inadvertently glanced against her breast and a shocked breath escaped her.

Gravel-voiced, he said, 'Stop hiding yourself…I want to look at you.'

'I'm not hiding! You—you make me nervous sometimes. That's all.'

As if her words surprised him, he dropped his hands to his hips, and another easy smile broke free from his sensual lips.

'Well, I do not mean to make you nervous. Not today, anyway. You are a very beautiful woman, Briana, and I intend to appreciate that fact. You cannot tell me that no other man has called you beautiful since we parted?'

Where was this leading? Was he jealous? For a moment the thought made her heart leap. To be jealous of compliments paid by other men suggested he still cared…even a little. If he had feelings towards her other than just anger and blame, then that had to bode well for the future, didn't it?

'I haven't been interested in other men since—'

'Since you left me?'

The dark eyes that resembled the most stunning jet in the world briefly reflected their disappointment and pain, and Briana came crashing back down to earth again.

'I hope that's true…that you haven't seen any other men since me,' Pascual continued somberly. 'I do not like to think of you with someone else… someone who has spent time with you and my son when I could not.'

'Well, you don't have to worry. I told you…I've been too busy raising Adán and trying to run a business to have time to even *think* about dating!'

Just as she was about to quiz him on whether *he* had dated other people since they parted—yet perversely not really wanting to hear about that at all— their son diverted her.

'Mummy, can I see the garden?' Running back into the bedroom from the balcony, Adán glanced hopefully from Briana to his father.

'Yes, of course you can see the garden! We have more than one, you know? In fact we call it a park, and it has many things to see in it—like fountains, marble statues, and a very large lake!' Catching hold of the little boy's hand with a grin that was more than a match for the dazzling Argentinian sunshine, Pascual looked as pleased and happy as his son at the prospect of showing him round his home. The sight of them together squeezed Briana's heart. 'Come with me and I will give you the guided tour. Then you can come back and tell Mummy what you think.'

'Can I, Mummy?'

'Yes, that's fine. Just stay with Daddy and don't go getting yourself lost!' She faltered on the word 'Daddy' just the tiniest bit, but told herself she would soon get used to using it. One astonishing fact was becoming more and more obvious...Adán was having no trouble using it at all!

'He will never leave my sight...I promise.'

Once again Pascual confounded Briana with a smile that was laden with warmth, and once again she sensed all her defences dissolve beneath its devastating impact.

'Why don't you take a shower or a bath while you have the chance? It might help you relax after all the travelling. Carlo will leave our luggage by the door.'

'Thanks...maybe I'll do that.'

'*Bien*! We will see you later!'

He had instructed Sofia to make ready the smaller, more intimate dining room in the house, rather than the grand one used for entertaining. And now, as they sat round the large ebony table that had been beautifully and lovingly laid with the best silver cutlery and colourful patterned native crockery, Pascual surveyed his small family with pride and a growing possessiveness he could not deny. His chef had prepared the most appetising meal in honour of his son and wife-to-be, and they were lingering at the table long after they'd finished dessert. He poured Briana another glass of Malbec—a popular wine often drunk in the region—his avid glance surveying her for probably the hundredth time, in a demure white gypsy dress that showed off her pretty shoulders to perfection.

'I wanted to discuss something,' she said, fingering the delicate stem of her wine glass but not raising it to her lips.

'Of course.'

Feeling more relaxed than he had in ages, Pascual settled comfortably back into his chair.

'When we return here for good—' she briefly pulled her gaze from his to let it momentarily rest on their son '—we'll need to find a school for Adán. He's in kindergarten back home, but in a few months' time he'll be five. Is there anywhere nearby that might be suitable?'

'I will do some research. Sabrina de La Cruz— Diego and Marisa's daughter—goes to a small private school not far away, and she is extremely happy there so they tell me. I will ask them for some more information.'

'Thank you. I'd appreciate that.'

'Of course I will not just take their word for it. In the next few days we will arrange a visit there and go and see the place for ourselves. I will also find out if there is a kindergarten at the school for Adán. It might be nice for him to continue going if he has become used to it, and he will make some new friends too. Being with the other children will also help him to learn Spanish.'

'Will there be any English-speaking teachers?'

'Of course. Argentina is home to many different cultures, as you know, and we have many English-speaking inhabitants…including teachers.'

Noisily laying down his dessert spoon beside the second bowl of chocolate ice cream he'd eagerly asked for but clearly could not finish, Adán yawned and rubbed at his eyes.

'I think it's past your bedtime, my angel.' Fondly, Briana squeezed the small chubby hand on the table next to her. 'It's been a long day for you, hasn't it?' Keeping a close eye on the sleepy little boy, she turned her gaze back to Pascual. 'There is one other thing…'

He frowned. 'What is it?'

'I know you suggested I should fold my business and put it behind me now that you've paid off my debt…but what am I to do all day when Adán is at school, Pascual? I want to pay back the money I owe you. I have to have a job of some sort. I can't just sit around and be idle.'

He thought of several of his friends' wives, who didn't work at all and seemed more than content to shop, travel, and dress in the most up-to-date *haute-couture* fashion, being a decorative adjunct to their successful well-heeled husbands at dinner parties and polo matches.

Pascual had known from the first time he had met Briana that she was not a woman who would be remotely satisfied with such a way of life, and he did not blame her. He had even suggested she go to college and train for a career that appealed to her. *Until such time as their children came along, of course...* Now he took his time considering what she had said. He sensed her concern. Understood it too. They might not be contemplating the most idyllic of unions, after what had transpired between them, but the trouble was, as he gazed at her lovely face across the dinner table, Pascual kept forgetting that he wasn't in love with her any more.

A wave of heat consumed him at the thought that she would be sharing his bed tonight...and *every* other night for the foreseeable future, if he had his way.

'What if I have a word with some of my own business contacts and see if there isn't a demand for the kind of hospitality services you offer in the UK? We could set you up in business here in Buenos Aires. How would that be?'

The relief and pleasure in her expression was instantaneous. 'Really? You would do that for *me*?'

He did not know right then why he should think
of what she told him about her 'schizophrenic' upbringing, her father who had called her his 'regrettable mistake', but once the thought had surfaced it
was not easily relinquished. He wondered how any
father could not recognise the many gifts a lovely
daughter could bring and—not only that—want the
best that life could offer her.

'*Sí,*' he answered thoughtfully. 'I would do that for
you.'

'Señor Dominguez! Señor Dominguez! I am so
sorry to interrupt, but—'

'Take a breath, Sofia!'

The small party glanced towards the dining room
entrance in unison as the plump, flushed-faced
housekeeper suddenly appeared in the doorway,
looking as if she'd negotiated the long and winding
staircase up to their landing at breakneck speed.

'What is the almighty panic?'

'Your parents and your cousin have arrived! They
heard that you were back and—'

'How did they hear?' Immediately Pascual got to
his feet, his dark gaze narrowing suspiciously.

'Your mother rang earlier this morning and I told
her you were returning with your fiancée and your
son… Did I do wrong, Señor Dominguez?'

Sighing, Pascual pushed his fingers through his
thick dark hair. Frankly, this was one impromptu

visit he could do without! His plan had been to phone his family the following day, after a good night's rest, and inform them of what had transpired in England—how he had met up with Briana again and learned that he had a son.

He hardly needed to be a mind-reader to know *exactly* what his suspicious mother's thoughts would have been when she'd heard the news! Top of the list would no doubt be that Briana had somehow blackmailed him into taking her back, wrongly convincing him that the child she'd borne was *his* when in actual fact he was the offspring of some other man. Well…she would only have to set eyes on Adán to know immediately who his father was!

'What shall I do, *señor*?' Looking a little distressed, Sofia waited for instructions.

'Show them into the downstairs drawing room and get them some drinks,' he answered curtly. Then, deliberately softening his tone, he said, 'Tell them we will be down in a few minutes. *Gracias*, Sofia.'

'*Sí, señor.*'

Abruptly the housekeeper turned and went back the way she'd come.

The tension in the room was as taut as the atmosphere in an aeroplane after take-off had been inexplicably delayed. Immediately Pascual met Briana's large grey eyes, and saw the worry and strain reflected there.

'It will be okay,' he said lightly, privately knowing that nothing was *ever* that simple or clear-cut when it came to his passionate-natured mother, and wishing again that he could have delayed this meeting until tomorrow at least.

'Will it?' She was rising to her feet, and with her hand on top of their son's curly dark head she sighed. 'I don't mind so much for myself if accusations are going to be leveled,' she told him, raising her chin, 'but I *do* mind that Adán might be upset in any way.'

She was as protective and fierce as any feral creature around her cub, Pascual saw, and an unexpected bolt of admiration jolted through him at the knowledge.

'You'll see she's done a good job in raising him,' Briana's mother had asserted, and already he was finding that to be perfectly true.

Considering his visitors downstairs, he reflected that it was fortunate his father was there tonight—because if anyone could get Paloma Dominguez to see sense and calm down then it was Iago. He had been far less judgemental of Briana, he recalled, regret shooting through him that he had not addressed the matter of his parents' less than warm reception of his bride-to-be before.

'I will simply introduce him to my parents and then ask Sofia to take him up to bed. I promise you I will not tolerate any upset caused to him either.'

He saw her slender shoulders relax a little before

she leaned down towards Adán, helping him out of the large dining chair that left his little legs dangling several inches from the floor.

'Thank you,' she murmured. Reaching for a starched linen napkin, she cleaned the chocolate ice cream stains from around his mouth, then kissed the top of his head. 'There, poppet…now you're fit to be seen by the Queen of England herself!'

'We had better go down, then.'

Gesturing towards the door, Pascual waited for them to precede him into the long, high-ceilinged corridor, with its six suspended crystal chandeliers, and privately vowed that if his mother caused any distress to either of them then he would not hesitate to tell her in no uncertain terms to leave his house and not come back until she could learn to be more civil…

CHAPTER NINE

As BRIANA and Pascual entered the room, with Adán between them, the three adults who had been waiting for them stood up in unison from the luxurious armchairs they'd been occupying. Immediately the sight filled Briana's heart with apprehension and dread. *They must despise her for what she'd done to their son.* A reunion hardly boded well under the circumstances…how could it?

But just then Pascual gently touched his hand to the back of her waist, and, intuiting that he was giving her his support, she felt a surge of deep gratitude ripple through her. Her determination not to be intimidated renewed, she lifted her chin and made her lips form a smile.

'*Holà!*' His resonant voice impinging on the tension-filled silence, Pascual walked forward to embrace his parents and cousin in turn, before returning to Briana's side.

The frighteningly elegant and slim Paloma Dominguez—with her slanted feline eyes, faultless make-up and classically beautiful *haute-couture* clothing—was a formidable sight at the best of times, and she was not one to be slow in vocalising her opinion on anything. But everyone appeared to lapse into a stunned silence as they glanced in Briana's direction, and she was acutely aware that their attention was focused on the little boy holding her hand, rubbing his eyes and yawning.

In English, and with pride in his voice, Pascual smiled and announced clearly, 'This is my son—Adán.'

It was Iago Dominguez—his father—who moved first. A little broader of girth these days, than Briana remembered, he was still an extremely imposing and attractive man for his age. Now, with no trouble at all, he dropped down easily to the same level as Adán and, his brown eyes clearly emotional, in wonderment reached out to stroke the tips of his fingers across Adán's baby-soft cheek. '*Holà,* Adán. *Soy su abuelo…* I am your grandfather… Did you know that you look just like your *papà* did when he was your age?'

Adán was shaking his head in reply and his small hand gripped Briana's a little tighter.

'Well, little one…you do. The likeness is incredible!' Standing up to his full height again, Iago now surveyed Briana with an emotional glance. 'He is a fine boy,' he declared a little gruffly. 'But you were wrong to walk out on my son and cause him such distress…also to keep from us all the fact that you had had his child! What can have possessed you to do such a thing?'

Before Briana could get past the dryness in her mouth to speak, Pascual stepped in, his hand reassuringly at her back again. 'Have you ever thought that you and rest of the family might have played your part in driving Briana away, Father?' he suggested. 'Think how hard it was for her to come and live amongst us— to leave her home, her family, her friends, and then not to feel exactly welcomed by my own family?'

'We did not know her very well back then. She was unknown to us…all but a stranger…and it takes time to get to know someone, does it not?'

'You did not act as if you wanted to get to know her at all! You kept her at a distance, and I fooled myself that it was not happening instead of telling you that your behaviour was unacceptable.'

It warmed Briana beyond measure that Pascual was standing up for her. It gave her the courage to speak out as she had never spoken out to his parents before.

'I wanted you to like me…to accept me—at least for Pascual's sake, if not my own. My own father rejected me, and when I saw that it might be the same again for me, living here in Buenos Aires amongst people who treated me in a similar manner…well, it brought back some of those unhappy feelings I'd had as a child and I was naturally apprehensive.'

Behind Iago—who was suddenly looking thoughtful—his wife Paloma moved towards them with an expression that was completely bereft of the new consideration reflected in her husband's. Her cool gaze seemed as distant as it had always been to Briana as it haughtily scanned her features.

'Why did you keep my son's child from him?' she demanded without preamble.

Even Iago looked uncomfortable at her outburst. Her heart thudding heavily inside her chest, Briana resolved to just be herself when answering the blunt question. *No more hiding behind a mask of politeness or not feeling good enough*, she vowed, or she might inadvertently cause Adán to believe *he* wasn't good enough either.

'I made a mistake,' she answered quietly, brushing her hair from the side of her face and sensing Pascual's hand behind her back, stroking her. 'No doubt I made *lots* of mistakes when Pascual and I were together. But we both should have been more open and not kept our fears and worries to ourselves. I can see that now. It was wrong of me to keep Adán from him and I honestly regret it.'

'My son is a good man. Even if you did not feel that *we* accepted you, you should have stayed with him regardless. Not run away!'

Feeling torn, Briana bit down anxiously on her lip. But then Pascual was sliding his arm completely round her waist, giving her a brief smile before addressing the woman who stood before them.

'Unfortunately Briana witnessed something between myself and Claudia the night of the party that made her believe I would not stay faithful to her in our marriage. *That* was what forced her decision to leave.'

'Something happened between you and Claudia?' Iago asked in surprise, his dark gaze probing his son's.

'It was nothing. She had had too much to drink, that's all. But to Briana it looked like I was encouraging her foolish attentions when I categorically was not!'

Her cheeks flushing a little, Paloma Dominguez added her own comment—and it was not what Briana expected at all.

'My husband is right…Adán *does* look very much like Pascual as a child.'

As if the annoyance she had previously emitted had ebbed away beneath the infiltration of a much stronger, more powerful emotion, the older woman bent down to the little boy and kissed him soundly on both cheeks. With tears in her eyes she impelled his small body into her arms and threaded long slim fingers with an array of dazzling jewelled rings affectionately through his mass of dark curls.

Amazingly, Adán did not struggle or put up a

protest. Hardly able to believe what she was seeing,
Briana was all but lost for words.

'I am starting to feel left out!' Grinning, Pascual's
handsome cousin Rafa suddenly appeared before her
and enfolded her in a friendly hug. '*Holà*, Briana.
You are even more bewitching than I remember!'

Unable to help herself, Briana wondered if he was
still going out with Claudia, Pascual's ex. Her pulse
raced a little at the memory of that night five years ago,
when Rafa had arrived with her at the party and the
evening had ended so disastrously with her seeing the
beautiful blonde model kissing her husband-to-be.

'You're looking well yourself Rafa.' She smiled,
and suddenly her pulse was racing again, because
Pascual had drawn her even nearer to him, and the
sensation of his warm, hard body next to hers made
her knees feel suddenly and alarmingly weak.

'He was hoping you would say that,' he teased, but
there was a distinct warning in his glance as he rested
it briefly on his cousin, Briana noticed. A warning
that said *Do not overstep the mark because she is
mine.* It made her insides flutter.

'Mummy, I'm tired!'

Feeling a tug on the hem of her dress, she saw a
wan-faced Adán, gazing hopefully up at her.

'I should take him to bed.' Turning towards the man
at her side, she waited until he nodded in agreement.

Without preamble he scooped his son up into his

arms and surveyed the assembled company. 'He has had a very long day,' he told them. 'Enjoy your drinks, and Briana and I will be back shortly.'

They all kissed the bemused and by now *very* sleepy child goodnight, and before she knew it she and Pascual were climbing the impossibly grand winding staircase with its opulent tread up to the little boy's bedroom.

'You are very quiet tonight.'

Leaving the dressing room that was adjacent to the master bedroom, Pascual found Briana seated on the bed. The sleeves of her cotton knee-length pink robe were rolled up to the elbows and she was smoothing lotion onto her pale exposed forearms. With the light application of make-up she usually wore cleaned away, and her dark hair swept up behind her head with wisps of escaped tendrils framing her face and neck, he thought she had never looked more lovely…or more alluring.

As had been the case from almost the very first moment he had ever set eyes on her, desire followed swiftly and intensely on the heels of that captivating thought, like a waterfall plunging down over a cliff-face.

'I was miles away, actually.'

Shyly surveying him, her ethereal grey eyes were like twin beams of silver starlight in the softly lamp-lit room, and Pascual sensed the heat in him move fiercely through his body like a sirocco wind threatening a previously calm desert.

'What were you thinking about?' Dropping down next to her, clad only in black silk pyjama bottoms, he realized even the minimum of clothing was too hot against his skin at the mere sight of this woman. Quizzically, he smiled at her.

'I was thinking about seeing your parents and Rafa again,' she replied, continuing to rub the lotion into her skin, seemingly oblivious to the effect she was having on him. 'I am glad that we all seemed to let down our guard a little. Perhaps in future my relationship with them can be a little better than I imagined it ever could? I hope so, anyway.'

'I should have listened to you before—when we were first together. If I had spoken to my family then perhaps our own relationship would have had a proper chance…hmm?' Pascual reflected, becoming more and more fascinated by the rhythmic movements of her small hand with its lilac-painted fingernails back and forth across her arm.

Sliding his fingers beneath her chin, he made her turn to face him. Her enchanting lips in their naked beauty quivered a little. Immediately he wanted to plunder them and wet them, make them look beestung, as he remembered they had whenever they'd made love in the past…

'But you stood up for me tonight…that makes all the difference in the world.'

'I wish I had done it before…I am well aware that my mother in particular can be a little aloof sometimes, and with people who do not know her well that may easily be misinterpreted. But I want you to know that underneath that difficult exterior she only wants the best for her family. I hope that in time you will discover that for yourself, Briana. Building good relationships will take time for all of us. But you and I are back together, after a long time apart, and feelings on all sides are bound to be tender. Can we not just put any hurts aside…for tonight at least?'

'We can. At least your parents were happy to meet Adán.'

'They were completely overjoyed at the realisation that they have a beautiful grandson. How could anyone not love him on sight? He is perfect…just perfect.'

'Already he seems to be comfortable with you and your family… It's extraordinary, really. He's only had just my mum and me for so long, and now we've come all this way to Argentina and he's totally taken everything in his stride. Sleeping in a huge bedroom on his own on his first night here is a really big deal for a small boy, do you know that? If he wakes in the night and is fearful you don't mind him coming in with us, do you?'

'Of course not. I want my son to be happy, not frightened.'

'Good. The fact is, he'll probably be missing my mum too.'

He thought of Frances Douglas, and the way she had taken him aside the day he had collected Briana and Adán to drive them to the airport—the beseeching, yet steely look in her eyes when she'd ordered him to, 'Take good care of them both, won't you? They mean everything in the world to me.'

Pascual suddenly knew a surprising need to reassure the woman by his side. 'She is welcome to come and stay whenever she wants to. I will organise the flights and pay for everything. As you can see…there is plenty of room for guests here.'

'Thanks…I appreciate that. I expect she's missing Adán too, even though we've only just left. They're naturally very close.' Stifling a yawn, Briana capped the tube of lotion and laid it down on the silk coverlet beside her. Her glance was apologetic. 'Sorry. All of a sudden I feel immensely tired. Must be all the travelling today.'

'Here.' Picking up the discarded lotion, Pascual flipped opened the top again. 'Let me apply some for you.'

'I'm done, Pascual. I don't need you to—'

'It smells of peaches…a peach for a peach…' He smiled, squeezing some of the cream into his hand. 'Turn round and loosen your robe. I will massage your shoulders for you.'

'It's all right. I don't really—'

'You do not like me touching you?'

The idea made him freeze. Already he was having immense trouble keeping his hands off her heavenly body, just sitting near her. The idea that Briana might not welcome his touch after all was akin to ice water being poured down his back, and the memory of her rejection of him as her prospective husband five years ago still had the power to wound him greatly.

'I—I didn't say I didn't like you touching me. It's just that it's late, and…'

It came to him that she was suddenly somehow shy with him. He wondered if what had happened the last time they were in bed together was on her mind. With all his heart he wanted to erase the unfortunate scene from her memory and replace it with a far happier one. So, with a slow, teasing smile, utilising his free hand, he undid the belt of her robe and eased the material down over her shoulders. Conveniently, the thin satin cerise nightgown she wore underneath had narrow spaghetti straps. Silently speculating if she had worn it especially for his benefit, Pascual saw how easy it would be to do as he'd suggested.

'Turn round, Briana. This will make you feel good…I promise.'

He had the magical touch of a healer, Briana thought in delight, with a heartfelt inner sigh. And not only did those amazing hands heal as they massaged her already overheated skin, they stirred the passion slumbering inside her into a restless wild sea that engulfed her. So much so that it was almost impossible for her to sit still on that magnificent opulent bed with the heat of Pascual's semi-naked taut-muscled body behind her, goading her imagination to ever more stimulating heights.

When he eased her robe off completely, in an orchestrated sensual manoeuvre that couldn't help but elicit a startled response from her, then slipped the thin straps of her nightgown down so low over her arms that her breasts were suddenly exposed to the warm scented night air, she sucked in a shaky breath that seemed to echo round the entire room.

'*Amante*…you are so beautiful you make my very *soul* ache for wanting you!'

His hot mouth suckled her bare shoulder as his hands circled her ribcage to massage and cup her breasts, his thumbs and forefingers stroking, then squeezing the rigid nipples, until Briana cried out and tipped back her head against his chest to allow him even greater access.

This time Pascual kissed her in the sensitive hollow between her neck and shoulder, his hands moving hungrily down to her hips, moulding them seductively in his palms. Kneeling on the bed behind her, he pressed himself against her, so that she felt the hard silk contours of his amazing body, smelled the masculine scent that had always had the power to drive her crazy. She ached so hard for his possession that she thought she might lose her mind if she couldn't have what she so desperately craved…

As if reading her mind, Pascual urged her round to face him and helped her dispense with her nightgown and robe completely. Lying down on the bed, his dark head against the silk pillows, he encouraged her to straddle that taut hard middle of his. Immediately her soft inner thighs made contact with the deliciously warm skin beneath her Briana was devastatingly reminded of the unmatched intoxicating pleasure his touch could arouse. Feverishly seeking his mouth, she bent her head for his equally feverish kiss, lips, teeth and tongues clashing hungrily, until she thought the world could come to an end right then and she wouldn't even notice.

'I need to see to something.' His ebony eyes glazed with passion, Pascual reached towards one of the elegant oak cabinets beside the bed. His lips parting in the most bone-melting smile known to woman, he opened the slim foil package he'd retrieved and handed the contents to Briana. 'Put it on for me.'

The timbre of his captivating voice was like brushed velvet to her already impossibly heightened senses, and with her heart racing she sat back a little, to ease the black silk pyjamas down over bronzed hips as lean and straight as an arrow and release him.

His sex was silky, hard and impressive, and as she nervously rolled the latex protection down over its erect length her hands were trembling.

'Now, come here…' He smiled, sliding his hands onto her thighs and urging her across him.

He entered her in one smooth, shattering thrust, and Briana's ensuing moan resonated with relief, pleasure, longing and a deep sense of being home at last. Home with the man she irrevocably now knew she had never stopped loving…not even for an instant. All the years they'd spent apart had done was increase that longing and love for him. Helplessly she thought back to when she'd given birth to Adán, and how her heart had cracked loud enough for the whole of London to hear because Pascual had not been with her to share her joy.

'That feels so good…'

Reaching for her hand, he kissed the inside of her palm as she moved over him, her hips rhythmically meeting his, feeling his possession become deeper and deeper, until she thought the deliciously wild feelings building inside her could only implode and take her straight into another stratosphere altogether.

'*How* good?' she teased, gripping and then releasing her feminine muscles tightly round him, eliciting a melting groan from deep inside his chest.

'Do you want to make me lose my mind, *amante*?' he answered, gravel-voiced, sliding his hands up her ribcage to her breasts and palming them.

Meeting his hungry, melting gaze that was like all the midnight-black skies she had ever known melded into one, Briana touched her aching mouth to his and kissed him. Voraciously his tongue slid between her lips and took command of the erotic little dance she had started, his hands sliding up and down her slim back and round to her bottom.

After a while she raised her head and now, on the most intimate terms with those black-coffee-dark eyes with their sweeping long lashes, she smiled. 'Why don't we lose our minds together?'

'Why not?' he agreed, and thrust high into her core, holding himself there as he sensed her unravel around him, showing no mercy as her shuddering soft cries littered the air.

The action was the catalyst for Pascual's own undoing. Just as he felt Briana come apart, the intense need and hunger for release that had gripped him almost from the moment she'd obligingly and so erotically sheathed him with the protection he'd given her peaked, taking him hotly and irrevocably over the edge. Now it was his turn to cry out, and as he did so he impelled Briana towards him, hungrily drowning out his own voice with the pressure of her sweet strawberry and vanilla mouth gliding against him. Then, pushing his fingers though her soft dark hair, he kept her there for long, heart-pounding seconds…

CHAPTER TEN

SHE woke to the fragrant twin scents of jasmine and jacaranda, drifting up through the opened French doors that led onto the ornate bedroom balcony. She remembered that although it was now autumn in London, it was spring in Buenos Aires. Breathing out a sigh of deep contentment—instigated, she was sure, by the pleasant 'well-loved' feeling in her body this morning—Briana was a little taken aback to find Pascual already gone from their bed.

Just as she was reaching for her cotton robe, which lay across the silk counterpane, the door opened and Adán—still dressed in his short-sleeved pyjamas—raced across the room and flung himself beside her.

'Mummy! I slept *all* night in my new bed!' he announced happily, winding his soft childish arms round her waist.

Briefly nuzzling the warmth of his sweet-smelling neck, Briana hugged him hard and gave him a kiss.

'I know you did, my darling…well done! You're getting more and more grown up every day!'

'But not *too* grown-up, hmm?' remarked the man
who'd entered the room behind him. Fully dressed
in light blue denim jeans and a fitted black T-shirt that
instantly drew her appreciative glance to his bronzed
skin and tight toned biceps, Pascual gave her a smile.
'Childhood is a precious time…we do not want him
growing up too fast!'

Before she could raise a comment he reached the
side of the bed and, bending down, pressed his warm
lips to her cheek. Instantly the provocative drift of his
spicy cologne and his own unique male scent made
a devastating assault on Briana's senses, and the
passion of the night they had shared came back to her
in all its never-to-be forgotten glory. *She blushed.*

'Buenos diás,' he added, dark eyes twinkling.

His comment about Adán not growing up too fast
was all the more poignant, she reflected, because he had
already missed over four years of his son's life. Her eyes
briefly smarted as she fought to hold back her tears.

'Good morning. You should have woken me. Adán
needs a shower—and so do I.'

'Take your time. I will see to Adán and you can
shower and dress at your leisure. Then we will meet
downstairs for breakfast. How does that sound?'

'Good…if you don't mind seeing to him? His
clothes are folded away in the bureau in his bedroom.'

'Come on, *mi hijo*! Let us leave your *mamà* in peace for a little while, to do all the things that beautiful ladies have to do in the morning to get ready for the day…*sí*?'

Catching Briana's eye, Pascual gave her the most lascivious wink, and her skin suddenly felt like ice cream melting beneath the blaze of a scorching sun. To disguise her disturbing reaction and divert herself, she gave Adán a brief, affectionate squeeze, and helped him off the edge of the bed onto the floor.

'Go with—go with Daddy, sweetheart, and I will see you soon.'

'Can I play in the park again today?' She heard his sweet voice beseeching Pascual as they went towards the door, hand in hand. 'I want to see the fountain and the lake again!'

'Of course. But first we must have breakfast with your mother…*sí*?'

Jogging across the lush grass, with his small son just ahead of him, Pascual thought that he was possibly the most content that he had been for a long, long time. *God had sent him a miracle, in the shape of the sweet child before him, and the woman he had once adored with all his heart had returned to him.* Even now his body was fiercely and vibrantly awake, after their long night of passionate lovemaking, and it was as though the force and strength of the Igazu Falls themselves were running though his veins!

But then, as if to cast a shadow over his newfound contentment, the thought came to him of how it must have been for Briana when she had first agreed to marry him and his family had all but made her feel like an unwanted usurper. *How he regretted the fact he had not spoken out against their treatment of her before!* Running his mind back over the days leading up to Briana leaving, there were two occasions that suddenly stood out like a newly lit beacon in his memory.

The first was when he had been discussing his forthcoming marriage with his mother over coffee at a hotel owned by a friend of his in Recoleta. She had made a comment to Pascual then about Briana that had made his blood boil.

'Her beauty is the kind that fades. She does not possess the extraordinary bone structure of someone like Claudia, whose beauty will only become even more exquisite as she grows older.' That was one of the things she had said, and then, *'She knows nothing of our way of life, my son...how to conduct herself in illustrious company, what clothes to wear... I would hate it if she ever embarrassed you in any way because of her ignorance.'*

If she had said those things to *him*, then had she made similar disconcerting remarks to Briana herself? he wondered painfully. If so, then it was no wonder his fiancée had felt doubtful and insecure about marrying into such a family. A family she had believed thought themselves far superior to everyone else! Given her own background, and an upper-class father who had called her his 'regrettable mistake', Pascual began to see for himself just *why* she had decided she could not go through with marrying him—even though she had professed to be in love with him.

And if she had been uncertain that she would have his support *whatever* his family thought of her, he reflected soberly, then surely he was partly to blame for her leaving? With a troubled sigh he saw his son's curly head disappear over the rise that loomed up before them, and he instantly increased his stride to catch up with him, the acute realisation bolting through his insides that he was heading towards the lake.

'Adán! Stop! Wait for me, *hijo*!'

'I want to take you to lunch.'

Briana was gazing out onto a pretty section of the vast garden filled with the most dazzling display of African violets, roses, lilies and asters from the opened patio doors in the drawing room, and Pascual's rich voice interrupted the quiet reflection she had fallen into. Her pulse leapt as he slid his arms round her waist from behind, and kissed the top of her head.

'That sounds nice…can Adán come too?'

'I want you to myself for a while, so I have asked Sofia to look after him for us. He is quite happy about the arrangement. When we return I have promised to show him the ponies.'

'I should go and get myself ready, then.'

Shyly, Briana turned so that she was facing him and, as usual, the sight of those strongly delineated handsome features, the glossy black hair and disturbing dark eyes took her breath away. Right now he was being lovely to her…considerate, kind, and—dare she say it?—*loving, even*… But how long would that last if in his heart he still couldn't forgive her for leaving?

Last night they had at least made some headway towards understanding, when Pascual had defended her against his parents. The fact that he was reflecting on his own past behaviour was a significant turning point. It meant that Briana could at last speak to him frankly and be heard. But lingering at the back of her mind was the still wounding memory of seeing him with Claudia, and the fear that she might not be enough for him even after they had married—even though he had explained that it had all been an unfortunate misunderstanding. Maybe having lunch together would be an opportune time to finally put some of her fears to bed?

'Put on something sexy for me,' he suggested now, his gaze lowering to her startled slightly opened mouth, looking as if he could eat her.

'What do you suggest? My underwear?' she

quipped, barely able to still the violent tremors that had taken hold.

'That works for me, *amante*, but I might not be able to deal with the stampede of admiring males that that would attract! Now, hurry up and get ready. We will go to Florida Street and see the street tango before we eat. I remember how much you used to love that.'

Thinking back to the many vibrant and exciting displays of street tango she had seen last time she had lived in Buenos Aires—from San Telmo to La Boca, and the more up-market end of Florida Street— Briana thought about the silky red dress she had hanging in the voluminous wardrobe upstairs. She couldn't deny the warm buzz of excitement that rippled through her at the idea of wearing it especially for Pascual…

The way the two bodies moved together was mesmerising. It was impossible to take her eyes off the woman in her short, strapless black dress, her slim, shapely legs encased in sheer black stockings and matching high-heeled shoes on her feet. Her partner was older, with a thick mane of silver hair tied back in a black band, but his lithe body moved like a much younger man's and his profile was fiercely proud. The raw sensuality of the background music, and the sight of the dancers' limbs entwining then parting—

the woman stalking away as though offended, the man striding after her and tipping her back into his arms—sent gooseflesh flying all over the surface of Briana's skin.

In the smart tiled square where a small crowd had gathered to watch the riveting display, she felt her enjoyment intimately heightened when Pascual slid his arms round her waist and drew her next to him. She could feel his heat through the thin silk of her dress, and everything in her tightened to contain the sudden flare of desire that spread like wildfire throughout her body.

'Enjoying it, *amante*?'

His voice low against her ear sent more goosebumps flying.

'It's wonderful. They're incredible!'

'Has it sufficiently fuelled your appetite to eat now?' he teased.

'Can we stay a minute or two longer?' She turned to look at him, and he gave her one of those long, slow-burning smiles of his.

'Why not?' He shrugged, 'it pleases me to see you happy like this.'

In the restaurant afterwards, with its tall wooden-framed windows providing a perfect view of the colourful throng of passers-by—tourists and locals alike—and with the distant music of the tango still echoing in her ears, Briana excused herself to go to the ladies' room.

While she was gone Pascual found himself pre-disposed to smile at anyone who happened to glance his way, his contented mood of the morning easily reinstated. As he finished ordering the wine, a hand tapped him on the shoulder, and he glanced round to see his friend Diego de la Cruz and his pretty wife Marisa. After greeting them with an affectionate hug each, he invited the couple to join him.

'It is a day for bumping into old friends!' Marisa announced, settling herself in a chair, her exquisite perfume punctuating the air. 'We just saw Claudia with her new husband too.' She frowned, her slim dark brows arching. 'You *did* know she'd got mar-ried, didn't you, Pascual?'

He shrugged. 'How could I *not* know? Her wed-ding photos were in all the papers.'

'Once upon a time we really thought you and she would—' Her gaze narrowing briefly at her husband as she said this, Marisa quickly turned back to Pascual. 'But then you met Briana, and we knew straight away that she was the right one for you. Hearing that she was back in Palermo with you and that you have a son together was so exciting! I cannot tell you how the news lifted us.'

'I expect the news will be surprising to everyone who hears it. Initially she will be staying for a holiday, and then, when she has tied up all the loose ends in the UK, she will be moving here for good.

And you will get to meet our son soon, I promise. His name is Adán, he is absolutely amazing, and I am still feeling quite overwhelmed that he is mine.'

'Where are they now?' Diego enquired, his thoughtful gaze on his friend as the waiters bustled round behind them, serving food to the other waiting customers.

'Adán is being looked after by Sofia back at the house, and Briana has just gone to the ladies' room. She will be back at any moment.'

'There is something I must tell you before she comes back, Pascual.' Covertly, Marisa bent her dark head towards him. 'We have been friends for a long time, haven't we?'

'Where is this leading?' Immediately aware of a more serious undertone to the innocent-sounding question, Pascual felt sudden disquiet arise inside him.

'I pray you will not take offence at me saying what I am about to say, but when I heard that Briana was back with you, and that she had had your son while you were apart, I guessed why she had decided not to go through with the wedding—and I knew it was *not* because she didn't love you with all her heart!'

His chest tightening almost painfully, Pascual could hardly take his eyes off Marisa as he waited for her full explanation. 'Go on,' he said, voice low.

'Remember the party that Claudia unexpectedly turned up to with Rafa? Do you know who *really* invited her? It was Paloma. Your mother persuaded her to come and make mischief between you and Briana. She was convinced Claudia was the woman you should really be marrying, and she hoped if Briana saw you two together she would call off the wedding and leave the way clear for you to get back with her.'

'How do you know all this?'

'Claudia told me. She is still fond of you, Pascual, and she only wants your happiness. She truly regrets what happened at the party, and the idea that she might have helped drive Briana away. Her own happiness has made her see that she did a very bad thing. It is her hope that one day you will forgive her.'

'I can hardly believe what I am hearing.'

Feeling slightly dazed, Pascual reached for the jug of iced water on the table and poured a glass. He took a long draught to ease the sudden aching dryness in his throat, then wiped the back of his hand across his mouth. *His own mother had helped drive away the woman he loved and consequently prevented him from knowing that she had had a son by him!* It was almost beyond belief. Now he saw that he had been right to reflect on some of his mother's more acerbic comments before his planned marriage. If only he had reflected more on them at the time, he thought again. If only he had made his feelings towards Briana much more clear to everyone. Then maybe his mother would have seen for herself how much she meant to him, and would have stayed well clear from making mischief of any sort!

'Pascual?'

'It is all right, Marisa.' The semblance of a rueful smile touched his lips. 'I am not upset that you told me this. In fact…I appreciate your frankness. Too many things have been pushed under the carpet for too long, and it is time they were aired. So, thank you.'

'I thought it was you! Oh, how lovely to see you both!'

Briana had returned, the red silk dress that so lovingly complemented her gorgeous figure drawing many appreciative glances as she returned to their table, Pascual saw. And none were more appreciative than *his*.

Hugging Marisa, then a smiling Diego, she dropped back down into her seat. The elegant young woman she'd once worked for was smiling warmly, and Briana genuinely felt for the first time as though she were among friends. 'Pascual was telling me that Sabrina is quite the young lady now. I would love to see her some time, if that's possible?'

'And we would love to see your son too, Briana,' Marisa responded eagerly. 'As soon as we learned of his existence we could not wait to hear all about him. We have just been pestering Pascual for information!'

'I would talk about him all day if you want me to.' He smiled and reached for Briana's hand, gripping it as though he never wanted to let it go again.

Something in him had changed, she saw, and her heart fluttered. He was behaving more and more like the Pascual of old—the man she'd fallen head-over-heels in love with almost from the start. Now, as much as she adored seeing Diego and Marisa again, she wished they were alone so that she might enjoy his company even more, talk frankly to him about all the things that were left unsaid between them.

'A toast!'

The waiter had brought more glasses, and Pascual was busy filling them with wine.

'To good friends, and to the best of futures for all of us!'

And Briana knew in that moment that to contemplate a future without this man would be like contemplating any mother's worst fear...that of something dreadful happening to her child. It was simply unbearable and unthinkable, and if she wanted this day to end in the same optimistic spirit as this lovely moment amongst friends then she would think of it no longer...

CHAPTER ELEVEN

SOFIA and Carlo the groundsman were running towards the car as Pascual drove down the drive towards the house's main entrance.

'What's going on?' Briana glanced nervously at Pascual, but he didn't answer. He was, instead, winding down his window and leaning out, conversing in Spanish with his clearly agitated staff. Nonetheless she quickly and horrifyingly understood what the two retainers were telling him.

Adán had been playing in the garden outside the drawing room. He had lifted the latch on the gate there and disappeared into the park. Carlo had been out looking for him, but as yet had not had any luck. He had only just returned to the house to see if the boy had come back to Sofia, but he hadn't.

Briana's first thought was the lake and so—judging by the colour rapidly draining from his face—was Pascual's.

'We've got to find him!'

She grabbed at his sleeve, the bright future she'd seduced herself into believing could come true suddenly obliterated by an unseen wrecking ball that had smashed all her hopes and dreams into devastating dust.

'Trust me, *mi amor*, we will. We will go and search together. Come!'

They were out of the car and running into the park, leaving a stricken Sofia standing at the entrance and a determined-looking Carlo heading out into the expanse of forested and lush green behind them. Turning briefly, Pascual instructed the older man to expand the search into another area nearby, where Adán might have wandered.

Shouting out her son's name as she ran, the man by her side doing the same, Briana's throat was hoarse with strain and anxiety by the time they approached the rise that preceded the lake.

'I will go on ahead. Don't worry…everything will be all right. We will find him safe.' Briefly clasping her to him, clearly registering the fear and terror in her white-faced countenance, Pascual touched his lips tenderly to her brow.

'You promise?' she begged, heart pounding, not caring that she was coming unglued in front of him.

'*Con todo mi corazón!* With all my heart!'

He left her then, and the tall, lithe black trousered and white shirted figure quickly disappeared over the top of the grassy rise. Breaking into a run too, with every stride she took Briana prayed her son would be found safe and well. *If only she hadn't gone to lunch without him! If only she had got in touch with Pascual as soon as she'd learned that she was pregnant and asked him to forgive her for running away! If only...*

A million regrets and thoughts flowed unstoppably through her mind, and only when she heard her name being called with the kind of urgency that turned her limbs into cooked spaghetti did she realise she was weeping. Freezing where she stood for a moment, in the next instant she forced herself to run. At the top of the hill she glanced down, to see Pascual carrying Adán in his arms. The lake was a vast smooth mirror speared by glinting sunlight behind them. Her son was talking to his father, and she saw Pascual press the small curly head against his chest for a moment, before glancing up and waving to her. Even from a distance she saw the unrestrained joy on his handsome face, and her heart turned over with gratitude and love.

'Where did you go, Adán? I was so worried!' Out of breath, and crying at the same time, as she drew level with the smiling pair Briana grabbed her son's small hand and reverently touched his face, as if surveying its innocent beauty for the very first time.

There were smears of dirt on his flushed cheeks, but he didn't appear as though he was hurt or injured.

'I wanted to see the ponies, but then I got lost and fell down the hill, and I landed near the lake!'

'Promise me you wouldn't have gone into the water?'

'Only if I was in a boat or I had my water wings and you and Daddy were with me!'

'But *why* did you leave the garden without telling Sofia?'

'Is she cross with me, Mummy?'

'I'm sure she's not cross, sweetheart, but she's worried out of her mind. She was in charge of making sure you were safe while Daddy and I went out. Imagine what she must have felt when she looked into the garden and you weren't there!'

'I'm sorry…'

'I have already told him it was not a good idea to do what he did, and I have made him promise me that he will never do such a thing again or I will not be taking him to see the ponies. Isn't that right, Adán?'

'Yes, but you *will* take me to see the ponies when I've washed my face, won't you? You said everyone should always keep their promises!'

The child gave him such a solemn yet hopeful glance that Pascual felt his heart splinter. *He'd thought he had lost him…* Just as he had lost Fidel and then Briana when she had left him. But this potential loss—the loss of the son he had only just come to know—would have been the most heart-breaking of all. The devastation that had swept through him at the idea Adán could be dead from a fall or drowned in the lake had left him shaking, feeling as if a hurricane had tossed him high into the air and then swept his body onto jagged rocks. Now that he had discovered him safe and well, the eu-phoria that pumped through Pascual's bloodstream was like the headiest, most potent cocktail he had ever imbibed.

'I will take you to see the ponies, *hijo*, when your *mamà* has washed your face and hands and we have got you a drink from the kitchen.'

He turned to survey Briana, her light make-up streaked with her tears, and her face paler than he'd ever seen it. A cooling breeze had sprung up, and it plastered the thin silk of her pretty red dress against her body, teasing the silken strands of her dark hair into a gentle tangle. She was *ravishing*.

He sensed something else besides euphoria move through him, and it was equally powerful and exhilar-ating. *He loved this woman—heart and soul. He always had and always would—no matter what had transpired between them before.* People talked about the one they loved making them feel complete, and *that* was what he experienced being with Briana. If only he had been more open with her right from the start, had made her feel that she was safe with him, know that he would always love and protect her no matter what…then maybe she would not have run away.

After he had lost his best friend, Pascual had vowed he would be more open and honest in his relationships, would not waste time prevaricating or being inauthentic. Life was the most precious gift, and every day should be lived in acknowledgement of that. But he had *not* shared those views with the woman he loved, and consequently she had believed him to be a very different man from the one he knew himself to be. An arrogant, uncaring man who gave more credence to his status in life than nurturing the people he loved. Well, fate had given him a second chance to demonstrate the truth to her, and he would not waste another second of it in unhappiness or doubt.

'Are you all right?' he asked her.

She nodded and smiled, though her eyes were still moist. 'I'm fine. Just so relieved and grateful that he's all right!'

'Then let us go back to the house,' he said, reaching for her hand and lightly squeezing it. 'Sofia and Carlo will be anxious to know the little one is safe.'

'And *then* you can take me to see the ponies!' Adán piped up with a disarming grin.

Ruffling his curly hair, Pascual laughed and planted a kiss on his brow. 'I can see that you do not give up easily, Adán. That is a quality I very much

admire. When you have a goal in life—whatever it
is—you should never give up believing you can attain
it.' His gaze met Briana's, and she held it for a long
second before glancing away again and blushing
slightly. Answering warmth curled inside him. 'So,
yes, *mi hijo*…I will take you to see the ponies—just
as I have promised!'

'Briana?'

The scented steam emanating from the partially
opened bathroom door told him immediately where
she was. Not long returned from viewing the polo
ponies with his son, and having left the boy with a
doting Sofia in the kitchen, eating some chocolate chip
cookies that she had made especially for him, Pascual
could wait no longer to see the woman he loved.

He knocked lightly on the door, and when she
didn't answer, slipped off his shoes and stepped
inside the room. The luxurious bath was an opulent
affair, set on a marble plinth up two surrounding
marble steps, and as the steam cleared Pascual saw
a long pale arm draped over the side, and Briana
lying with her head back and her eyes closed. *At the
height of her beauty Cleopatra herself could not have
looked lovelier or more desirable.* The scented water
lapped gently over her luscious form amid a myriad
of foamy pink bubbles, and her hair was piled on top
of her head in a dark silken cloud.

Crouching down beside the bath, Pascual feasted his hungry gaze for several long, appreciative moments before dipping his fingers into the sea of bubbles, gathering a few, and touching them gently to her nose. She opened her eyes—those incredible silvery grey eyes, whose power to shake him to his very core had never diminished—and it was like gazing into a sparkling moonlit lake. 'I didn't hear you come in. I must have dozed off. Where's Adán?'

'He is with Sofia, eating cookies, and he is quite happy.'

'He'd better not eat too many or he won't eat his dinner tonight.'

'I told Sofia not to let him overdo it.'

'Is she all right now? She was so upset about Adán running off like that.'

'I reassured her that there is no blame involved, and she is fine. She literally turned her back for a minute and he was gone. In future we will all make doubly sure we watch him like a hawk. As for you dozing off, you know you should never fall asleep in the bath, *mi amor*…you might drown!'

'I always do it.' Her delectable lips parted in the most edible smile. 'And I've never drowned yet.'

'I am almost tempted to get in there with you and teach you a lesson for being so reckless with your own safety.'

'What *kind* of lesson?'

'Are you teasing me, Briana Douglas—soon to be Señora Briana Dominguez?'

In surprise, she sat bolt-upright in the bath, and Pascual watched, fascinated, as the tiny pink bubbles clung to her glistening skin and inevitably provoked the already rising heat inside him to new and unsettling temperatures.

'Are you asking me to marry you, Pascual?'

'You already know that was always my intention, *mi amor*.'

She expelled a soft sigh. 'But before you wanted to marry me because I had Adán, and you naturally wanted to assume your role as his father, not because…' The sentence drifted away unfinished.

Striving to maintain the most serious expression he could muster, Pascual frowned. 'Because what?'

'You're making this very hard for me.'

Seeing the uncertainty in her eyes, and not wanting to prolong one more second of doubt, he cupped her jaw and stroked his thumb over her damp cheekbone.

'Then I will not make it hard for you any longer, *amante*. I want to marry you because I love you with all my heart and I do not want to live without you!'

'Oh, Pascual, I love you too! I've never stopped loving you…not in all these years!'

'In that case—' his fingers were already unbuttoning his white shirt as he grinned and got to his feet

'—you leave me with no choice but to get into that bath with you.'

'Really?'

'Yes—really!'

As he settled his magnificent nude body into the bath opposite her, Briana was almost delirious with happiness and delight. *Pascaul loved her! He really loved her!* She wanted to pinch herself to make sure she wasn't dreaming, but she only had to study the arrestingly handsome face before her to know that she was looking at pure, twenty-four-carat diamond reality, and the love she saw blazing at her from his gorgeous dark eyes was no fantasy.

'I was wrong to leave you like I did,' she told him now, her throat tightening with regret and not a small amount of sorrow. Seeing father and son together earlier, after Adán's frightening little escapade getting lost, had brought that home to her more than anything else. 'Can you ever forgive me, Pascual?'

He looked reflective for a moment. 'I let you down too, Briana. I should have made you know that you were more important to me than anything else in the world, and clearly I did not. If you had known that, and had been confident enough to talk to me about your fears and doubts, to confide in me about your difficult childhood, then perhaps you would have stayed, *mi amor*?'

'And if only I hadn't jumped to conclusions about

you and Claudia. If only I had confronted you with my fears instead and listened to your side of things,' she heard herself say, her heart racing slightly. 'But I was completely devastated when I thought you and she might be having an affair.'

'I have a confession to make to you about what happened that night.'

Briana stared at Pascual and hardly dared breathe. Steam from the bathwater had risen up and dampened his tanned skin with tiny little droplets of moisture. His shoulders were broad and powerful, and the eyes gazing back at her were darker than molasses. *What was he going to tell her?* That the old attraction between him and his ex had been helplessly aroused that night, and it had only been afterwards that he had regretted kissing her?

'It was as I said before…Claudia had too much to drink and more or less threw herself at me. But it was not entirely her fault.' He took a deep, steadying breath before continuing. 'My mother put her up to it. It was she who invited her to the party and got her to play up to me, because she hoped you would see her and believe that I was still attracted to her. When we saw Marisa and Diego at the restaurant today I finally learned the truth. Claudia is now happily married, and she told Marisa that she truly regrets going along with my mother's little plan. I owe you a big apology, Briana. You were right when you indicated that Paloma was less than welcoming towards you. My mother is an inveterate snob, I am afraid, and she allowed her prejudices to influence her behaviour in the worst possible way. I will be phoning her tonight and telling her in no uncertain terms what I think of what she did to you…to *us*. Please believe me when I tell you it will never happen again. If she should act with anything less than genuine warmth towards you in the future I will have no hesitation in cutting her out of our lives completely! And I know how much that would hurt her…especially now that she has seen Adán.'

'At least now we all know the truth. But I think we can extend our forgiveness towards your mother, too, Pascual, don't you? With my own mum living in the UK, Adán is going to need *both* of his grandmothers as he grows—*and* his grandfather. Can we not put the past behind us and start over again? We're young and in love and we have the most beautiful son in the world! Our future can start right here and now, if you're willing?'

'*Mi amor*, I am *more* than willing to let that be the case.'

Moving towards her, Pascual covered Briana's mouth in damp erotic kisses that made her weak with joy and desire, his hands moving over her slippery warm body with all the ardour of the most insatiable of eager lovers. And when they emerged from the bathroom, quite some time later, it was only to rekindle the flame they had stoked all over again in the bedroom…

All the dancing had made her hot. Seeking the cooler air that the early hours of the morning so blissfully provided, Briana went outside. The entrancing music of the ball faded a little the more she walked away from the house, but was still easily discernible just the same. She had left Pascual waltzing with Marisa—utterly ravishing in a glittering Venetian-style ballgown and harlequin mask studded with pearls. He was in the costume of a nineteenth-century Venetian nobleman, complete with a black velvet half-mask that made him look almost too handsome and charismatic for words!

Traditionally in Argentina, because there was such a mix of cultures, a wedding was a chance for couples to remember and pay homage to their ancestry, and as Pascual's family had originally come from Italy he had suggested the Venetian masked ball theme. *He had given her a wedding to remember*, she thought with gratitude and love, hugging herself against the suddenly cooler temperatures.

The voluminous skirts of her ivory silk ballgown wedding dress rustled a little like the wind in the trees as she walked. Wearing it, she had never felt more beautiful or feminine in her life…even though the heavily boned corset beneath the figure-hugging bodice had forced her to keep her enjoyment of the lavish banquet to a minimum, so that she could at least breathe!

Glancing behind her, she saw every window in the palatial mansion blazed with light, and the long gravelled path that led away from the house was lit with glowing lanterns on either side. It really was like the most incredible dream. A month ago she, Adán and Pascual had travelled back to the UK, so that Briana could put her affairs in order in preparation for moving to Argentina for good, and they had brought her mother Frances back with them—for an extended holiday and to be there at her daughter's wedding.

Paloma Dominguez had been sweetness itself to Frances *and* Briana, and had even issued her daughter-in-law with a clearly genuine apology for what had gone on before. Adán had given her a new lease of life, she'd enthused, and both women had insisted on tucking him into bed tonight before coming down to the ball. Two more doting grandmothers would be hard to find!

But the thing that had amazed and heartened Briana the most was that she had made friends here. *Genuine*, caring friends she could laugh and be herself with. Nobody looked down on her because of her background, and Pascual's family had welcomed her with open arms. She saw that she had been mistaken before in imagining she wouldn't fit in and that everyone would despise her because she'd had such a different upbringing from her wealthy husband. It made her realise that some of her fears had indeed prejudiced her into not recognising that there were good people everywhere—no matter *what* their background or history—she only had to have her eyes open to see!

She walked on to a stand of trees in the distance, silhouetted against the night sky like menacing dark sentinels. The air was full of luscious scents as well as the evocative sound of cicadas. The perfume of exotic flowers mingled with the more earthy notes of the land itself, and the legacy from the sunshine earlier in the day permeated the atmosphere with faint but subtle baked warmth.

Was that the rumble of thunder she had just heard? She came to a standstill for a moment, suddenly realising that what her ears had picked up was the distant sound of a horses' hooves not the thunderous precursor to a storm. Peering into the inky night ahead, she shivered.

A rider on a black stallion bedecked in nineteenth-century livery was heading towards her at a steady canter. Briana's heart missed a beat. She hardly knew what to make of the strange scene unfolding. But when the obscured full moon emerged from behind a bank of low-lying dark clouds above the trees, shining its ethereal light on the rider and his horse, she honestly thought she had never seen anything more spine-tingling and dramatic in her whole life!

Horse and rider pulled up beside her. *'Buenas noches, mi señora,'* a richly sensual male voice greeted her.

Wishing she had brought a shawl with her, Briana shivered again. Even though the rider wore a mask, immediately she knew it was Pascual, and she stared up at him in wide-eyed wonder behind her own ivory half-mask—a disguise that she thought made the women who wore it resemble exotic and mysterious cats.

'Pascual! I left you dancing with Marisa…how did you get away so soon?'

'This house has many secret passages and exits that you do not yet know about, *mi amor*!' There was a pleased smile in his voice. 'When I saw you leave and go outside, I also saw the perfect opportunity to spirit you away from the party and take you somewhere private, where I can be alone with my new wife!'

'Where are we going?'

Gazing down at the vision in silk and satin before him, her beautiful face partially obscured by the very sexy mask she wore, her shoulders and the tops of her breasts bared by the revealing and ravishing neckline of her gown, he felt the most delicious tension coil deep inside him—as well as pride and love. *It was true what he had said. He could not wait to get her alone.* The wedding reception had started that evening and—as tradition dictated—would continue on until breakfast. Daybreak was too far away for him to wait for the privilege of making love with his gorgeous new wife, Pascual had decided earlier, and he was not going to wait a moment longer!

'Give me your hand,' he ordered.

'You don't mean—? Pascual, I can't get up on that horse in this gown! It's impossible!'

'*Nothing* is impossible!' He laughed, and hauled her up into the saddle in front of him.

After a little patient adjusting of her voluminous gown, and sliding his arms round Briana's slender waist to reach the reins, Pascual clicked his teeth and his steed broke into another steady canter.

Directing the stallion away from the path, and crossing the wide open grassy area beside it towards the woodland that lay in darkness beyond, he murmured soft-voiced against the delicate pale lobe of Briana's ear. 'Hold on, *mi amor*. This will get us there quicker!' and he schooled his horse into a near gallop.

Yelping in fright, Briana felt her body go almost rigid in the saddle in front of him, before pressing even more deeply against Pascual's chest. 'Please don't let me fall!' she begged.

'Never!' he answered. 'I am an extremely accomplished horseman, and the last thing in the world I would do would be to let the woman I love fall or injure herself in any way when in my care.'

When they came to the spot deep within the forested area that he sought—a secluded semicircle of grass and bracken beneath the shade of some very tall trees—Pascual dismounted first, then reached up for Briana to help her down onto the soft grass. As she spilled into his arms in a warm, delectable bundle of satin and silk, the feel of her body was utterly divine to his hungry senses.

'How did you enjoy your riding adventure?' he teased, reluctantly releasing her.

'It's a wonder my legs can hold me up, they're shaking so badly!'

'Well, you will not have to stand for very much longer, my sweet…I can promise you that.'

Leading the stallion a little further away, he reached for the small bundle he had secured behind the saddle before tethering the reins to a tree branch and returning to join Briana. The bundle he had collected was a generous-sized soft wool blanket, and now he shook it out and laid it at the foot of the tree they were standing beneath.

'You think of everything!' Her expression delightfully shy, Briana walked into his arms.

*It was like walking into heaven…*Briana thought. He kissed her gently at first, then, as hunger spilled over into unstoppable need for both of them, with loving hands urged her down onto the blanket. Mindless with desire and love for the wonderful man who was now her husband, she hardly knew how they accomplished the removal of her exquisite gown, with all its tiny hooks and eyes and layers of silk, but somehow they found a way.

When Briana lay beneath Pascual wearing only a cream-coloured suspender belt and matching sheer stockings he was still more or less fully clothed, except for the silk shirt that she had feverishly pulled open so that she could touch that wonderful hard-muscled chest of his. They eagerly sought the connection and release they had both been craving all day. Suspended above her, Pascual gazed down at Briana with the most emotional glance he had ever given her, and a tiny muscle flickered at the side of his perfectly sculpted cheekbone.

'I never want to lose you again,' he vowed, his tone not quite steady.

'You won't,' Briana promised, touching his cheek and wanting to keep him right there inside her for the rest of this unbelievably magical night. 'What can I do to convince you that I'm here to stay, my love?'

'Give me another child,' he answered huskily and, turning his head, pressed his warm lips against her palm.

Not even hesitating, she let a tremulous welcoming smile lift the edges of her mouth. *'Gladly,'* she replied—and meant it with all her heart…

Argentinian Playboy, Unexpected Love-Child

CHANTELLE SHAW

Chantelle Shaw lives on the Kent coast, five minutes from the sea, and does much of her thinking about the characters in her books while walking on the beach. She's been an avid reader from an early age. Her schoolfriends used to hide their books when she visited—but Chantelle would retreat into her own world and still writes stories in her head all the time. Chantelle has been blissfully married to her own tall, dark and very patient hero for over twenty years and has six children. She began to read Mills & Boon® romances as a teenager and, throughout the years of being a stay-at-home mum to her brood, found romantic fiction helped her to stay sane! She enjoys reading and writing about strong-willed, feisty women and even stronger-willed, sexy heroes. Chantelle is at her happiest when writing. She is particularly inspired while cooking dinner, which unfortunately results in a lot of culinary disasters! She also loves gardening, walking and eating chocolate (followed by more walking!). Catch up with Chantelle's latest news on her website, www. chantelleshaw.com.

**Chantelle Shaw's exciting new novel,
The Ultimate Risk, is available from
Mills & Boon in May 2011.**

CHAPTER ONE

DIEGO leaned against the paddock fence, his dark eyes narrowed against the glare of the early evening sun as he watched the horse and rider soar over the triple jump with impressive ease. The six foot wall was next. The horse was gathering pace and the rider stretched forwards along its neck in preparation for the jump.

The display of riding skill was fascinating to watch. Unwittingly, Diego held his breath, waiting for the horse's hooves to leave the ground. But at that moment a motorbike emerged from the woods, the high-pitched scream of its engine shattering the quiet air. The bike braked on the track which ran alongside the paddock with a squeal of tyres. The horse was clearly scared by the noise, and Diego knew instantly that it would refuse the jump. But there was nothing he could do, and he watched helplessly as the rider was thrown out of the saddle, sailed over the horse's head, and landed with a sickening thud on the sun-baked earth.

Rachel was winded by the force of the impact with the ground and she struggled to draw oxygen into her lungs. Her head was spinning and sensation was returning to her body, bringing with it various points of pain on her arms, shoulders, hips… She was going to have some spectacular bruises, she thought ruefully. It seemed easier to keep her eyes closed and sink into the welcome blackness where pain was obliterated, but she could hear a voice and she forced her lashes up and stared dazedly at the man looming over her.

'Don't try to move. Lie still while I check to see if you've broken any bones. *Dios*—You are lucky you are still alive,' the voice said roughly. 'You flew through the air like a rag doll.'

Rachel was vaguely aware of hands running over her body, working up from her legs to her hips and then skimming her ribcage and, despite the lightness of the man's touch, she winced when he found the tender area on her lower rib. Still stunned by the fall, her lashes drifted down again.

'Hey, don't pass out. I'm going to call an ambulance.'

'I don't need an ambulance,' she muttered fiercely, forcing her eyes open again. The blackness was disappearing and above her she could see the blue sky dotted with wisps of cotton wool clouds. But then the stranger leaned over her, his face so close to hers that she could feel his warm breath graze her cheek, and for a moment she wondered if she was concussed—or hallucinating.

She recognised him instantly. Diego Ortega—international polo champion, multimillionaire and playboy who, according to the press, was as successful in his pursuit of beautiful women as he was of polo titles. Rachel had no interest in gossip columns, but since she was twelve years old she had devoured every riding magazine she could lay her hands on and there was no doubt that the Argentinian was a legend in his chosen sport.

She supposed she should not be surprised by his sudden appearance when, for the past few weeks, the main topic of conversation among the other stable-hands had been his impending visit to Hardwick Hall. But seeing him in the flesh was still a shock, and the realisation that he had been watching her take Piran over the jumps was disconcerting.

He had already extracted his mobile phone from his jeans. Rachel forced herself to sit up, biting down on her lip to stop herself from crying out as her battered body protested.

'I told you to lie still.' Diego Ortega's heavily accented voice was terse with a mixture of concern and impatience.

She instinctively rebelled against his authoritative tone. 'And I told you I don't need an ambulance,' she replied firmly as she curled her legs and managed by sheer determination to get onto her knees.

'Are you always so disobedient?' Diego made no effort to disguise his irritation and muttered something in his native tongue, in a tone that made Rachel glad that she could not understand Spanish. Once she was on her feet she would feel better, she told herself. She certainly didn't have a couple of hours to waste sitting in the waiting room at the local hospital. Gritting her teeth, she forced herself to move, and then gave a yelp of surprise when strong, tanned hands settled around her waist and she was lifted into the air.

She could not have been held against Diego Ortega's muscular chest for more than a second, but the feel of his powerful arms around her and the tantalising waft of his cologne that assailed her senses made her head swim. Her heart was beating too fast, and it was no good trying to kid herself that its accelerated speed was a result of the fall. Up close, he was awesome. Her eyes strayed to his broad chest where his casual cream shirt was open at the throat, revealing dark hairs that she noticed also covered his forearms. Slowly she lifted her head and studied his square jaw, the sharply chiselled cheekbones and wide mouth with its perfectly curved upper lip.

What would it be like to be kissed by that mouth? The thought hurtled uninvited into her mind and the blood that had drained from her cheeks due to the shock of the fall now flooded back, scalding her skin. Her gaze skittered over his face and clashed with amber eyes that at this moment were glinting warningly beneath heavy black brows.

His eyes had the golden hue of sherry, Rachel noted distractedly, desperately trying to hide the fact that her legs were wobbling when he set her on her feet. She was bound to feel peculiar after hurtling over Piran's head and meeting the ground at speed. The shaky feeling had nothing to do with the man who was looming over her, she told herself as her eyes strayed to his gleaming mahogany-coloured hair which fell to his shoulders.

His rugged good-looks were entirely masculine, and with his olive-gold skin he reminded her of a picture she'd once seen of a Sioux chief—dark, dangerous and undeniably the sexiest man she had ever laid eyes on.

He was still gripping her arms, as if he feared she would topple over if he let her go. He was too close, too big and way too overwhelming, and she needed to put some space between them.

'Thanks,' she murmured as she stepped back from him.

For a moment it seemed as though he would not release her, but then he took his hands from her arms, his eyes narrowing when she swayed unsteadily.

'You need to see a medic,' he said tersely. 'Even though you're wearing a hard hat, you could be suffering from concussion.'

'I'm fine, honestly,' Rachel assured him quickly, forcing a smile and trying to ignore the feeling that she'd been run over by a steamroller. 'I've had far worse falls than that.'

'I'm not surprised,' Diego growled. 'The horse is too big for you.' His mouth compressed as he relived those gut-churning seconds when the horse had refused the jump and its rider had been flung through the air, to land in a crumpled heap on the hard ground.

He turned his head and cast an expert eye over the black

stallion which had first captured his attention when he had strolled down to the practice paddock. His interest in the rider had come afterwards, when the braid of golden hair hanging beneath the riding hat had told him that the boyishly slim figure astride the horse was in fact most definitely female.

The horse was easily seventeen hands, Diego estimated. It seemed calm now that the noise of the motorbike had faded but it was clearly a nervy creature and its highly strung nature, teamed with its physical size and strength, would make it a difficult animal for a man to control, let alone the slender woman standing before him.

She was startlingly beautiful, he acknowledged, feeling a tug of interest as he studied her small heart-shaped face. Her skin was bare of make-up and porcelain smooth, her cheeks flushed like rosy apples from her exertions over the jumps. She was a true English rose, and he was captivated by her cornflower-blue eyes, which were regarding him steadily from beneath the brim of her riding hat.

Diego frowned, astonished by the sudden realisation that he was staring at her. He was used to women staring at *him*—with varying degrees of subtlety and frequently a blatant invitation in their glances, which he responded to when he felt like it. Never had he been so fixated by a woman that he could not take his eyes off her. But this woman was simply exquisite—and so fragile looking that he was amazed she had not broken every bone in her body in the fall.

Riding the big stallion was plain folly, he brooded. 'I'm amazed your father allows you to ride such a powerful animal.'

'My father?' Nonplussed, Rachel stared at him. Neither her real father nor her mother's two subsequent husbands, who she had insisted that Rachel call 'Dad', had ever been sufficiently interested in her to care what sort of animal she rode. But Diego Ortega knew nothing of her complicated family, or the fact that her mother was a serial bride, and she frowned as she focused on the word *'allow'*.

'Neither my father nor anyone else "allows" me to do anything,' she said sharply. 'I'm an adult, and I make my own decisions. And I am more than capable of handling Piran.'

'He's too strong for you, and you're a fool to think you could control him if he decided to bolt,' Diego replied coolly. 'You plainly couldn't control him when he refused the jump—although, to be fair, that was not entirely your fault. Who the hell was that on the motorbike? I can't believe Earl Hardwick is happy for a yob to tear around the estate like a lunatic.'

'Unfortunately, the Earl allows his son to do whatever he likes,' Rachel said tersely, still incensed by Diego's remarks that she could not control Piran. 'The *yob* you're referring to was Jasper Hardwick, and I couldn't agree more with your description of him. He spends much of his time carving up the fields on his wretched bike. He shot out of the woods without warning, and it was no wonder Piran was startled. I'd challenge any rider to have been able to handle him in that situation.'

'Perhaps so,' Diego admitted with a shrug. 'You ride well,' he acknowledged grudgingly. When he had first arrived at the paddock he'd witnessed the empathy between the girl and the horse—that instinctive understanding that could not be taught or bought but was so vital in whichever competitive arena you were in. The girl was fearless in the saddle. There had been absolutely no hesitation when she had approached the six-foot jump and, although Diego had given up showjumping in favour of polo in his late teens, he knew enough about the sport to recognise her undoubted talent.

He walked over to the stallion, now standing patiently by the fence, and took hold of his reins. 'How old is he?' he queried, running his hand over the animal's flank.

'Six—I've been jumping him for two years.'

'He's a fine animal. What did you say you call him?'

'Piran. He comes from a stud in Cornwall, and his name means "dark"—rather appropriate for his colouring,' Rachel said softly, running her fingers through Piran's jet-black mane at the same time as Diego reached out to stroke the horse. His hand brushed against hers and she caught her breath at the brief touch of his warm skin, and then blushed furiously at the sudden gleam in his eyes that told her he had noticed her reaction to him.

His voice was so gravelly that it seemed to rumble from deep in his massive chest as he spoke again. 'So…the horse is Piran…and his rider is…?'

'Rachel Summers,' she answered briskly. She was head groom at Hardwick Polo Club, and it was likely that she would be in charge of Diego's horses at the upcoming polo match, where he would be the star guest. She wanted him to think she was a professional and experienced stable-hand, not a simpering idiot. She unfastened the strap under her chin and removed her riding hat. 'And you are Diego Ortega,' she said politely. 'Everyone here at Hardwick is excited about your visit, Mr Ortega.'

Dark eyebrows winged upwards and Rachel cringed. Why hadn't she said *everyone has been looking forward to your visit* or *talking about your visit*—instead of using the word 'excited'? She sounded like a naïve teenager and Diego must have thought so too because he gave her an amused smile.

'In the same way that the meaning of Piran suits your horse's colouring, I see that your name matches the shade of your hair. It is the colour of ripened wheat in mid-summer, Miss Summers,' he murmured, his eyes drawn to the wisps of gold curls that framed her face and the long braid that had slipped forwards over one shoulder. She was tiny—probably not more than a couple of inches over five feet tall—and when he had lifted her in his arms she had weighed next to nothing. Remarkably, she seemed relatively unscathed by her fall, although he could tell she was in pain around her ribs. But, despite her delicate appearance, she was as feisty and spirited as one of the prize colts from his stud at the Estancia Elvira, back home in Argentina.

'You look as though you are barely out of high school,' he drawled, his mouth twitching when she glared at him. 'How old are you?' he asked her.

'Twenty-two,' Rachel snapped, drawing herself up and wishing heartily that she was six inches taller. She knew she looked younger than her age and, as she rarely bothered to spend more time on her appearance than it took to wash her face and braid her hair, she accepted that it was her own fault Diego Ortega had probably mistaken her for a teenager. She did not care about his opinion of her looks, she told herself irritably, but she was proud of her riding skills and she was incensed that he had questioned her ability to control Piran.

She was breathing hard, her chest lifting and falling erratically, and she felt a jolt of shock when Diego's dark eyes trailed slowly over her body and focused deliberately on her breasts. Rachel swallowed and reminded herself that there was nothing much beneath her shirt to excite him. Riding was more than just her passion—since she was a teenager it had been an obsession that exceeded any vague interest in her appearance, and it had never bothered her that she had failed to develop a big bust. Now, for the first time in her life, she wished she looked more feminine and possessed curves rather than boyishly slender hips and a couple of minuscule bumps that did not require the support of a bra.

Diego's gaze caused the tiny hairs on Rachel's body to stand on end. Her legs suddenly felt weak and her breath seemed to be trapped in her chest—the same feeling she'd experienced a few moments ago when Piran had thrown her and she had struggled to her feet—winded and wobbly and strangely light-headed.

During her adolescence she had been so busy with her riding that she'd had no time for boys, and although she'd had a couple of relationships since she had left school they had quickly petered out through a lack of interest on her part. Diego Ortega was nothing like the men she had dated—and he was looking at her in a way that no man had ever done before. Her experience of the opposite sex might be limited, but she sensed Diego's interest. Some primal instinct inside her recognised the chemistry between them, and she could not restrain the little shiver of awareness that ran down her spine.

Diego's eyes narrowed. Rachel wasn't wearing a bra—he could clearly make out the darker flesh of her nipples—and as he watched they hardened into tight little peaks that jutted provocatively towards him. Heat surged through him, shocking him with its intensity. He hadn't felt this aroused for years. He did not understand why he was so acutely aware of her but, to his intense irritation, his heart was pounding and his jeans suddenly felt uncomfortably tight.

It was time for him to move, to break out of the sensual web that entrapped them both. A glance at his watch warned him that he should return to the Hall and change in time for dinner with the Earl and Lady Hardwick and their attractive but tediously overeager daughter, Felicity. He wondered if the idiot son who had nearly caused a serious accident would be present. He certainly intended to inform the Earl that he would not permit noisy motorbikes to be ridden near to the thoroughbred polo ponies he had been invited to Hardwick Polo Club to train.

His eyes strayed back to Rachel Summers's face and focused on her soft mouth, his stomach clenching when he imagined crushing those moist lips beneath his and exploring her with his tongue. She would taste as sweet as a light summer wine, and she would respond to him willingly—he noted how her eyes were now the colour of wood-smoke, her pupils dilated with sensual promise.

She could prove an interesting diversion over the next couple of months, he mused idly. He wondered who she was. He knew that the aristocratic Hardwick family had many off-shoots, and he assumed that Rachel must be a relative.

'Are you staying up at the Hall?' he demanded abruptly, forcing himself to step away from her.

'Earl Hardwick isn't in the habit of inviting his stable-hands to live in,' Rachel replied dryly. 'Not even his head groom.'

'So you work here.' Diego frowned. 'Do you own Piran?' He knew that most yards paid low wages, but the stallion was a thoroughbred and must have cost several thousand pounds.

'No, I have him on loan. His owner is Peter Irving, from the farm adjoining the Hardwick estate. Peter used to be a world-class showjumper, and he's my sponsor.'

'Irving—the name is familiar.'

'Three times Olympic gold medallist and top rider with the British Equestrian team for many years. Peter is my inspiration,' Rachel explained.

Diego caught the note of fierce determination in her voice and glanced at her curiously. 'You hope to be selected for the British team?'

'The next Olympics are my dream,' Rachel admitted, blushing and wondering why on earth she had revealed her life's ambition to a man she had never met before. She had never told anyone, apart from Peter Irving, of her hopes of competing at the highest level—not her friends, and certainly not her family. Since her parents had divorced when she was nine, they had both been too wrapped up in their lives with their new partners and children to take much interest in her, and the few times she had mentioned her riding to her mother it had led to the old argument about getting a proper job, somewhere decent to live rather than an old caravan, and a boyfriend.

'The Olympics are a long way off,' she murmured. 'For now I'm working hard in the hope of being picked for the team for the European championships next year. Peter and Earl Hardwick both think I have a good chance. The Earl has been very supportive of my career,' she added. He allows me to stable Piran here, and he always gives me time off to go to competitions. The facilities at Hardwick are excellent, and working here is a fantastic experience.'

'But not quite so fantastic when your horse refuses a jump,' Diego said dryly, his sharp gaze noting how she had crossed her arms over her chest and was surreptitiously rubbing her ribs. 'I'll ride Piran back to the stables for you.'

Without giving Rachel time to argue, he deftly adjusted the stirrups and swung into the saddle with a lithe grace and expertise. Piran did not usually take to strangers but, to Rachel's annoyance, he stood as docile as a lamb while Diego spoke to him in Spanish. The deep-timbred voice was strangely hypnotic; Piran's ears pricked up and he whinnied—almost as if he were talking back, although that was just fanciful imagination, Rachel told herself irritably. It was a pity that the Argentinian horseman did not have such a soothing effect on her. She felt decidedly rattled, and she knew it was not only because of the fall.

She opened the paddock gate and Diego took Piran through, but then halted and waited for her. 'I still think I should call a doctor,' he said, his mouth thinning when he noted how she winced with every step she took. 'You're as pale as a ghost and clearly in agony.'

'I'm just bruised, that's all,' Rachel argued stubbornly.

Diego gave her a hard stare. 'You're going to be black and blue and you'll ache tomorrow. To be on the safe side, you shouldn't ride for the next week.'

'Are you kidding?' Rachel looked scandalised. 'I've got a competition coming up and I'm going to take Piran round the course again tomorrow. He'd have managed that last fence fine if he hadn't been startled by the bike.'

Diego let out a curse, torn between impatience and admiration at her mulish determination. 'You are the most argumentative woman I have ever met, Miss Summers.' He moved before Rachel could guess his intention, and she gave a startled cry when he reached down and lifted her effortlessly onto Piran's back, placing her at the front of the saddle and clicking his tongue so that the horse immediately began to walk. One arm remained around her, holding her against his chest, while he held the reins in his other hand and controlled the stallion with impressive ease.

Attempting to scramble down would be futile, Rachel acknowledged as she stared at Diego's muscular forearms. She would just have to sit still until they reached the stable block, but she absolutely would not give in to the temptation to relax and lean her head against his chest. He was too close as it was, and the feel of his hard thighs pressing against her bottom seemed shockingly intimate. She was agonisingly aware of him—of the heat that emanated from him and the sensual musk of his cologne mixed with another subtle scent that was excitingly male and utterly intoxicating.

She was thankful when they reached the yard. Diego dismounted first and then carefully lifted her down. He seemed to think she was the rag doll he had described when he had witnessed her flying out of the saddle, she thought irritably as he strode into the barn, still holding her in his arms. His heart was beating steadily beneath her ear, but hers was thudding erratically and she was supremely conscious of his hands holding her beneath her knees and around the upper part of her body so that his fingers brushed lightly against the side of her breast.

She was pink-cheeked when he sat her down on a hay bale, and she glared at him when he leaned over her to prevent her from jumping to her feet. 'I need to see to Piran,' she said angrily.

'I'll ask one of the other grooms to rub him down. Every breath you take is agony—I can see it in your eyes, even if you are too stubborn to admit it,' Diego said grimly.

Rachel stared at his hard-boned face and it slowly dawned on her that she had finally met someone whose determination to have his own way matched her own. 'I've told you I'm fine,' she muttered. 'And Piran doesn't like anyone else to groom him.'

'Well, he's going to have to get used to it because I don't want to see you around these stables until you've had your ribs X-rayed and been thoroughly checked over by a doctor. My chauffeur, Arturo, will drive you to the hospital,' Diego informed her coolly. 'I would take you myself, but Lady Hardwick is giving a dinner party this evening—and I believe I'm the star guest,' he added dryly.

'Don't waste your breath arguing with me, Miss Summers,' he warned, placing his finger beneath her chin and exerting gentle pressure so that she had no option but to shut her mouth and swallow the angry words that were bursting to escape. 'I will be in charge of the stables for the duration of my stay at Hardwick Hall, and I refuse to have anyone working here who can't pull their weight. If you've broken your ribs, or sustained other injuries today, you'll be a liability I can do without.'

Unfazed by her furious expression, he smiled, revealing his gleaming white teeth that contrasted with his bronzed skin. 'I can't keep on calling you Miss Summers all summer—can I, Rachel?'

His voice had altered, and was now as thick and sensuous as molten honey, but Rachel was determined not to be impressed. Clearly he was an outrageous flirt, as well as the most arrogant man she had ever met, and she was furious with her treacherous body for responding to him. She was aware of a tingling sensation in her breasts and a shocking yearning for him to push her down into the hay, lower himself onto her and kiss her like she had never been kissed before.

'What do you mean by "all summer"?' she croaked. 'I know you're here for the polo tournament, but surely you'll be going back to Argentina straight afterwards.'

Diego shook his head, his smile widening at Rachel's look of dismay. 'As a matter of fact, I usually spend a couple of months—when it is winter in Argentina—at my polo school just outside New York. But this year the Earl has invited me to Hardwick to train the polo ponies.

'So you see, Rachel,' he drawled softly, moving his finger from under her chin and gently tracing the shape of her lips with his thumb pad, 'for the next month or so I will be your boss, and you will have to abide by my rules. Go to the hospital with Arturo, get yourself checked over, and when you can come back to me with a clean bill of health you will be welcome here. Until then, if I catch so much as a strand of your pretty blonde hair near Piran's loose box, there will be trouble. *Entiendes?*'

There was a hint of steel behind his mocking tone that warned Rachel he would be a dangerous man to cross. Incensed by his high-handedness, she jerked her head away, disgusted to find that she was trembling. The feather-light caress of his thumb over her lips had been shockingly intimate, and the idea that she would be working for him over the summer was downright disturbing.

'Earl Hardwick personally appointed me as head groom, and I'm sure he'll have something to say when I tell him you've banned me from doing my job,' she said furiously.

'The Earl had a hard job persuading me to come to

Gloucestershire rather than New York, and I think you'll find
that he'll go along with anything *I* say,' Diego replied with a
breathtaking arrogance that made Rachel itch to slap him.
'Besides, you are not banned, Rachel. I am very much looking
forward to working with you once I am assured that you
suffered no serious injuries today. I have great plans for
Hardwick Polo Club, and I have a feeling that you and I will
be spending a lot of time together.'

The sensuous gleam in his eyes was unmistakable, and a
quiver ran down Rachel's spine. She wanted to jump up and
tell him to get lost—tell him that she'd rather work for the
devil than him. But she couldn't move. For one thing, her ribs
were seriously painful—but the real reason, she acknowledged dismally, was that she was trapped by his magnetism
and utterly captivated by his raw masculinity. He was the most
potently virile man she had ever met; she could not tear her
eyes from his sensual mouth and when he lowered his head
slowly towards her, she ceased thinking, almost ceased
breathing, her heart hammering with frantic excitement when
it seemed that he was going to kiss her.

To her intense disappointment, he did not. Instead, he
straightened up abruptly and moved away from her, giving her
a mocking smile that added to her humiliation.

'Wait here for Arturo,' he ordered. He strode across the barn
and halted in the doorway to glance back at her. 'It promises
to be an interesting summer, don't you think, Rachel?' he
taunted softly.

CHAPTER TWO

To Rachel's relief an X-ray showed that she had not broken any bones when Piran had thrown her, but her ribs and shoulder were badly bruised and the doctor was adamant that she should not ride for a few days.

'I doubt you'll be able to move tomorrow,' he told her as he handed her a prescription for strong painkillers. 'Take two of these twice a day, and if I were you I'd go to bed and stay there.'

It was the most ridiculous suggestion Rachel had ever heard. She had never spent a day in bed in her life, and as far as she was concerned the fact that she hadn't suffered any fractures meant that she would be fit to work at the stables tomorrow.

But the following morning she woke in agony and the sight of her purple bruises forced her to accept that she was in no fit state to ride her bicycle up to the stables, muck out loose boxes and then spend the morning exercising the horses.

Besides, even if she managed to get to the stables, Diego Ortega was likely to send her straight home again. The Argentinian was the most arrogant individual she had ever met. Infuriatingly, he was also the sexiest man she had ever laid eyes on, she acknowledged grimly. She cringed when she remembered how she had been so mesmerised by him that she had stared at him, hoping he would kiss her, and his amused smile had told her that he had known exactly what she was thinking.

The day dragged endlessly, but fortunately the painkillers worked well and by early evening Rachel was feeling less like she had been trampled on by a herd of bulls and was bored of her enforced isolation. One of the other stable-hands sent her a text saying that Diego had returned to the Hall, where he was staying as a guest of Earl Hardwick. He was unlikely to visit the stables again tonight, Rachel decided as she cycled through the woods to the Hardwick estate, wincing every time she hit a pothole on the path.

Piran was gratifyingly pleased to see her. From his gleaming coat she guessed that someone must have groomed him, but she gave him another brush and fed him a couple of peppermints, and did not notice she had company until a figure came up silently behind her.

'Jasper, you'll give me a heart attack if you creep up on me like that,' she snapped when a faint sound made her swing round and she almost collided with Earl Hardwick's son and heir. 'It's a pity you weren't so quiet on your bike yesterday,' she muttered, feeling the same uneasy tension that always gripped her when she was alone with Jasper. The young Englishman was reputedly one of the most eligible bachelors among the landed gentry and, with his blonde hair flopping onto his brow, Rachel could see why women might be attracted to him. But he did nothing for her, and she hated the way he looked at her as though he were mentally undressing her.

'Yeah, I heard Piran threw you when you were jumping him yesterday.' Jasper lounged in the stable doorway, blocking Rachel's path so that she instinctively stepped backwards away from him.

'It was your fault, not his. The noise of your bike scared him. I wish you wouldn't ride it near the paddock.'

Jasper gave a careless shrug. 'It's my land—or it will be one day. You know, it would pay you to be nice to me, Rachel,' he said with a sly smile, reaching out and running his finger down her cheek. 'One day I'm going to be very rich—as long as my dear papa doesn't blow the family fortune on the polo club. God knows how much he's had to fork out to persuade Diego Ortega to come here and share his "expertise",' he added petulantly. 'Ortega is already a multimillionaire, and the money the old man's paying him could have gone on increasing my paltry allowance.'

'Mr Ortega is reputed to be one of the best trainers in the world,' Rachel murmured. 'And his appearance at the Hardwick Polo Tournament has trebled ticket sales, which must be good for the club.'

'Ortega is a notorious playboy,' Jasper said sulkily, clearly resenting Rachel's defence of him. And why *had* she spoken up for Diego when the first thing he had done since his arrival had been to ban her from the stables? she wondered irritably. 'My sister was all over him like a rash at dinner last night,' Jasper added sneeringly. 'Don't tell me you've fallen for his smarmy charm too?'

'Of course not,' she replied quickly; perhaps too quickly because Jasper stared at her intently and she felt herself blush. She could not bear for Jasper of all people to guess the effect that Diego had on her and so she added, 'From my brief meeting with Diego Ortega, I found him to be the most objectionable man I've ever met and, like you, I'll be glad to see the back of him.'

'Is that so, Rachel? How disappointing. I had such high hopes for our relationship,' a familiar, heavily accented voice drawled mockingly behind her. Rachel gasped and jerked her head round to see Diego strolling in through the doors of the stable block. 'Our working relationship, of course,' he added, giving Jasper Hardwick a bland smile when the young Englishman glowered at him.

Diego turned his attention back to Rachel, and she felt a fluttering sensation in her stomach as her eyes clashed with his gleaming amber gaze. He had obviously changed for dinner and looked stunningly handsome in tailored black trousers and a white silk shirt. Presumably he would don a tuxedo and bow tie before dinner with the Hardwicks, but for now his shirt was open at the throat, revealing his golden skin.

'I'm afraid you'll be seeing a lot of me over the next few weeks—back and front,' he said sarcastically, while she stared at the floor and wished a trapdoor would miraculously open beneath her feet. 'Earl Hardwick has challenged me to turn Hardwick Polo Club into a top sporting venue—and I can never resist a challenge,' he murmured silkily, his eyes focused on Rachel's flushed face.

He glanced dismissively at Jasper. 'I'm afraid you will no longer be able to ride your motorbike around the estate. I'll be doing some intensive training with the polo ponies and I don't want to waste my time calming them down after you've terrified them. Your thoughtless actions yesterday caused Rachel's accident, and it was sheer luck the outcome wasn't more serious.'

An angry flush stained Jasper's face. 'It's not my fault Rachel can't control her horse,' he said sullenly. 'Everyone knows Piran is too strong for her.' He gave Diego a look of active dislike. 'You can't tell me what to do. My father…'

'Your father agrees with me that the bike should be banned from anywhere near the stables and practice paddocks,' Diego interrupted with a quiet authority in his tone that brought another wave of colour to Jasper's face. 'Miss Summers's riding skills are not in question. I was watching her yesterday, and in my opinion she is an excellent horsewoman.'

Rachel blushed at the unexpected praise. Jasper glanced furiously from her to Diego and swore viciously before he swung round and stormed out of the stables. In the silence that fell after his departure Rachel felt her tension rise and she busied herself with putting Piran's grooming brushes away.

'He may be a member of the British aristocracy but he's a charmless individual, isn't he?' Diego drawled. 'But perhaps you don't think so, Rachel? Did you arrange to meet Hardwick here, when you knew the other grooms would have finished work and the two of you would be alone?'

Stunned by the accusation, she spun round and saw that his amber eyes were coldly assessing her. 'Of course not,' she denied sharply. 'Why would I? I'm not the slightest bit interested in Jasper.'

Diego stepped into the loose box and patted Piran. 'Well, he's interested in you,' he said harshly. 'A word of advice, *querida*—don't flirt with Hardwick unless you intend to follow it through. He wants you badly, and it's not a good idea to lead him on.'

'I wasn't *flirting* with him!' Rachel's eyes flashed with temper. 'He must have seen me arrive here and followed me into the stables.' She trailed to a halt, remembering how Diego had expressly banned her from visiting the stables. 'I came to see Piran, not to ride him,' she muttered and then, as her temper sparked again, added, 'although the X-rays were clear. I didn't break any bones yesterday, and there's no reason why I can't ride.'

'Apart from the doctor's recommendation that you take a break from riding for a few days—Arturo overheard your conversation at the hospital,' Diego murmured dryly, feeling a mixture of amusement and impatience when she glared at him. She was infuriatingly stubborn—a trait they shared, he acknowledged. He understood her obsession for riding and her addiction to the adrenalin boost when she took her horse over the jumps. She clearly pushed herself to the limits, just as he did on the polo field, but he wondered what demons drove her and made her careless of her safety—as his demons drove him to take risks which had taken him to the top of his sport, and on several occasions within a whisker of the grave.

He was torn between wanting to shake some sense into her and kiss the mutinous line of her mouth until she parted her lips and allowed him to push his tongue between them. He was irritated by the effect she had on him. Yesterday he had thought she would be an interesting diversion while he was staying at Hardwick, but after spending a restless night when he'd been unable to dismiss her from his mind he had decided that she was a complication he could do without. He had confidently assumed that when he saw her again he would have his inconvenient attraction to her under control, but as soon as he'd walked into the stables and felt his heart jolt at the sight of her he had been forced to admit that his aware-ness of her had not lessened.

Her hair was the colour of spun gold, falling to halfway down her back. He wanted to run his fingers through the thick, silky mass and then pull her into his arms so that her hips cradled the hard evidence of his arousal. His body was as taut as an over-strung bow and he felt an overwhelming urge to tumble her down in the hay, but instead he called on all his willpower and stepped out of Piran's loose box.

'As you can see, Piran is fine, and he gave me no trouble when I groomed him earlier.' He followed Rachel out of the loose box. 'I'll drive you home. I understand you live at Irving's farm.'

'Yes, but there's no need for you to give me a lift—I cycled here.' Rachel nodded towards her bike, propped up against the barn wall. 'It's quicker for me to ride through the woods.'

'I want to discuss the horses I've brought over from Argentina for the polo tournament. If you are going to oppose everything I say, I will have to seriously question whether I can have you working here,' Diego snapped.

Was he threatening to sack her? Rachel chewed on her lip as panic surged through her. How could she admit that her reluctance to sit next to him in the close confines of the sleek silver sports car she could see parked in the yard was due to her acute awareness of him? But he gave her no further opportunity to speak and was already striding out of the barn. She hurried after him and when he held open the car door she slid into the passenger seat and stared determinedly ahead, her senses flaring when he sat behind the wheel and she inhaled the exotic scent of his aftershave.

'You were going to tell me about your horses,' she murmured tentatively when he had driven almost to the boundary of the Hardwick estate in a taut silence that played havoc with her nerves. Diego exhaled deeply, as if he too was aware of the prickling tension between them, but then proceeded to give her detailed information about his polo ponies. Rachel listened intently so that it was a surprise when the car came to a halt and she realised that they had turned into the farm.

'I've left notes about feeds and medical histories, et cetera in the tack room. You can read through them when you come back to work after the weekend,' he said in a tone that brooked no argument about when he would allow her back to the stables.

'Fine. Well, I'll see you next week then,' Rachel replied flatly, wondering how she was going to survive for three long days without riding. The prospect of not seeing Diego for days had nothing to do with the deflated feeling that had settled over her, she told herself firmly.

'Before you go…these are for you.' He reached behind his seat and handed her a huge bouquet of yellow roses, his mouth curving into a smile at her expression of stunned surprise. 'To wish you a speedy recovery,' he explained. 'When I visited the florist's the colour reminded me of your bright hair—and the sharp thorns were a painful reminder of your prickly nature,' he added dryly, showing her several deep scratches on his hand. 'I almost bled to death removing them.'

'I don't mean to be prickly; I'm just used to doing things for myself and making my own decisions, that's all,' Rachel mumbled, burying her face in the scented blooms because she could not bring herself to meet Diego's gaze. Unaccountably, her eyes filled with tears and she blinked fiercely to dispel them. She wondered what he would say if she revealed that she had never been given flowers in her life—and then wondered where on earth she was going to put them when she did not possess a vase.

She sensed he was waiting for her to say something, and forced herself to speak. 'They're beautiful. Thank you.'

'You're welcome.' Diego paused, and wondered impatiently why he felt as edgy as a teenager on a first date. Rachel was a stable-hand, with an attitude problem and a sharp tongue—not the sort of woman he would usually be interested in. But he was intrigued by her and as he watched her tongue dart out to moisten her lips the tug of desire that had kept him awake for half the night intensified. 'I was hoping they would persuade you to invite me in and offer me a cup of coffee.'

Rachel glanced at him, caught the unmistakable sensual gleam in his amber eyes and stared back at the golden bouquet, her heart beating very fast. It was only coffee, she reminded herself, and it seemed churlish to refuse when he had presented her with two dozen roses. 'You're welcome to come in for coffee. But I don't live at the farmhouse. I live up there.'

Following her gaze, Diego restarted the engine and drove up the track that wound out of the farmyard and through a small copse of trees, his brows lowering in a frown when the track ended at a small shabby caravan nestled in the shade of a towering oak tree. 'You don't seriously expect me to believe you live in *that*?'

'And the coffee is cheap instant,' Rachel said sweetly. 'Welcome to my home, Mr Ortega.' While Diego stared out of the windscreen in patent disbelief, she jumped out of the car and unlocked the caravan, the heat that had built up inside hitting her as she pushed open the door. He had probably changed his mind about the coffee, she decided, trying to ignore her disappointment as she rummaged around in the cupboard under the sink, searching for a suitable vessel to hold the roses. She had unearthed a couple of jam jars when he climbed up the steps, ducking his head as he stepped through the door and instantly seeming to dominate the cramped space.

He glanced around the interior of the caravan and Rachel gave a silent groan when his eyes fell on the bed, which she had left down this morning because her shoulder had hurt too much to pack it away.

'It's what an estate agent might call a compact residence,' she said brightly. 'When the bed is folded away there's actually a surprising amount of room—for me, anyway,' she added when she glanced up and saw that Diego's head was brushing the ceiling.

'This can't be your permanent home.' He could not disguise his shock at her living conditions. 'You just camp out here during the summer—right?'

'No, I moved in here when I was seventeen, after my mother married for the third time and my twin half-sisters were born.'

Diego's brows rose. 'Family life sounds complicated.'

'Believe me, it is. I went to live with my father for a while, but he and his new wife had also just had a baby and it was easier for everyone when Peter Irving offered me the caravan.'

Rachel's voice was carefully controlled, giving no hint of

how she had resented feeling like a spare part in her parents' lives—unwanted, apart from being an occasional babysitter to her various half brothers and sisters. She had spent most of her childhood being passed between her mother and father, but she often thought that the bitter custody battle they had fought over her had been more about them trying to score points off each other than because either of them had actually wanted her to live with them.

It had been a far from idyllic childhood, and by the age of twelve she had been fiercely independent—getting up early every morning to do a paper round to pay for her riding lessons. She preferred horses to people and, after witnessing her parents' various failed marriages, she was adamant that she never wanted to get married or be reliant on another human being.

'The caravan is sound and dry, although it does shake a bit in strong wind,' Rachel admitted as she spooned coffee granules into the two least chipped mugs she could find. 'But it's got all the basic amenities—a shower, and Peter rigged up a generator to provide me with electricity. I can't afford to rent a house,' she explained when Diego gave her a look that said he seriously questioned her sanity. 'Property is very expensive around here, and everything I earn goes on Piran's upkeep and competition fees.'

Diego noted that the caravan might be small and old, but it was immaculately clean. The collection of china horses arranged on the shelf above the cooker were free from dust, and on the miniature kitchen worktop stood a jar filled with wild daisies. Rachel's home was as unconventional and dainty as its occupant, and he felt like a giant who had somehow squeezed himself into a doll's house.

He would drink the coffee and then leave, he decided, shaking his head when she offered milk and sugar, and grimacing when he took a sip of the foul black liquid she handed him. He didn't know why he hadn't simply dropped her off at the farm entrance.

His eyes strayed to her slender figure and her pert derrière, moulded by her jeans, and he felt a tightening sensation in his groin. He was used to dating sophisticated socialites who wouldn't be seen dead in anything other than designer labels, but there was something wholesome and incredibly sexy about Rachel's scrubbed face and simple clothes. He wondered if she was aware that the sunlight streaming in through the window made her shirt semi-transparent. He could clearly see the outline of her breasts, and liquid heat surged through his veins.

He took a gulp of the hot coffee and felt it scald the back of his throat. 'Do you live here alone?' he asked shortly.

Rachel glanced around the cramped living space, her brows lifting expressively. 'There's barely enough room for me, let alone anyone else,' she murmured.

'So, no boyfriend sharing your bunk?'

'No! I told you, I'm training hard in the hope of being picked for the British Equestrian team. I don't have time for boyfriends.' Much less the desire for one, she thought, her mouth firming. But that did not mean she was completely oblivious to men, or at least this man. She could not tear her eyes from Diego. He looked faintly incongruous, standing in her tiny caravan in his formal black trousers and beautifully tailored shirt. He reminded her of one of those impossibly gorgeous male models from a glossy magazine—and he should be somewhere exotic like Monte Carlo or Rio, not a field in rural Gloucestershire. But he *was* here, with her, and he was looking at her in a way that was making her heart race and her face feel hot.

She should have suggested that they drink their coffee outside, she thought frantically. But her garden furniture con- sisted of two upended feed buckets, and she could not picture suave Diego Ortega sprawling on the grass. The atmosphere inside the caravan suddenly seemed to be charged with electricity and she was agonisingly aware of his hard, lean body standing inches from her. She held her breath when he closed the gap between them, and her eyes darted nervously from his chest up to his face and focused helplessly on his sensual mouth. Her heart seemed to stop beating when he slid his hand beneath her chin and lowered his face so close to hers that she could see the tiny lines that fanned out from the corners of his eyes.

'What…what do you think you're doing?' she demanded, dismayed that her voice sounded so weak and breathless when she wanted to give the impression that she was in complete control of the situation.

'I think I am going to kiss you,' Diego drawled, patently amused by the question. 'In fact, I know it, *querida*—just as I know that you want me to.'

Rachel's heart was jerking painfully beneath her ribs. 'I don't,' she said desperately, her cheeks flaming as she recalled how she had silently urged him to kiss her in the stables yesterday.

'Liar,' he said with gentle mockery which disguised the tension that gripped him. Her skin was almost translucent, her peaches-and-cream complexion as exquisite as a work of art, and her mouth, pink and moist and slightly parted, was a temptation he could no longer resist. The sexual awareness between them was white-hot—and mutual. Rachel might try to deny it, but her eyes were huge with excitement, the invitation in their depths unmistakable. He hesitated for a second, wanting to savour the anticipation, but as he brushed his lips over hers in that first explorative caress and felt her tentative response, hunger coursed through his veins and with a muffled groan he crushed her mouth beneath his and kissed her with unrestrained passion.

It did not cross Rachel's mind to resist him—and, even if her brain clung to some last vestige of sanity, her body had a will of its own and demanded her complete and utter surrender. Diego's lips were warm and firm, sliding over hers with such erotic skill that she simply melted against him and opened her mouth, her heart thudding in her chest at the first bold thrust of his tongue.

Nothing in her life had prepared her for the storm of sensations that swept through her. She had never experienced true desire before; not this desperate need for something she did not even understand but which raged inside her as wild and dangerous as a bush fire.

Perhaps her subconscious mind had deliberately subdued her normal sexual urges? she wondered vaguely, finding it hard to think straight when Diego slid his arms around her and drew her against the hard wall of his chest.

But now those urges had been awakened, and she could not control them. The pressure of his mouth on hers was as addictive as a drug, and she wanted more. She placed her hands on his chest and felt the heat of his body through his silk shirt. What would it be like to feel his bare skin pressed against hers?

But, before she could give in to her heated fantasy, Diego suddenly dropped down so that he was sitting on the edge of her makeshift bed and pulled her onto his lap.

'That's better, hmm…?' he murmured against her mouth, before he kissed her again, moving his lips on hers with undisguised passion which sent a shiver of need down her spine. She was trembling, every nerve-ending tingling, and when he brushed his hand lightly over her breast she shivered in anticipation of a more intimate caress.

'Do you like that, *querida*?' His voice was a husky growl, but Rachel was beyond giving an answer, the feelings he was arousing in her were new and wondrous and she was swept away to a place where nothing mattered except that Diego should continue to kiss her and touch her. She heard him mutter something in his own language, and was vaguely aware of his fingers gently stroking her waist before inching up towards her ribs once more. The bright sunlight streaming through the window made her squint, and through her half closed eyes he seemed dark and forbidding—a stranger who had kissed her until she could not think straight.

As he gently increased the pressure of his caresses, Rachel suddenly drew in a sharp breath. Aware that her rapid intake of air had nothing to do with arousal, Diego quickly removed his hands before he gently pushed her shirt over her shoulder, revealing the fragile line of her collarbone—and the mass of purple bruises that contrasted starkly with her pale skin.

'Your injuries are worse even than I imagined,' he said harshly, the sound of his voice shattering the last of the sexual haze that had held Rachel a willing prisoner in his arms. The fire in her veins cooled as quickly as if he had thrust her beneath an ice-cold shower, leaving her feeling slightly sick. What had she been thinking, allowing a man she barely knew to kiss her, and touch her…?

Diego was staring at her bony shoulder with a look of undisguised horror, and she felt embarrassed that he was clearly repelled by her body. With a jerky movement that jolted her ribs and caused her to wince in pain, she snatched the edges of her shirt together to hide the offending bruises from his gaze. 'I'd like you to leave,' she said tightly. 'You've had your fun.'

'My fun?' Diego stiffened, his eyes narrowing on her flushed face.

Rachel was aware that she sounded abrupt to the point of rudeness, but she was dying of mortification as she recalled her wanton response to him. What must he think of her? She had made no attempt to stop him kissing her. The moment he had taken her in his arms, she had melted against him and kissed him back; and her soft moans of pleasure when he had caressed her must have sent out a message that she was his for the taking.

Since she was old enough to understand adult relationships, she had proudly announced that she would never act like her mother, lurching blindly between marriages and affairs with no thought to the consequences. She would never allow any man that kind of power over her, she'd stated confidently. Yet here she was, practically making love with a stranger just because he was the most gorgeous male she'd ever met.

'I don't know what you were expecting,' she snapped, taking her anger with herself out on him, 'but I am not the kind of woman who jumps into bed with a man five minutes after meeting him.'

'You could have fooled me,' Diego drawled, the warmth that had blazed in his amber eyes turning rapidly to an expression of icy arrogance. 'I was not expecting anything,' he snapped, furious with himself that he had come on to her like some callow youth. It was not his style. He always played it cool with women, and he had meant to stop after one brief kiss. Rachel's passionate response had blown him away, but he wasn't prepared to take all the blame. 'Do you seriously expect me to believe that if I hadn't stopped just then, you would have called a halt?' He gave a disbelieving laugh that sparked Rachel's temper. 'Don't kid yourself, Rachel. Your need was as great as mine—and still is,' he said coolly as he trailed his hand insolently down the front of her shirt and noted how her nipples jutted to attention.

He watched her cheeks flood with colour, and with an impatient movement he stood up and strode over to the door of the caravan, snatching oxygen into his lungs as he stared over the lush green English countryside. He was only going to be here for a few weeks, and he had a job to do that promised to be interesting. Rachel played an important role at Hardwick. He had learned from talking to the other grooms that she was highly regarded for her dedication to the horses and the polo club, and he needed to establish a good working relationship with her. The attraction between them was seriously inconvenient—but if Rachel could fight it then so could he.

'This was a mistake,' she said huskily. For some reason the discernible tremor in her voice tugged at Diego's insides. He turned his head and saw that she had buttoned her shirt right up to the neck. 'I wasn't expecting you to kiss me…and I admit I got carried away. I can't believe I fell for the "can I come in for coffee?" line,' she choked. Her eyes fell on the glorious yellow roses and she felt sick. 'Is that what the flowers were for—to soften me up for a quick sex session?'

'Of course not,' he grated, outraged at the accusation. She was making it sound as though she was some virginal innocent and he was an utter bastard who had cynically planned to seduce her, but neither was true. 'It was just a kiss,' he said coldly. 'I assure you I had no intention of asking you to jump into bed with me.'

It might have been 'just a kiss' to him, but for Rachel it had been the most devastatingly sensual experience of her life. Still, she would rather die than let him see how much he affected her, and she preferred to carry out a post-mortem of her behaviour away from his mocking gaze. 'Please go,' she said shakily. 'I think it would be best if we both forgot this…this…'

'Fascinating interlude?' Diego suggested sarcastically.

'Get out!' The glittering amusement in his eyes was the last straw and she clenched her fists and dared him—*dared* him—to say another word.

'I'm going.' He sauntered down the caravan steps and glanced back at her, his tone no longer mocking but quietly serious as he murmured, 'I agree we should try to forget the sexual chemistry that exists between us, Rachel. But I wonder if we can.'

CHAPTER THREE

THE heatwave, which had been unusual for early May, broke and on Monday morning Rachel walked up to the stables in the rain, dreading facing Diego again. Over the weekend she had come to the dismal conclusion that she had seriously overreacted. Of course he hadn't kissed her as a prelude to persuading her to sleep with him. He was a gorgeous playboy and a sporting hero who was frequently photographed in the tabloids in the company of beautiful models. He was hardly likely to have felt uncontrollable lust for a scruffy stable-girl.

His scathing dismissal of their kiss emphasised how unimportant he regarded the whole episode, but she had acted like a shocked virgin from a Victorian melodrama. No doubt that was because she was a shocked virgin, she acknowledged gloomily. Diego had made her feel things she had never felt before, and now she felt restless and unfulfilled.

She did not see him until later in the afternoon, when she and a few of the other grooms had been out exercising some of the polo ponies and gave them one last gallop back to the stables. Diego was wearing a knee-length black oilskin coat and matching wide-brimmed hat that shielded his face, but his height and the width of his shoulders made him instantly recognisable, and Rachel's heart lurched when she reined in her horse and they trotted into the yard.

'Are you sufficiently recovered from your accident to be riding?' he greeted her as he strode over and caught hold of her pony's bridle.

'I'm fine,' she replied automatically, ignoring the nagging pain in her ribs. Her eyes were drawn to his mouth, and she blushed as she recalled the tingling pleasure of his kiss. She saw something flicker in his eyes and hastily looked away from him. 'I'd better go and rub Charlie Boy down. He's covered in mud.'

'You both are,' Diego said dryly. He did not understand how he could possibly be turned on by Rachel when she was wearing a bulky waxed jacket and mud-spattered jodhpurs. He usually liked women to look feminine and alluring—as if they'd spent their days in the beauty parlour and came to him beautifully groomed and coiffed and dressed in exquisite couture gowns. Rachel looked as though she had rolled in every muddy puddle she'd come across but, to his self-disgust, he imagined undressing her slowly, layer by layer, until he exposed her slender, pale body.

'How are the bruises?' he asked roughly.

'Fading,' she mumbled, remembering how he had unfastened her shirt and discovered the ugly purple marks on her shoulder, and how the desire in his eyes had rapidly disappeared. What would he make of her now that the bruises were turning an unattractive greenish yellow? She would never know, she told herself firmly. She was never going to allow him to touch her again, let alone undress her—and, from the cool expression in his eyes, he obviously regretted the whole episode as much as she did.

'You could have taken another day off,' he murmured. 'I can see that your shoulder is still stiff.'

'It's fine—and I'm not used to sitting around doing nothing. I'm not the world's most patient patient,' she owned honestly.

Amusement glinted in his eyes at her understatement. 'No, I don't suppose you are. When you've seen to your horse I'll give you a lift home. I have to go into the village and the farm is on my way.'

'Oh, no, it's okay—I'm not going home just yet.'

He frowned. 'There's nothing more to do here today.'

'I want to take Piran over the jumps,' Rachel admitted reluctantly.

He shook his head. 'That's not a good idea. It's your first day back and you must be tired.' He had watched her on several occasions during the day, when she had been unaware of him, and he was astounded at how hard she worked. She was so petite, and the life of a stable-hand was physically demanding, but from the moment she had arrived at the stables early this morning she had taken on more than her fair share of the workload.

If Rachel was honest, she was worn out and ached all over, but her innate stubbornness rebelled at Diego's dictatorial tone. 'Olympic champions don't get to the top of their sport by giving in every time they're tired,' she said briskly. 'Piran and I both need all the practice we can get before our next competition.'

'*Santa Madre!* You are the most headstrong, argumentative…' Diego inhaled deeply, trying to control his temper. 'I understand your desire to succeed as a showjumper, but it's sheer folly to take unnecessary risks.'

'Jumping is a dangerous sport—as is polo,' Rachel said tightly. 'How can you warn me about taking risks when your whole career has been built on the fact that you consistently risk your safety when you play? I've watched footage of you competing in tournaments, and you ride with a crazy disregard for your safety—almost as if you've got a death-wish,' she added, her voice faltering when the hard gleam in Diego's eyes warned her that she had gone too far.

'Don't be ridiculous,' he snapped coldly. 'I've been at the top of my sport for the past ten years and I know what I'm doing.'

Rachel shrugged. 'Fine—let's agree that I won't give you advice on your sport, and you won't tell me how to do mine.'

Diego glared at the mutinous line of her mouth and was seriously tempted to kiss her into submission. She was as strong-willed and reckless as…as he had been at twenty-two, he owned grimly. She thought she was infallible, just as he had a decade ago, and he wanted to warn her that she wasn't—no one was.

Once he had been headstrong and impetuous, but it had been those traits that had caused his brother's death. Diego closed his eyes briefly, trying to stem the wave of pain that swept through him as he pictured Eduardo's lifeless body. Even after all this time the memories were agonising and the pain still raw. The ache in Diego's heart had never eased—nor had the belief that he had no right to experience happiness in his life when he had unwittingly caused Eduardo's accident.

Rachel was wrong about one thing; he brooded grimly as he watched her dismount and lead her pony into the stable. He did not have a death-wish—it was simply that his survival or otherwise was something that did not interest him unduly. He had spent the last ten years pushing himself to the limits and daring death to take him as it had taken his brother, and it was ironic that his recklessness had made him a national sporting hero in Argentina and a world renowned polo champion.

Hardwick Polo Tournament was always a popular event, but this year more tickets had been sold than usual because Diego Ortega would be playing for the home team. For the past two weeks Rachel had arrived at the stables at dawn and worked until dusk, helping to prepare the estate for the influx of twenty thousand visitors. Somehow she managed to fit in riding Piran. She'd felt apprehensive the first time she had taken him over the jumps after he had thrown her, and Diego's brooding presence at the edge of the paddock had only made things worse. But she forced herself to control her nerves—aware that Piran would pick up on her tension, and she was euphoric when he jumped the six foot fence with no problems.

She was less happy that Diego seemed to have appointed himself as her minder and turned up without fail every evening when she took Piran down to the practice paddock. His presence unsettled her. *He* unsettled her, she admitted when she watched him stride into the yard on the morning of the polo tournament. He looked breathtakingly handsome in the Hardwick team colours—a gold shirt, taupe jodhpurs and black leather boots. As usual the sight of him made her pulse-rate quicken and she blushed when he looked over at her, the slight smile on his lips telling her that he was aware that she had been staring at him.

She had developed a monumental crush on him, she acknowledged ruefully, feeling a shiver of excitement run the length of her spine when his gaze lingered on her. She worked with him closely every day and was finding it increasingly hard to hide her attraction to him. And it was not just her physical awareness of him. Watching him train the polo ponies, she had been impressed by his skill and patience, and his amazing affinity with horses. He was an outstanding horseman, and she knew she could learn a lot from him. She wished she could relax and chat to him as easily as the other stable-hands did, but she felt tongue-tied whenever he spoke to her, and was terrified he would guess how much she longed for him to kiss her again.

Diego had been chatting with the other members of the Hardwick team, but now he detached himself from the group and walked over to collect the first of the four horses he would ride during the match. 'Do you have a partner to escort you to the after-tournament party, Rachel?' he queried casually as he swung himself into the saddle.

He hadn't yet donned his hard hat and in the sunlight his hair gleamed like raw silk on his shoulders, blown back from his face by the breeze. Rachel's heart jolted beneath her ribs and her voice emerged as a strangled sound. 'Alex asked me to go with him,' she mumbled. Alex was another groom and one of her closest friends. She saw Diego glance across the yard to where the copper-haired young man was leading out a polo pony, and he gave a slight shrug.

'What a pity. I was hoping I could persuade you to partner me tonight.' He gave her a bland smile, but the expression in his eyes stole her breath. It was gone before she could define it—yet she was sure she had not mistaken the look of feral hunger in his gaze, and she felt a surge of gut-churning disappointment that she had missed her chance to attend the party with him.

But what chance did she realistically have with Diego? she brooded later as she watched him tear around the polo pitch, controlling his horse with awesome skill. He dominated the field, and she doubted there was a woman present among the spectators who was not bowled over by his stunning looks and blatant virility.

At the end of the tournament he was presented with the winner's trophy by Felicity Hardwick, who looked pink cheeked and flustered as she gave him a congratulatory kiss. Afterwards he posed for photos with the promotional glamour models, and as Rachel stared at the bevy of beautiful blondes crowded around him, and then glanced down at her mud-stained jodhpurs, she wondered why she had thought he could ever be interested in her. He was going back to Hardwick Hall for a champagne reception, but she still had hours of work to do at the stables. They were worlds apart, she accepted with a heavy heart, and for her own good she had to stop mooning over him like a lovesick teenager.

Dusk was falling by the time she returned to her caravan, and she could summon little enthusiasm for the party which Earl Hardwick gave every year for guests and staff of the polo club. But she had promised Alex she would go, and so she stripped out of her filthy clothes and squeezed into the tiny shower cubicle.

'You look fantastic,' Alex greeted her when he arrived to drive her to the party. 'You should dress up more often, Rache. I can't remember the last time I saw you in something other than jodhpurs.'

'I can hardly trip around the stables in a skirt and heels,' she pointed out. She felt ridiculously girly in her pink floral skirt and a silky chemise with delicate shoestring straps that left her shoulders bare. She had swept her hair up into a loose knot on top of her head, but it was so fine and silky that stray tendrils had already worked loose and framed her face. On an impulse, which she assured herself had nothing to do with the knowledge that Diego would be at the party, she was even wearing make-up—just a touch of mascara to darken her lashes and a pale pink gloss on her lips.

A huge marquee had been erected in the grounds of the Hardwick estate and the party was already in full swing when they arrived. Rachel's eyes were immediately drawn to Diego. Taller than everyone else in the room, his black tailored trousers and matching silk shirt emphasised his height and the breadth of his shoulders. With his dark hair falling onto his shoulders, and his gleaming olive skin, he was exotic and different, and other men paled into insignificance beside him.

She was not the only woman watching him, she noted moodily when she glanced around the marquee and saw that Felicity Hardwick and a gaggle of her aristocratic friends, all dressed in haute couture, were openly ogling him. Rachel instantly felt underdressed in her cheap skirt, which she'd bought from a market stall. Her arms ached from grooming fifteen polo ponies, and the evening suddenly seemed very flat. She was on her way over to the bar to tell Alex she was going home when Diego stepped into her path.

'Do you think your red-haired friend will object if I ask you to dance?' he murmured, his eyes gleaming with amusement and something else when Rachel's face flooded with colour.

'Alex and I are simply friends, and I'll dance with whoever I like,' she replied breathlessly, her heart racing as Diego caught her hand in his and slid his other arm around her waist.

'Then dance with me, *querida*,' he invited with a sultry smile that made her heart thud. 'You value your independence, don't you?' he commented, trying to focus on their conversation rather than the fire coursing through his veins when he drew Rachel's slender body against his thighs.

'More than anything,' she told him seriously. 'The most important lesson I learned from my mother's tangled love-life is that I don't want to be beholden to any man.'

She sounded so fierce that Diego's brows rose. 'Perhaps you have not yet found a man who excites you sufficiently that you would want to be beholden to him?'

'That's not likely to happen.' Rachel wondered what Diego would say if she admitted that *he* excited her unbearably. Since he had kissed her in her caravan they seemed to have been playing a waiting game where the sexual chemistry between them had simmered beneath the surface and they had both tried to ignore it. But the look in his eyes tonight told her that he was bored of the game. She could feel the tension in his body, and when he held her close so that her head rested on his chest she could hear the erratic beat of his heart and knew that it matched her own.

'What about marriage and children?' he queried curiously. 'Don't you want those?' Every woman he'd ever met had seemed to regard him as suitable husband material, and their first demand for commitment was invariably the point at which he ended a relationship. Rachel was a novelty in more ways than one, he brooded as he glanced down at her simple skirt and top and acknowledged that she looked sexier than any of the women at the party who were wearing designer outfits.

Rachel shrugged. 'I believe children deserve to have two parents who are committed to each other and, as I don't want to get married, I guess I won't have them. Perhaps I'll feel different in the future, but right now I don't have any maternal urges. I'd rather concentrate on my riding career.'

Diego's mouth curved into a smile that stole her breath. 'So, you are a free spirit and you can do whatever pleases you?'

'Yes.' The word escaped as a little gasp as he stroked his hand down to the base of her spine and exerted gentle pressure so that he brought her pelvis into direct contact with his. The hungry gleam in his eyes filled her with a feverish anticipation. Did he know how much he was pleasing her, holding her like this? How much she longed for him to lower his mouth to hers and kiss her as he had done two weeks ago?

He knew, she thought dreamily as their bodies swayed together in time with the music, one tune spilling into another so that she lost all sense of time and place and was conscious only of Diego—the hardness of his body and the subtle perfume of his aftershave, mingled with male pheromones that tantalised her senses. She didn't want to ever stop dancing, and felt a lurch of disappointment when the band announced they would be taking a break while the firework display took place. But, instead of releasing her, Diego kept his arm firmly around her waist as he led her outside and drew her to the edge of the crowd.

Starbursts of gold and silver shot across the sky and were reflected in the inky blackness of the lake. Rachel tilted her head to watch, supremely aware of Diego standing behind her, and she gave a little shiver when she felt him brush his lips down her neck in a feather-light caress.

The pyrotechnic display ended with a cascade of sparkling colours falling down to earth. There was a round of applause and, as the guests returned to the marquee, silence fell around them, a prickling, shimmering silence so intense that Rachel was aware of the faint, uneven whisper of her breath.

'It's not working, is it?' Diego murmured in her ear, his accent very pronounced and heart-stoppingly sexy.

Rachel turned to face him and shook her head, bemused by the question. 'What isn't?'

'Trying to ignore the hunger that is eating away at both of us,' he said softly.

She understood immediately, but understanding did not lessen her confusion. 'But you never gave any indication during the past two weeks that you wanted…' She broke off, her face flaming, and his smile widened into a predatory grin.

'You?' He finished her sentence for her. 'I promised myself that I would behave in a professional manner in the workplace. But that doesn't mean I have not secretly fantasised about barricading us in the hay barn and making love to you until we were both utterly sated.'

'Oh.' Rachel made a muffled sound, shocked not so much by his bluntness as the image in her head of him fulfilling his fantasy.

'Yes. *Oh*, Rachel.' Amusement lilted in his voice, but the expression in his eyes made her blood pound in her veins. 'The question is, *querida*—if we cannot ignore it, what are we going to do about it?'

His words hovered in the air between them, shredding her fragile composure. 'I don't know,' she whispered. But she did know, she acknowledged as every nerve-ending in her body tingled. He had aroused her sexual curiosity, and she wanted to explore the feelings he evoked in her, just as she wanted to explore the hard contours of his body and run her hands over his golden skin. There was no reason why she shouldn't go to bed with him. She was a single, independent woman who could live her life as she chose—but was he free?

'Are you involved with anyone at the moment?' she demanded baldly. She knew from what she'd read about him that Diego was seldom without female companionship!

'Definitely not.' Diego's eyes narrowed. 'Nor do I have any desire to be,' he told her firmly, needing to establish right away that he was not in the market for a relationship that demanded permanency or commitment. The past weeks had been purgatory as his desire for her had become a hungry monster that clamoured to be fed, and tonight, watching her dancing at the party in her floaty skirt which revealed her slender figure, he'd no longer been able to deny his fierce need. But, as with all his previous lovers—and there had been many, he owned unashamedly—a relationship with Rachel could only be on his terms.

'The party is almost over,' he said, flicking back the cuff of his dinner jacket and glancing at his Rolex. 'Do you want to come back with me—for coffee? Proper Argentinian coffee beans—' he tempted her with a smile '—not cheap powdered stuff.'

Rachel recalled his expression of disgust when he had sipped the coffee she had made him at her caravan. Diego was a millionaire and clearly never had to shop in discount supermarkets. It was a little thing, yet it emphasised the huge social divide between them. But, despite their different backgrounds, they were still just a man and a woman, and when passion had blazed between them two weeks ago the fact that she was a stable-girl and he was a wealthy world renowned polo player hadn't seemed to matter.

She could barely believe that he was asking her back—they both knew that the invitation was for more than coffee. With his stunning looks and blatant sex appeal he was spoilt for choice. He could have any woman he wanted. But the undisguised hunger in his eyes filled her with a fierce excitement that refused to listen to caution. Right now, Diego wanted her, and the knowledge made her tremble.

'All right,' she said shakily, but then paused as she remembered that he was staying at Hardwick Hall. 'I can't turn up at the Hall without an invitation from the Earl,' she murmured, wondering if Diego intended to smuggle her up to his room via the staff staircase.

'I am no longer the Hardwicks' house guest.' Diego ran his hands up her arms, savouring the feel of her satiny skin beneath his fingertips as he moved up to her shoulders and traced the fragile line of her collarbone. Every night since he had arrived in Gloucestershire, he had lain awake thinking about kissing her again, but now the waiting was over and he bent his head and brushed his mouth over hers, felt her tremble and wrapped his arms around her, aware that he couldn't kiss her as he wanted to yet.

'I like my own space, and I'm renting a cottage on the estate. It's situated in a very secluded part of the woods,' he added softly, grazing his lips over hers in a tantalising caress that promised so much more. 'I can guarantee we won't be disturbed all night.'

And if she left early in the morning, no one would know she had been there, Rachel realised, her excitement escalating once more now that her last nagging doubt had been dismissed. She would prefer not to be the subject of gossip and speculation among the estate staff.

'Well, then…' she murmured, her breath snagging in her throat when she glimpsed the predatory gleam in his eyes. Diego's mouth curved into a smile that made her pulse-rate accelerate. But, instead of kissing her again as she'd hoped, he caught hold of her hand and led her away from the marquee.

CHAPTER FOUR

DIEGO was staying in the old gamekeeper's cottage. The house was small and simply furnished, but Rachel barely noticed the décor when he ushered her inside and immediately pulled her into his arms. She couldn't quite believe she was here with Diego Ortega—internationally famous polo player and the man who had featured in the shockingly erotic fantasies she'd been having lately.

But her doubts were outweighed by a compelling certainty that this was somehow fated. She felt as though she had been waiting all her life for him, which was a dangerous thought, she acknowledged, because she was well aware that he would not be a part of her life for very long. She was under no illusions that Diego wanted anything more than sex with her—and perhaps he only wanted her for one night. But, far from being disappointed, she felt a sense of relief. She wasn't ready for a love affair; she valued her independence too much. Still, that didn't mean she had to live the life of a nun.

She found it difficult to think straight when he was sliding his fingertips lightly up and down her spine, and she could not restrain a little shiver when he brushed his lips along her collarbone and hovered over the pulse beating frenetically at the base of her throat.

'Would you like coffee, or a drink?' He eased away from

her and took the two steps necessary to cross the tiny kitchen. 'There's champagne…or champagne,' he said, his sultry smile making her heart flip. He wasn't joking, Rachel realised when she glanced inside the fridge and saw that it was devoid of any basic necessities and instead contained two magnums of champagne and a jar of caviar.

He popped the cork with the same familiarity as most people would open a carton of milk, filled two glasses and handed her one of them. Rachel already felt dizzy—as if the bubbles fizzing in the glass had somehow entered her bloodstream, and when she sipped the pale gold liquid it seemed to be an elixir that swept away her doubts. She wished he would kiss her, and he must have read her mind because he put down his glass with a deliberation that set her heart thudding.

'Come here.'

His eyes gleamed gold beneath his heavy lids. Tiger's eyes, Rachel thought as she moved towards him. He was powerful and dominant and a part of her was appalled at how easily he could control her, but when he snaked his arm around her waist and jerked her up against him she could think of nothing but the hardness of his thighs pressed against hers, and the tantalising warmth of his body beneath his black silk shirt.

He took the clip from her hair and threaded his hands through the mass of gold silk that rippled down her back before claiming her mouth in a searing kiss that was shockingly demanding. 'You are so tiny,' he murmured when he finally lifted his lips from hers and straightened up so that he was once more towering over her. 'And so very lovely.' His gut clenched as he stared down at her delicate heart-shaped face. He couldn't remember ever feeling this overpowering need for a woman, this heavy drumbeat of desire that seemed to throb through his entire body. He had watched her and waited for her for two long weeks, and anticipation had added a certain piquancy to his desire, but now he could not wait a moment longer to possess her. 'We will definitely be more comfortable horizontal, *querida*,' he muttered hoarsely.

Horizontal meant bed, Rachel thought shakily, feeling a frisson of nervous excitement as the enormity of what she was about to do sank in. But he gave her no time for second thoughts. She gasped when he lifted her up, and she had no option but to wind her legs around his hips and curl her arms around his neck as he strode through the living room and up the narrow staircase to his bedroom. His hands cupped her bottom and, as he mounted the stairs, the feel of his hard arousal nudging between her thighs was so intensely erotic that heat flooded through her and she felt a heavy sensation deep in her pelvis.

'You see, much more comfortable,' he said thickly as he deposited her on the big bed and immediately stretched out next to her. Rachel had a vague impression of an airy white-walled room with dark wood ceiling beams and the bed with its carved headboard and crisp white cotton sheets. But then Diego leaned over her and the stark hunger she glimpsed in his eyes before he brought his mouth down on hers drove every thought from her mind except that she was lying on a bed with the man she had secretly idolised even before she had met him in the flesh.

His tongue probed between her lips until, with a gasp, she parted them and he thrust deep into her mouth in a sensual exploration. It was mind-blowing and she responded to him helplessly, sliding her fingers into his thick, silky hair as he trailed his lips down her throat and then lower to the faint swell of her breasts. Rachel held her breath, waiting for him to slide the straps of her top down her arms, but instead he slanted his mouth over one taut nipple straining against the silky material and sucked her wetly until she twisted her hips restlessly and felt a flooding warmth between her thighs.

He transferred his mouth to her other breast, and the feel of his tongue laving her through the now wet silk heightened her senses and her need to a level that was almost unbearable. But when he drew the straps of her top over her shoulders she could not prevent herself from tensing. No man had ever seen her naked before and she suddenly felt shy and unsure. Diego had dated some of the world's most beautiful women, super-models with stunning figures. But she was thin and her breasts were unexcitingly small, and she squeezed her eyes shut to block out the disappointment she was sure she would see in his as she felt him tug her top down to her waist.

'*Perfecto…*' he said raggedly. 'You are exquisite, *querida*.'

Startled by his husky tone, her eyes flew open and she swallowed at the expression in his dark gaze. 'You don't have to lie,' she mumbled, colour stealing into her cheeks when he cupped one pale mound in his hand. 'I hate being skinny and shapeless.'

'Not shapeless,' he insisted as he stroked her soft flesh and watched in fascination as her nipple hardened into a provocative peak that seemed to beg for him to take it into his mouth. 'You are as delicate and fragile as a porcelain figurine, and so fine boned that I'm afraid I will crush you beneath me.'

She trembled at the image in her head of him covering her body with his and bearing his weight down on her. Would he take it slowly? A bubble of hysteria rose in her throat as she imagined his response if she asked him to be gentle with her. She knew instinctively that if she revealed she was a virgin he would refuse to make love to her, and she could not bear for him to reject her. Before she had met Diego, she had believed she must have a low sex drive as none of the men she'd dated stirred her. Now she knew she had been waiting for the right man, but she needed to prove that she was not like her mother, and she would not confuse lust with love. She wanted to have sex with Diego, but that was all she wanted, and she was in complete control of her emotions, she assured herself.

'You won't crush me, I'm stronger than I look,' she told him softly, running her hands over his chest and fumbling with his shirt buttons, trying to disguise the fact that her fingers were shaking. She pushed the black silk aside and stroked his bare chest, loving the feel of his satiny skin overlaid with a covering of dark hairs. She had never touched a man before, and she studied his rippling abdominal muscles in fascination before sliding her hands up to explore his tight male nipples.

'I knew you would be a witch,' Diego said unsteadily. 'You have cast your spell over me. But now it is my turn to torment you, *mi belleza*.'

Rachel caught her breath when he lowered his head to her naked breast and painted moist circles around her nipple before taking the swollen peak fully into his mouth. Lost in the world of sensory pleasure he was creating, she lifted her hips so that he could remove her skirt, and she shivered when he slid his hand between her legs and stroked the sensitive flesh of her inner thigh. She could feel the sticky wetness between her legs and she was embarrassed by the unmistakable evidence that she was desperately aroused, especially when he hooked his fingers in the waistband of her tiny lace knickers and drew them slowly down.

'So lovely,' he said thickly as he ran his fingers over the triangle of gold curls he had exposed, before he gently parted her and eased between her slick velvet folds. 'And so very ready for me.' His voice was laced with rampant male satisfaction, but Rachel could not deny it and she arched her hips when he slid his finger deeper into her while his thumb pad found the ultra-sensitive nub of her clitoris and he caressed it until she sobbed his name.

'Please…' Everything was new and incredible and she

wanted more, needed him to soothe the burning sensation in her pelvis.

'Soon, *querida*,' he promised as he suddenly sprang from the bed and tore off his shirt. 'I'm afraid this won't be a leisurely seduction. I want you now, and I can't wait—but you share my impatience, don't you, my Rachel?'

Her brain was barely capable of conscious thought, but as she dwelled on the phrase 'my Rachel' something tugged at her heart. It made her feel special, as if she was truly his, but no doubt he used the same endearment with all his lovers, she reminded herself, aware that it was important she took this for what it was—sex with no emotions involved on either side.

Diego dropped his shirt carelessly on the floor and as his hands moved to his belt Rachel stopped thinking and watched, wide-eyed, as he stripped off his trousers. His underwear could not disguise his fierce arousal, and her mouth ran dry when the boxers joined his trousers and she was faced with a naked and proudly erect male for the first time in her life.

Her immediate thought was that he wasn't going to fit—that sex between them was surely a physical impossibility. Up to this moment she had been driven by curiosity, and each new caress from his hands and mouth had increased her excitement. But now, as she stared at his rigid length, her doubts came storming back and she shrank back against the mattress when he came down beside her. Diego seemed unaware of her sudden tension, and when he brought his mouth down on hers and his long silky hair fell forwards to form a curtain around them both she forced herself to ignore her apprehension and kissed him back, running her hands over his muscular torso and feeling the hard ridges of his muscles.

'It has to be now, *querida*,' Diego muttered hoarsely. He hadn't been this turned on in years. He was so desperate for her he felt as though he was about to explode, and he swiftly positioned himself over her—and then stilled abruptly and cursed savagely in his native tongue.

Rachel could not understand the words, but the anger in his tone was unmistakable. She stared at him in bemusement. Had she done something wrong? she wondered fearfully. Could he have guessed that this was her first time?

'I'm sorry, Rachel. I did not expect to invite anyone back tonight and I don't have any protection,' he growled harshly, his frustration palpable.

Did she come under the label of 'anyone'? The unsettling thought came into Rachel's head and brought home to her that Diego might just as easily have brought another woman from the party back to his cottage for casual sex. She pushed the thought away and concentrated on her relief that he was not rejecting her because he had somehow discovered that she was in unchartered territory.

'It's all right. I'm on the pill,' she murmured. After years of monthly misery her doctor had advised her to take it to regulate her periods, but she was aware that it was also the most reliable method of contraception.

The agonising frustration that had gripped Diego's body dissipated and excitement thundered through his veins. He was on fire for her and relieved that there was no reason why he could not make love to her. He refused to admit to the fleeting feeling of disappointment that her air of innocence which so intrigued him was not real, and that she was obviously sexually experienced.

Instead, he slid his hands beneath her bottom and angled her for his possession. His penis strained urgently against her moist opening and he slowly eased forwards, a shudder running through him as her tight muscles closed around him and clasped him in a velvet embrace. As he entered her, his eyes locked with hers and he was puzzled by her expression—the look of wonderment and surprise, as if this was all new to her. She was so incredibly tight… He frowned as he withdrew a little and then thrust deeper into her, heard her faint gasp. 'Rachel…?'

'It's been a while,' she mumbled shyly.

He stared down at her pink cheeks and saw that she was embarrassed, and he felt an unexpected surge of tenderness mixed with arrogant male satisfaction that she had obviously not had a lover for months—or maybe even longer.

'Then we'll take it slowly,' he assured her. But, as he sank deeper inside her and established a sensual rhythm that matched the pounding beat of his heart, his resolve was tested to its limits. She was the most responsive lover he had ever known, he could already feel his pleasure building and knew that he would not be able to hold back for long.

The slight discomfort she had felt when Diego had first thrust into her was less than Rachel had expected and soon forgotten as he slowly filled her. It was good; better than good—awesome, amazing, she thought shakily as she curved her legs around his hips and drew him deeper into her. She caught her breath when he withdrew almost completely and then drove into her again and again, faster now as his pace became more urgent.

She could not think, could only feel, every cell in her body attuned to the intense sensations he was arousing in her. She had not expected the act of lovemaking to be so beautiful; to feel that not just her body but her soul was joined with Diego, and for some inexplicable reason tears stung her eyes. She blinked them away frantically and pressed her face into the tanned column of his throat, brushing her mouth over the pulse that jerked beneath his skin.

She never wanted him to stop, and yet there had to be an end—he could not keep up this frenetic rhythm for ever. The throbbing ache low in her pelvis was growing ever more insistent. And then suddenly she was hovering on the brink of the unknown, and she was almost afraid of what would come next as Diego thrust deeper and harder than before and she felt herself explode in a shattering wave of ecstasy. Spasm after spasm of pleasure ripped through her, so intense that she cried out and clung to his sweat-slicked shoulders while he slammed into her and then gave a harsh groan, his big body shuddering and his head thrown back as he reached his own spectacular climax.

For a few moments afterwards they remained joined, and Rachel revelled in the weight and warmth of his body pressing down on her. She could stay like this for ever, she thought dreamily as she slid her fingers through his hair and stroked her hands across his massive shoulders. She felt safe and protected in the arms of this big, powerful man—and after her childhood, where she had received little care or affection, the feeling that she somehow belonged with Diego was sweetly seductive. But it was also dangerous, she conceded when he finally rolled off her and tucked his arms behind his head. For a few seconds she felt bereft and longed to cuddle up to him, but instinct warned her that he would be horrified if she clung to him.

Instead, she affected a tiny yawn, even though she had never felt more awake in her life, and allowed her lashes to drift down so that she could stare at him without him being aware of her compulsion to study every minute detail of his face until it was imprinted on her memory for ever.

Diego turned his head and glanced at Rachel. Her long eyelashes fanned her cheeks and her lips were slightly parted, reddened and swollen from the demanding pressure of his mouth. With her golden hair spilling over the pillow, she looked young and ridiculously innocent, and he felt a curious tugging sensation in his chest. He had known that sex with her would be good, and it had exceeded all his expectations, but he had not expected the experience to be so…shattering—

a complete union of body and mind that had left him feeling more content than he could ever remember.

'You haven't done this much before, have you?' he murmured.

Her lashes flew upwards and cornflower-blue eyes regarded him warily. 'What do you mean?' Had he realised that it had been her first time? If so, he did not appear to be annoyed, Rachel decided, her flutter of panic fading.

'I mean, I do not think you have had many lovers,' Diego said carefully. He did not understand why he was probing for information about her exes. Never before had he been curious about a woman's past history, and it shouldn't matter to him if Rachel had had dozens of other men, he brooded irritably.

Rachel was silent for so long that he thought she was not going to answer. 'Not many, no,' she admitted quietly, blushing profusely. 'I'm sorry if I disappointed you.'

Diego refused to question why he was so inordinately pleased with her reply. 'You were incredible, *querida*,' he assured her in a deep growl that made the tiny hairs on her body stand on end. 'Does this feel as if I was disappointed?' he murmured as he took her hand and placed it on his hardening manhood.

Rachel caught her breath when she felt him swell beneath her fingertips until his erection was a rigid shaft of muscle. 'Do you want to do it again?' she asked him in a startled voice. Her heartbeat was only just returning to normal, but the idea that he wanted her again, so soon after the first time, sent her pulse-rate soaring.

She must know the effect that her breathlessly innocent query had on him, Diego brooded as savage hunger surged through him. It was a clever trick designed to make a man feel as though he was her first lover, but the knowledge that she was an adept game player did not lessen his desire, and he gave a self-derisive laugh as he slid his hand between her legs and discovered her slick wetness.

'What do you think?' he said harshly and, without giving her time to reply, he moved over her and entered her with one hard, powerful thrust, smothering her soft gasp with his mouth as he began the whole delicious process of making love to her all over again.

Rachel was used to waking early, and when she opened her eyes the bedroom was shadowed with the pearly grey light that preceded dawn. She stretched, and winced as the effects of the previous night on her untutored body made themselves known. Diego was still asleep; she could hear the rhythmic sound of his breathing and she turned her head and studied him, absorbing the masculine beauty of his sculpted features and the faint dark stubble on his chin with a faint sense of desperation that she would probably never lie like this with him again.

She had no experience of how to behave after a one-night stand. Should she wait for him to wake up, and maybe they would share a leisurely breakfast? Recalling the sparse contents of his fridge, breakfast seemed unlikely. And she could not picture herself making small talk with him when memories of the incredible and sometimes shocking things he had done to her last night were making her blush.

She needed some time alone to come to terms with the fact that she had given her virginity to a man who was practically a stranger. She knew very little about him, other than that he owned a ranch just outside Buenos Aires. He never spoke of his family or his private life and although sex with him last night had been incredible, and she definitely did not regret it, she was no nearer to understanding what made Diego Ortega tick.

It seemed sensible to slip away now, before he or the rest of the estate were awake, but she was reluctant to move. Diego was lying on his back with one arm flung across her stomach—although, when he had finally allowed her to fall asleep, he had rolled away from her onto his side of the bed. Some time during the night their bodies had drawn closer together and she felt loath to break the connection between them.

But the feeling of closeness was a dangerous illusion, she told herself firmly as she eased carefully from beneath the sheet. The morning air was cool and she shivered as she donned her skirt and flimsy top. At this hour she would normally be wearing jodhpurs and a thick sweatshirt, and she prayed none of the estate workers would be about to comment on her appearance.

'What are you doing, *querida*? Do you know what the time is?' The seductive drawl—husky from sleep—sent a frisson of fierce awareness down her spine.

Diego propped himself up on one elbow and surveyed Rachel indolently. It had been an amazing night. He had known instinctively that sex between them would be mind-blowing, and he hadn't been wrong. His body had been utterly sated when he'd finally fallen asleep, but the sight of her in the pale light of dawn, flushed and still sleepy, with her golden hair rippling down her back, caused a familiar tightening in his groin and he acknowledged that one night of her was not going to be nearly enough.

'Why are you up so early?' he murmured.

'I'm a stable-hand—one of the requisites of my job is to get up early.'

His eyes narrowed as he caught the faint defensive note in her voice. 'Not on a Sunday,' he said lazily. He patted the sheet. 'Come back to bed.'

'Horses have to be fed and turned out, even on a Sunday.' Rachel ignored the fact that this was her Sunday off and fought her longing to do as Diego had said and get back into bed with him. The sultry gleam in his eyes told her that he was not inviting her to go back to sleep, and her body was clamouring to experience his soul-shattering brand of magic one more time. 'I need to go,' she muttered, forcing herself to walk over to the door.

'It's 5:00 a.m.' Diego could not hide his frustration when it became apparent that Rachel was actually going to leave. Women did not usually walk out on him after a night in his bed. In fact, this was the first time ever, and another first was his brief flare of self-doubt that he had not satisfied her last night. He dismissed it instantly as he recalled how she had writhed beneath him. No way had she been faking it. He had given her orgasm after orgasm, and the moans and cries she had emitted as she'd tossed her head from side to side on the pillow had been ample proof that he had pleased her.

'If I wait any longer people might see me leaving the cottage,' she mumbled.

'What *people*?'

'People who work on the estate—groundsmen, the other grooms—my colleagues!' Rachel said tersely, flushing when Diego stared at her as if she had taken leave of her senses. 'I don't want anyone to know I spent the night here.'

Diego shook his head, mystified by Rachel's change of mood from the sensual sex kitten of last night to someone who was decidedly on edge this morning. 'Why not?'

'Because word will get round that we had a one-night stand,' she told him impatiently. 'I'd prefer not to have my private life open to public discussion, and I assumed you would feel the same way.'

'I don't give a damn what anyone else thinks,' Diego stated with such supreme arrogance that Rachel's temper simmered. 'And what makes you think that either of us would be content with only one night together? We were dynamite between the sheets and I want you in my bed every night.'

Every night while he was staying at Hardwick, Rachel

quickly reminded herself as her heart leapt. She could not suppress her excitement that he seemed to want an affair with her, but it was vital to remember that their relationship would only be temporary.

'I don't object to seeing you again,' she said carefully, 'but I don't want anyone else to know about us. In a few weeks you'll go back to Argentina, but I'll still work here after you've gone and I hate the idea of being the subject of gossip.'

'So you don't object to seeing me again?' he repeated in a dangerously soft tone. Dark brows winged upwards in an expression of haughty disdain. 'How very magnanimous of you, *querida*,' Diego snapped, outraged that Rachel seemed to think she could call the shots in their relationship. 'But how exactly are we to meet up in secret? Do you intend for us to creep through the estate after dark like criminals? If you are ashamed of being with me, then I can see little point in continuing with this,' he stated coldly.

Rachel's stomach dipped at the finality in his voice, but at the same time her temper flared. 'I'm not ashamed of being with you, but I think you should try seeing it from my point of view,' she muttered. 'I don't want to be for ever known locally as the woman who once had a brief fling with the notorious playboy Diego Ortega. I do have some pride, you know.'

'Then I suggest you take your pride and get out,' Diego growled furiously, struggling to contain his outrage at the notion of engaging in some cloak-and-dagger affair with Rachel. In his past, every woman he had ever dated had been eager to broadcast their affair with him, and he had always hated the publicity. But, far from being pleased that Rachel wanted to keep her relationship with him a secret, he was deeply insulted. He glared at her, waiting for her to back down, but her mouth was set in a mutinous line and she glared right back at him.

'Fine,' she said crisply as she yanked open the door. 'Well, it was nice knowing you…' She broke off abruptly, and Diego felt a spurt of satisfaction when her face burned with fiery colour.

'Ditto,' he drawled sardonically, still not quite able to believe that she would walk out of the door. 'Just remember when you are tossing and turning in your lonely bed tonight that you can thank your pride for the sexual frustration which prevents you from sleeping.'

His arrogance was unbelievable! Rachel made a strangled sound as she marched out onto the landing and she vented her temper by slamming the door after her and then kicked it for good measure, incensed by the sound of Diego's mocking laughter following her down the stairs.

CHAPTER FIVE

RACHEL might have guessed that a day that had started off so badly would get progressively worse. Keeping to the woodland paths, she saw no one on her journey back to her caravan, but once there she was too worked up to relax—her anger with Diego mixed with a growing feeling that once again she had handled things badly. Far from regarding her as a one night stand, Diego had made it clear that he had hoped to have an affair with her, at least for the duration of his stay at Hardwick—and she had thrown his invitation straight back in his face.

She was thankful when one of the other grooms phoned her, pleading a hangover from last night's party and begging her to work his shift at the stables. At least being busy would stop her from dwelling on things she'd rather not think about, she brooded as she cycled into the yard. Things like her wanton response when Diego had made love to her, and the fact that, thanks to her stubborn streak and hot temper, he now wanted nothing more to do with her.

The cool dawn gave way to another unusually warm day for May, and by mid-morning Rachel felt hot and tired after a serious lack of sleep the previous night. Usually she always took extra care around Earl Hardwick's bad tempered mare, Poppy, but for once she was careless and forgot to muzzle the horse before starting to groom her. Poppy was at her most un-cooperative, shaking her head wildly before snapping her teeth into an expanse of bared flesh—eliciting a startled cry of pain from Rachel as she stared at the bite mark on her upper arm.

The bite had broken her skin and when she met Alex later in the afternoon the bandage she'd tied around the wound was soaked with blood. Alex took one look at it and ignoring her protests, bundled her into his car and drove her to the accident and emergency unit of the local hospital.

'You can't take chances, Rache,' he told her when she emerged two hours later with her arm swathed in a sterile dressing and clutching a week's course of antibiotics. 'Animal bites are prone to infection.'

The doctor who had dressed her wound had said the same thing, and as soon as Rachel got home she followed his advice and took a double dose of the antibiotic before she set about scrubbing the interior of the caravan in an effort to expend some of her restless energy. She would not waste another second thinking about Diego, she told herself when she dumped the now curled and brown roses he had given her two weeks ago in the bin. She was kneeling in front of her tiny fridge, debating whether the cheese would be safe to eat if she scraped the mould off it, when the sound of a familiar, toe-curlingly sexy voice made her jump to her feet.

'You can't possibly be contemplating eating that, not unless you want another trip to the hospital with food poisoning.' Diego walked up the steps of the caravan and filled the doorway, looking so gorgeous in faded denims and a white T-shirt which contrasted with his bronzed skin that Rachel's heart seemed to temporarily stop beating. 'How's the arm?'

'Fine,' she replied automatically, despite the fact that her wound was throbbing painfully. She frowned. 'How did you know…?'

He shrugged. 'Word travels fast on the estate.'

'Exactly my point,' Rachel muttered tersely. 'If anyone had seen me coming out of your cottage this morning in the clothes I'd been wearing the night before, gossip would have swept through the estate faster than wildfire.'

'I realise that now.' His quietly spoken comment was so surprising after their earlier row that Rachel stared at him, wishing she could see his expression, which was hidden behind his designer shades. 'Everyone at Hardwick seems to know everyone else's business,' Diego said, sounding faintly irritated. It was his first experience of life in a close-knit rural community and he was amazed by the fascination that everyone, from Earl Hardwick down to the assistant gardener, took in their neighbours' day-to-day affairs.

He had spent most of the day in a furious temper after Rachel had walked out on him, but by late afternoon his anger had faded as he acknowledged she had every right to want to protect her privacy. Last night had been amazing, and he'd come to the conclusion that the passion they had shared had been too electrifying to throw away.

He glanced at her, noting the wariness in her eyes, and wondered if she had any idea how badly he wanted her. What was it about this delicate English girl with her pale-as-milk skin and a dusting of gold freckles on her nose that he found such a turn on? he brooded irritably. Her close-fitting jodhpurs emphasised her boyishly slim hips and her tight, faded T-shirt looked fit for the rag bag. But, despite her lack of sophistica-tion, he ached to release the clip that secured her hair in an untidy knot on top of her head and run his fingers through the heavy silk, and he was already envisaging pushing her shirt up so that he could cradle her firm breasts in his hands.

'I was wondering if you'd like to join me for dinner. At the cottage, naturally, as we dare not risk being seen dining together in public at the Rose and Crown,' he added dryly.

Rachel went pink but ignored his jibe, her pulse quickening at the realisation that he seemed to be giving her another chance. 'Do you mean you're going to cook?' she queried, recalling the lonely jar of caviar in his fridge and trying to imagine him pushing a trolley around the local supermarket.

'*Santa Madre*. No!' He sounded as shocked as if she had suggested flying to Mars. He removed his sunglasses and shook his glossy dark hair back from his face. 'I've discovered an excellent French restaurant in Harrowbridge—and, even better, I've persuaded the manager to start up a home delivery service,' he explained, his eyes glinting with amusement when he noted the conflicting emotions on Rachel's face. 'Of course, you may not like French food, *querida*, in which case I will try my powers of persuasion on the Italian eatery at the other end of the town.'

'French will be lovely,' Rachel murmured after a long pause, ignoring the fact that she had never actually eaten French food. Dinner wasn't the real issue here, and they both knew it.

'I've left my car down by the farmhouse. Come with me now and I'll drop you back here early in the morning—before anyone's about,' Diego suggested casually.

His smile was a lethal weapon that numbed her brain and turned her legs to jelly, and she began to appreciate the very real danger he presented to her peace of mind. In the five years that she had worked as a groom at Hardwick she had fought to prove she was 'one of the lads' in an industry that was still rife with male chauvinism. But, for the first time in her life, she was tempted to sacrifice the respect she had earned among the other grooms and brazenly advertise the fact that she had slept with Diego to anyone who cared to know.

Nothing seemed to matter other than knowing he wanted her in his bed, and a little part of her longed for him to sweep her into his arms and kiss her senseless before carrying her to his car and driving her through the estate to his cottage, uncaring of the curiosity and speculation they would arouse. Although he was staring at her intently, he made no attempt to persuade her and the voice of caution in her head grew louder, reminding her of the lessons she'd learned after witnessing her parents' tangled love lives—no one was worth losing her independence for.

'I need to shower and sort out a few things, and then I'll cycle over to the cottage,' she told him in a cool voice that disguised her feverish excitement at the thought of spending another night with him. 'That way, I can ride my bike home again tomorrow.'

Diego's eyes narrowed, but he controlled his spurt of irritation. Everything with Rachel was a battle of wills, but that made his ultimate victory all the sweeter, he reminded himself. And it was satisfying to know that soon she would not be arguing with him, but pleading for his possession as she had done the previous night. 'Suit yourself,' he murmured with a faint shrug. 'But instead of a shower, why not have a bath at the cottage? I've always found that a long, hot soak is the best way to relax tired muscles.'

The wicked gleam in his eyes brought a rush of colour to Rachel's cheeks as she acknowledged that the reason why she ached all over was because of the demands he had made on her body last night. But the idea of sinking into the enormous roll-top bath at the cottage was irresistible. 'That sounds good,' she murmured. The sexual tension that had been smouldering between them since he had arrived was suddenly so acute that her skin prickled, and anticipation caused a dragging ache low in her pelvis.

He nodded and walked down the caravan steps, but halted at the bottom and turned back to her. His face was on level with hers and he dropped a brief, stinging kiss on her mouth that left her aching for more. 'Don't keep me waiting too long, *querida*,' he drawled. 'I'm ravenous!'

* * *

The predatory glint in Diego's eyes stayed with Rachel long after he strode down the track back to his car. Not knowing what she would need, she simply grabbed clean clothes for tomorrow and her toothbrush and bundled them into a backpack. Twenty minutes later she was cycling through the woods, retracing the path she had walked earlier that morning, back to the cottage.

She found the front door ajar, but when she walked into the hall there was no sign of Diego. From above came the sound of running water and she hurried up the stairs, coming to an abrupt halt when she pushed open the bathroom door and discovered him immersed in a bath full of foaming bubbles, sipping champagne.

'Hello, beautiful,' he drawled, raising his glass and greeting her with a smile that stole her breath.

'Didn't you say dinner is going to be delivered?' she croaked, her eyes locked on his muscular chest and the whorls of damp black hairs visible between the bubbles. He was so impossibly gorgeous. She felt weak with wanting him, but her instinct for self-protection warned her that it was imperative she did not allow herself to be swept away by his sexy charm.

'It'll be here in a couple of hours.'

Her heart began to thud unevenly as she speculated on how he intended to fill the time until dinner arrived. 'I thought you were hungry.'

'Join me in this bath and I'll show you just how hungry I am, *querida*,' he promised her deeply, the amusement in his eyes changing to an expression of such feral need that Rachel trembled. Last night this had all been new to her, but tonight she knew what to expect and she was overwhelmed by an urgent need to feel him inside her. She gripped the hem of her T-shirt—but then paused. Evening sunlight was streaming through the bathroom window and she felt reluctant to strip in front of him. It would be fine if she possessed voluptuous curves and was slipping out of a sexy negligee, but she was thin and bony and wearing jodhpurs and one of her oldest T-shirts.

'Diego…' She opened her mouth to tell him that she would undress in the bedroom, but he interrupted her.

'Take it off.' His voice was slurred and heavy with desire, causing molten heat to flood through her veins. Slowly she lifted her arms, tugged her shirt over her head and dropped it on the floor, blushing when his eyes focused intently on her breasts.

'Now the rest.'

There was no elegant way to kick off her riding boots and shimmy out of her jodhpurs, but Diego discovered that watching Rachel removing her clothes was the most erotic striptease he had ever witnessed. He was thankful that the bubbles hid the solid length of his arousal when he stared at her naked, slender body with her spun-gold hair spilling over her shoulders to cover her breasts, and the cluster of blonde curls between her legs.

'You are the most beautiful woman I've ever known,' he said harshly. The words were torn from him—he was shaken by his reaction to her. He was an expert in giving glib compliments to his lovers, but Rachel's pale loveliness evoked a curious ache inside him that he refused to assimilate. Instead he set down his champagne glass and held out his hand to assist her as she stepped gracefully into the bath.

'I need to keep the dressing on my arm dry,' she murmured when he drew her down into the foaming water. 'Diego—what is that…?' She broke off, her face flaming as he settled her on his thighs and she felt his rigid shaft push into her belly.

He laughed at her shocked expression and felt his heart-rate quicken as her shock turned to undisguised excitement when he slid his hand between her legs. 'Rest your arm on the side of the bath,' he bade her in a low growl, 'and allow me the pleasure of washing you.'

'Diego…' Rachel drew a sharp breath when he picked up a bar of soap and smoothed it over her breasts, washing her with a thoroughness that made her tremble. He rinsed her just as assiduously, first with his hands and then, when he had rolled her nipples between his fingers until they swelled and hardened, he lowered his head and took one and then the other into his mouth, sucking deeply until she gave a guttural moan and gripped his hair, desperate for him to stop and equally desperate for him to continue his sorcery.

He had positioned her so that she was lying back in the bath and he was kneeling over her, the dark curtain of his hair falling forwards to brush against her skin as he at last took mercy on her and lifted his mouth from her breast to her lips. And, while he kissed her, he slid the soap over her stomach and then lower, stroking and exploring her in an erotic foreplay that went beyond the wildest excesses of Rachel's imagination.

'I really think I'm clean,' she gasped as she twisted frantically, sending bath water slopping onto the floor.

'Then I'd better help to dry you,' Diego murmured as he stepped out of the bath, roughly dried himself and then scooped her out of the water and enfolded her in a towel. He carried her through to the bedroom and blotted the moisture from her body with the same dedication that he had washed her, until she was sure she would die with wanting him. She was on fire for him and ran her hands eagerly over his chest, trying to urge him down, but he laughed softly and drew her arms down by her sides.

'You should always moisturise your skin after a bath,' he told her, his amber eyes gleaming with a wicked intent that made her heart pound as he took a bottle of lotion from the bedside table and tipped fragrant oil into his palms.

This was a well-planned seduction—a routine he'd probably performed on numerous occasions with his previous lovers, cautioned a quiet voice of common sense in Rachel's head. But it didn't matter; nothing seemed to matter except that he should ease the ache of sexual frustration that was tearing at her insides.

He started at her feet, massaging the scented oil into her skin with sensuous strokes, and by the time he reached her breasts and brushed his fingertips back and forth across her nipples she sobbed his name and begged him to take her—now, this minute. He gave a husky laugh at her eagerness as he dipped slick, oiled fingers between her thighs, gently parted her and discovered the flooding sweetness of her arousal and, to Rachel's feverish relief, he finally positioned himself over her.

'Are you ready, *querida*?'

Was she? If she was any more turned on she would melt. 'Diego...*please*...' Last night she'd suffered a few last-minute doubts when he had rubbed the solid length of his erection up and down the outer lips of her vagina, but tonight she was frantic for him to fill her. She opened her legs, bending her knees a little and catching her breath when he entered her with one deep, powerful thrust which felt so incredibly good that she sighed her pleasure against his mouth.

He made love to her with all his considerable skill, exerting superb control and taking her to the edge once, twice, until she writhed beneath him, wantonly begging him to take her harder, faster, and crying out when he relented and thrust so deep that she climaxed in a violent explosion of ecstasy. Only then did he relinquish his grip on his self-control and he reached the heights seconds after her, giving a low groan as he pumped his seed into her.

In the aftermath Rachel felt limp and spent as her heart-rate gradually slowed. Diego was an incredible lover, she mused. She had no one to compare him with, but she knew instinctively that sex would never get any better than this. But there was no point in hoping that they would ever share anything more than passion. In a few weeks he would return to Argentina and it was likely that she would never see him again—and that suited her fine, she reminded herself, trying to ignore the way her heart leapt when he rolled off her and immediately curled his arm around her and drew her against his chest. She had her life mapped out—her riding ambitions were paramount but there was no reason why she should not enjoy a brief love affair with Diego, safe in the knowledge that neither of them wanted anything more than fantastic sex.

CHAPTER SIX

'CHECKMATE.' Diego moved his bishop and then leaned back on his elbow and grinned at Rachel.

'What…?' She stared down at the travel-sized chessboard set out on the picnic rug and shook her head in dismay. 'But I was about to win. I had my strategy all planned out.'

'But instead I win again. You know what this means, *querida*?' Diego's eyes glinted wickedly. 'The loser forfeits an item of clothing—and, as you have already lost your shoes and bracelet, this time it has to be your dress.'

'You can't really expect me to take it off here,' Rachel argued, feeling her heart begin to thud hard beneath her ribs. 'We're in a public place…and I'm not wearing a bra.'

'I know.' The look of devilment in Diego's gaze was mixed with a sensual gleam that sent a quiver of excitement down Rachel's spine. 'I have been painfully aware all day that the only thing hiding your breasts from my eyes is a very thin cotton dress. But you can't hide from me any longer. We're miles from the nearest village, and we've picnicked at this spot three times before and never seen a soul—so come on, hand it over.'

Rachel knew she was beaten. 'I can't believe you talked me into playing strip chess in the first place,' she grumbled, 'especially when I've only just learned the game.' She began to tug at the buttons that ran down the front of her dress, flushing beneath Diego's avid stare. Two could play at teasing, she decided—and, when she had unfastened the dress to her waist, she slowly drew it down to expose her shoulders and breasts, feeling a spurt of feminine triumph when dull colour flared along Diego's cheekbones.

'I bet it isn't one of the rules that the loser has to undress,' she said as she allowed the dress to slither down her thighs until it pooled at her feet and she stood before him wearing only a pair of minuscule lace panties.

They had spread the picnic rug beneath an oak tree, and the sun filtering through the leaves dappled Rachel's slender body. She looked like a woodland nymph, Diego brooded, feeling his body harden.

'It's in the Argentinian rule book,' he assured her gravely, his lips twitching. His eyes settled on the fragile wisp of lace between her thighs, and he gave her a predatory smile. 'Want to play again? Loser loses…everything.'

Rachel gave a little gasp as he suddenly tugged her ankle so that she tumbled down on top of him, and her pulse raced as he placed his hands on her bottom and clamped her tightly against him so that she could feel his arousal straining beneath his jeans. 'You might lose, and then you would have to strip,' she pointed out, her eyes dancing with amusement that swiftly darkened to desire when he grazed his lips along her collar-bone.

'That's the plan, *cariño*,' he said throatily.

Rachel's laughter echoed around the sunny copse, but the sound was soon lost beneath the pressure of Diego's mouth on hers. Life was a lot like chess—complicated and unpredictable—she mused as she anchored her fingers in his long silky hair. She had never had an affair before, and so hadn't known what to expect, certainly not that she and Diego would become friends, as well as lovers, over the last few weeks.

They shared everything and spent all their time together, although at the stables they tried to keep their relationship a secret from the other grooms.

Every night their passion grew more intense, but the bond that Rachel felt with Diego was based not just on sex, but on laughter and long conversations about every subject under the sun. On evenings and weekends they saddled up the horses and rode out together, exploring the beauty of the Cotswolds beneath cloudless blue skies.

Falling in love with him was not in the rule book, but day by day her emotions were becoming more entangled. The summer was racing past, and in a few more weeks he was due to return to Argentina. But he wasn't going yet, she consoled herself, and a lot could happen in a few weeks. They might fall out and be glad to see the back of each other—or he might fall for her…

While she had been daydreaming he had shrugged out of his clothes and she smiled at him as he moved over her, and felt the familiar tug on her heart when he smiled back. Who could tell what the future held?

Diego propped himself up on one elbow and stared at Rachel curled up beside him. Her lips were slightly parted and the sunlight filtering through the gap in the curtains turned her hair to a river of gold on the pillows. It was a month since they had become lovers, and he was faintly surprised that his fascination with her was even stronger than when he had first taken her to bed.

He could lie here watching her for hours, he mused, frowning slightly as he realised how quickly he had grown used to her sharing his bed—and his life. Usually she woke first—to the strident ring of her alarm clock, which was set for some ungodly hour before dawn—and normally she was dressed and about to sneak back to her caravan when he stirred. But last night he had switched off the alarm, and obviously making love to her three times during the night had worn her out because she was still fast asleep.

She would need food, he decided, swinging his legs over the side of the bed and carefully tucking the sheet around her. She would need to replenish the energy she'd used last night and, although he could not face anything more than strong black coffee in the mornings, Rachel was a breakfast girl.

Pulling on his robe, he padded barefoot down to the kitchen and found a saucepan, milk and the porridge oats Rachel ate every morning. He had watched her make her breakfast a dozen times, but he still managed to burn the milk, and he cursed as he stared at the lumpy grey goo he'd ended up with. A vigorous stir seemed to help and he added syrup, poured juice into a glass and, on an impulse he refused to question, he stepped outside and snipped off a pink rosebud, which he placed on the tray before he returned to the bedroom.

She was still asleep and looked so peaceful that he was reluctant to disturb her. He couldn't get enough of her, he acknowledged silently—and it was not just because she was a wild temptress in bed. She was good company and he liked having her around. He liked her sharp wit and her wicked sense of humour, and her infectious giggle that never failed to make him smile. He was even considering taking her to New York with him. He would only be at Hardwick for one more week and then planned to spend a month at his polo school in the States, before returning to Argentina. He was confident he would have tired of Rachel before he went home, and he certainly had no intention of inviting her to the Estancia Elvira. However, he was not convinced she would fit in with his lifestyle in New York—and, if he was honest, he'd arranged their forthcoming trip to London as a test to see how she coped in social situations.

Rachel stretched lazily beneath the sheets and slowly became conscious of soft golden sunlight stealing beneath her eyelids. Sunlight! Her lashes flew open and for a second she studied the chiselled perfection of Diego's face, his jaw shaded with dark stubble that seemed to enhance his sexiness. But then she grabbed her alarm clock and gave a horrified yelp.

'It's nearly nine o'clock!' She'd never slept that late in her life. 'My alarm can't have gone off.'

'It would seem so.' His amused drawl sparked her temper and she glared at him, pushing her tangled hair out of her eyes impatiently.

'I'm late for work. Why didn't you wake me?'

'Because you're not going to work for the next couple of days,' he said cheerfully. 'Here, I've made your breakfast.' He set the tray down on Rachel's lap and she stared at the brimming bowl of porridge in disbelief.

'*You* made it?' she said faintly. Diego was a sex-god and a world class polo player, but he was utterly clueless in the kitchen. She picked up the rosebud and gave him a smile that stole his breath. 'Thank you.'

'You'd better save your thanks until after you've tried it,' he said gruffly, dragging his eyes from the tempting curve of her breasts, barely concealed beneath the sheet.

'I'm sure it's lovely.' She would eat it even if it was foul because he had made it for her and, despite the lumps, she forced the porridge down, drank the juice and then remembered what he had said. 'What did you mean about me not going to work? Of course I'm going.'

'Uh-uh.' He put the tray on the dresser, slid out of his robe and joined her in the bed, tugging her down on top of him and clamping her hips when she wriggled to escape him. The frantic squirming of her hips intensified his arousal—and hers, he noted, watching the way her eyes darkened with desire.

'Diego…?' Rachel gasped and fought to retain her sanity.

'I have to attend a business meeting in London, and I thought you would like to come with me.'

'To your meeting?' She frowned in confusion.

'To shop—in preparation for our trip to Royal Ascot.' He grinned at her stunned expression. 'A friend of mine has hired a private box for Ladies' Day and invited me to bring a guest. I want you to be my guest, *querida*.'

'I've always wanted to go to Ascot,' Rachel admitted slowly, excitement at the idea of visiting the famous horse-racing event drowning out the voice in her head which pointed out that Diego had altered the rules of their relationship without asking her.

For the past month they had maintained the act of a professional working relationship in front of the other staff at Hardwick. Now he was suggesting being seen together in public—but it was unlikely that they would bump into anyone she knew at Ascot, she reassured herself. She stared down at him, feeling her heart give its familiar flip as she absorbed the male beauty of his face, and accepted that she was desperate to go with him.

'I don't need to go shopping,' she told him firmly. Ascot would be heaven, but trekking around the shops was her idea of hell. 'I bought a new outfit for a friend's wedding last summer and I'm sure it will do.'

'And I'm equally sure it won't,' he murmured dryly. 'You can't walk into the Royal Enclosure in a cheap, off-the-peg dress. While I'm at my meeting I've arranged for a personal stylist to take you to Bond Street and find you something suitable to wear.

'Humour me, *querida*?' he said softly when she opened her mouth to protest, and he took advantage of her parted lips to slide his tongue between them at the same time as he lifted her and guided her down onto his swollen length, smiling triumphantly when he heard her gasp as he filled her. It was the most effective way he knew of stalling the argument he could sense was brewing. Rachel was feisty and independent—but she was totally addicted to him and he had no compunction about using sex to get his own way.

They drove to London later that morning. Rachel wanted to go back to the caravan and pick up clothes and toiletries, and had hoped to dash up to the stables and see Piran, but Diego's meeting was scheduled for early afternoon and he was impatient to get away.

'You can buy everything you need in town,' he told her as they sped along the motorway, 'and I've arranged for one of the other grooms to exercise Piran for the next few days.'

She felt as though her independence was being subtly eroded, Rachel fretted silently. A month ago she wouldn't have dreamed of allowing anyone else to take charge of Piran, and she was disturbed that Diego had organised the trip—and her life, it seemed—without consulting her.

During her childhood she had lived through her mother's various love affairs—which had usually resulted in the upheaval of moving into a new home and being expected to get on with new step-siblings. Liz Summers had put everything into her relationships and sacrificed her independence without a second thought—only to be devastated when it all went wrong a few months down the line. Rachel had vowed that she would never allow a man to take over her life, but nothing had prepared her for Diego's charismatic personality—or her overwhelming need for him. For the first time she appreciated the power of sexual attraction. It would be very easy to be swept away by him, she acknowledged—she was already halfway there.

She had assumed that they would stay in a hotel in London, and she gave Diego a puzzled glance when he parked in a private car park close to the river. 'Who lives here?' she queried when he ushered her into a lift which whisked them up to a penthouse apartment with panoramic views over the Thames and Westminster.

'I do—although it would be wrong to say that I actually live here. I use the flat as a stopover whenever I'm in London—maybe once or twice a year,' he explained. His phone rang and he glanced at the caller display. 'I need to take this. Feel free to take a look around.'

She couldn't even afford one property, and lived in a caravan, while he owned a luxury flat in a prime city location and rarely stayed in it! Their lives were worlds apart, Rachel mused as she wandered around the apartment, admiring the elegant décor that was clearly the work of a top interior designer. She paused in the doorway of the master bedroom, her eyes drawn not to the spectacular view across the city but the huge bed in the centre of the room. Tonight Diego would make love to her on that bed. Heat flooded through her veins and she felt the familiar heavy sensation in her pelvis. This was the real reason she had agreed to come away with him, she acknowledged ruefully. Ascot would be a great experience, but she wouldn't care if they missed the racing and spent all their time indulging in a sensual feast. She only had one more week with him before he left for New York, and she was dismayed by the sudden ache in her chest at the knowledge that their affair was almost over. She had always known it would end, but she was unprepared for the sense of panic she felt at the prospect of her life returning to normal—without him.

When she returned to the sitting room, she found Diego chatting to a stunning brunette who looked as though she had stepped from the pages of a fashion journal. Rachel was immediately conscious that her skinny jeans and T-shirt were far from elegant, and she flushed when the woman gave her a speculative glance.

Diego strolled across the room. 'Rachel, I'd like you to meet Jemima Philips. Jemima is a personal stylist and she's going to guide you around the designer boutiques in Mayfair and help you select a few new outfits.'

Rachel stiffened. '*One* new outfit—for Ascot,' she said tightly. 'I don't need anything else.'

'You'll need something to wear to dinner tonight—I've booked a table at Claridge's,' Diego murmured, his mouth curving into a sensual smile that he knew with supreme self-confidence never failed to affect her. 'And of course you will want to buy some lingerie and a few items of smart casual wear as we'll be staying in town for a couple more days.' He noted her frown and dropped a brief tantalising kiss on the mutinous line of her mouth. 'Enjoy it, *querida*,' he bade her, a hint of steel beneath his teasing tone. 'I have a sudden yearning to see you dressed in clothes that flatter your figure rather than swamping it. Most women would jump at the chance to flex my credit card on Bond Street.'

It was on the tip of Rachel's tongue to point out that she was not most women, but his comment that he wanted to see her in flattering clothes stung her pride. He obviously thought she looked a mess in her uniform of jeans or jodhpurs and baggy sweatshirts, and she felt a sudden urge to prove that she could look as elegant as the gorgeous Jemima if she put her mind to it.

But several exhausting hours later, she wished she hadn't taken up Diego's challenge to improve her appearance. Jemima Philips had whisked her around the exclusive boutiques in Bond Street and Sloane Square: Chanel, Gucci, Armani, a boutique specialising in exquisite Italian shoes, and another which sold beautiful and eye-wateringly expensive lingerie. If Rachel had been on her own she would never have had the nerve to walk into any of the shops, and even with Jemima beside her she was horribly conscious of the haughty stares from the sales assistants who cast disdainful glances at her faded jeans. However, the mention of Diego's name seemed to act like a magic wand and the assistants were suddenly gracious and eager to help.

By the end of the day she owned a cream silk dress trimmed with black ribbon and a matching jacket, black stiletto shoes and handbag, and a chic black pillbox hat complete with curled ostrich feathers. Rachel had been determined to pay for her clothes herself, but the bill for her Ascot outfit was so exorbitant that she did not have enough funds in her bank account to cover a fraction of it. Horrified at how much of Diego's money she had spent, she refused to allow Jemima to purchase any of the evening gowns the stylist had nagged her to try on.

After shopping came a visit to a beauty salon favoured by A-list celebrities, where her unruly blonde hair was transformed into a sleek, glossy style with layers around her face and a long sexy fringe. Her face was made up with a range of cosmetics which again cost the earth, but here at least she insisted on paying the bill herself, and as the transaction went through she prayed that her credit limit would not be blown and her card refused.

Diego was waiting at the apartment when a taxi dropped her off. 'You should have had all your purchases delivered, rather than struggling to carry them,' he greeted her when she staggered through the door. When Rachel looked puzzled he indicated several flat boxes emblazoned with the name of the design house on the front. 'Jemima arranged for these to be sent on.'

'It wasn't my choice to buy them,' she muttered when she opened the boxes and discovered the three exquisite evening gowns she had tried on earlier. 'These dresses cost a fortune, Diego, and I can't allow you to buy them for me. I only need one dress for tonight. The other two can be sent back—with all these.' She sifted through the pile of filmy lace bras and knickers in a variety of colours. 'I didn't ask for them. Jemima shouldn't have…'

'Jemima Philips was simply following orders,' he murmured in the honeyed tone he used when he was determined to win an argument. 'You have no idea how beautiful you are, Rachel—but now you will see.' He gave her a gentle push towards the door. 'Go and change into one of the dresses so that I can take you out to dinner. And, Rachel…' She paused and glanced back at him, her heart thudding at the sultry gleam in his eyes. 'Wear the black underwear and the stockings,' he said softly. 'I'm looking forward to removing them later tonight.'

The following day, Rachel ached all over after Diego had made love to her countless times during a night of the wildest passion they had ever shared. She had read that men were turned on by women wearing stockings and now she knew it was true, she mused, her face growing warm as she recalled his reaction when he had unzipped her evening dress and she had shaken back her hair and posed before him in a sexy black basque, suspenders and stockings.

She'd barely had enough energy to crawl out of bed this morning, but they had left London early to drive to Berkshire and now they were here at one of the most prestigious sporting venues in the world. She turned her head at the sound of hooves thundering along the track and peered through her binoculars as the riders streaked towards the winning post. The racing at Ascot was fantastically exciting, and if she had been down in the main enclosure she would have unashamedly yelled and cheered with the rest of the crowd. But up in the private box, among Diego's wealthy friends, she felt ill at ease and desperate not to draw attention to herself.

She had quickly discovered that this was nigh on impossible when she was the subject of intense speculation among the sophisticated friends of the host of the party, Lord Guy Chetwin.

'Call me Guy,' the aristocratic Englishman had told her when Diego had introduced them. Guy seemed friendly enough—indeed, Rachel had been acutely conscious of his eyes lingering on her several times during lunch—but the other men in the group, and their glamorous socialite wives and girlfriends, were less welcoming and could not hide their curiosity about Diego Ortega's new mistress.

It was a title Rachel felt deeply uncomfortable with—just as she felt unhappy about the fact that every item of clothing she was wearing, and the eye-catching diamond choker Diego had fastened around her throat before they had left the flat this morning, had been paid for by him.

'Your glass is empty. Let's find some more champagne,' Diego murmured in her ear as he led her out onto the balcony, which offered spectacular views of the racetrack.

She forced a smile, but could not dismiss the feeling that she did not belong here. Diego looked utterly gorgeous in full morning dress—a black suit complete with coat-tails, a dove-grey silk waistcoat and tie and a grey top hat which surprisingly did not look odd with his long hair and gave him a rakish air that drew admiring female glances. This rarefied world of the super-rich was his world—but it was not hers. Despite her expensive clothes, she did not fit in with his friends and now that they were away from Hardwick she realised how little she had in common with him.

She glanced back inside and her heart plummeted when she caught sight of a man with a mass of blonde hair flopping onto his brow chatting to Guy Chetwin.

'Jasper Hardwick has just arrived,' she said in a tense whisper as she gripped Diego's arm. 'We'll have to leave. If we walk along the balcony we may be able to slip away without him seeing us.'

'Don't be ridiculous.' Diego frowned. 'I have no intention of leaving. Nor am I going to play a game of hide and seek for the rest of the afternoon. What does it matter if Hardwick sees us?'

'It matters because he'll guess that we're…that we're together,' Rachel snapped. 'And, knowing Jasper, he'll make sure everyone at Hardwick knows. I can't believe he's here,' she muttered.

Diego shrugged. 'He and Guy are old friends. They were at Eton together, although I hadn't realised Hardwick was on the guest list today. I can't believe you're still bothered about our affair being made public,' he added, making no attempt to hide his irritation.

'Doesn't it bother you?' she snapped.

'It has never bothered me, *querida*,' he drawled laconically. 'I respected your wish not to proclaim the fact that we've been sleeping together, but things are different now.'

'How are they?' Rachel demanded, puzzled not just by his statement but the sudden gleam in his eyes.

'Because I want you to come to New York with me next week.'

Diego felt a spurt of satisfaction at her stunned expression. She suddenly looked young and vulnerable, reminding him of the Rachel he had first met rather than the sophisticated woman he had turned her into by buying her designer clothes. When she had walked out of the bedroom this morning, dressed for Ascot, he had been pleased that she looked just as he had wanted her to look, with her hair expertly groomed and her face made-up—her lashes darkened with mascara which emphasised the dense blue of her eyes and her mouth coated in a scarlet gloss. But, for some inexplicable reason, he found that he missed the untidy stable-girl who smelled of the earth and fresh air rather than a cloying, expensive perfume.

It took a few seconds for Diego's words to sink into Rachel's brain, and she felt as shaky as when she had accompanied him across the lawn of the Royal Enclosure in her three-inch stiletto heels. Her heart began to thud erratically. 'To work at your polo school, you mean?' she queried carefully.

'No, *querida.*' His sensual smile stole her breath. 'To pleasure me in bed every night—although we do not have to confine our lovemaking to bed,' he teased wickedly. 'I own a large house in upstate New York, and we could be inventive in the jacuzzi, or on the leather sofa in the sitting room, or maybe I'll spread you across the big walnut desk in my study…'

'Diego…!' She could feel her face burning and was sure they were attracting curious glances from the other guests. But part of her did not care. Diego wanted to extend their affair by taking her to New York, and she was shocked by how tempted she was to say yes. She could not afford to take a break from jumping Piran—not if she was to stand any chance of being selected for the British Equestrian team, she reminded herself urgently. And she couldn't simply disappear from the stables for however long Diego's invitation extended—she noted he had not specified a time limit—and then expect her job to be waiting for her when their affair was over. There was every reason under the sun to refuse him and not one sensible one to accept his invitation, yet it was on the tip of her tongue to agree, to throw caution to the wind and take whatever he was offering for as long as he wanted her.

Dear Lord, she had criticised her mother for leaping into unsuitable relationships with no thought of the consequences, yet here she was, unbearably tempted to do the same thing. She licked her dry lips and forced herself to speak. 'I don't know. I'll have to think about it.'

She would have to think about it? Something kicked in

Diego's chest and for a moment he felt faintly incredulous. Never in his life had a woman told him she would have to think about agreeing to continue an affair with him. The situation rarely arose. He had a low boredom threshold and usually tired of his lovers after a few weeks. Rachel was different although, to his intense irritation, he could not work out why she continued to intrigue him. But he had no intention of letting her know that her answer mattered to him. Instead, he closed the gap between them and slid his hand beneath her chin, satisfaction surging through him when he saw the mixture of confusion and undisguised hunger in her cornflower-blue eyes.

'Perhaps this will help you decide,' he murmured as he lowered his head and crushed her soft mouth beneath his. He ignored the fact that he never kissed his lovers in public, intent on bending her to his will in the one way he was certain of victory. She was as stubborn as a mule, and if he was honest he admired her fierce independence. She was a challenge, and perhaps that was why he had not bored of her. All he knew was that he wanted her with him in New York, and from her unguarded response to him he was confident she would agree to come.

When he finally lifted his mouth from hers, Rachel could only stare at him dazedly. Her heart was racing, her face felt hot and she knew her lips must be swollen. So much for wanting to avoid drawing attention to herself, she thought numbly.

'Diego, when you've got a minute, old man, I'd like your tips for the next race,' a voice sounded from behind them.

Diego cast a brief glance at the guest who had interrupted them. 'I'll be right with you, Archie.' He looked down at Rachel's flushed face and smiled. 'Give me your answer tonight,' he murmured. But the triumphant gleam in his eyes when he stepped away from her told her that he was confident of her reply.

With an effort she tore her eyes away from him as he strolled over to a group of his friends, and her heart sank when she saw that Jasper Hardwick had stepped out onto the balcony and was staring at her. Something in his sneering expression made her blood run cold and when a waiter materialised at her side, offering champagne, she took a glass and quickly walked to the far end of the balcony, determined to concentrate on the racing for the remainder of the afternoon.

'What do you think of Ascot, Rachel? I understand this is your first visit.'

She had been standing alone for several minutes when the cultured voice disturbed her solitude. She lowered her binoculars and smiled hesitantly at Guy Chetwin. 'It is. And it's…' she gave a faint shrug, her glance encompassing the view of the crowds in the public enclosure below, the velvet green lawns and the racing track that sliced through the grounds like an emerald river '…spectacular.'

'I'm glad you are enjoying the day.' Guy moved until he was standing a little too close for Rachel's liking. His thin mouth curved into a smile, but the eyes that trailed slowly over her were coolly assessing. 'You look charming, my dear. Diego has always had exceptionally good taste.'

Guy made her sound like an object rather than a person. Something in his tone caused Rachel to stiffen and her hand moved unconsciously to the diamond choker around her neck.

His eyes followed her movement. 'A pretty trinket,' he commented. 'Cartier, if I'm not mistaken?'

'I believe so,' she murmured. 'Diego gave it to me.' She was going to add that she had only reluctantly agreed to wear the necklace to Ascot after intense persuasion from Diego, but Guy spoke first.

'I'm sure you deserve it.' He uttered the curious statement in a pleasant enough tone, but Rachel detected a nuance in his voice that made her skin crawl. 'I hear you're accompanying Diego to New York.'

'How do you know…?' She struggled to hide her shock that Diego must have discussed her with his friend. 'Actually, I haven't decided whether to go yet.'

'Ah…' Guy laughed. 'Well, I don't blame you for trying to up the stakes. But a word of advice, my dear. Don't keep him dangling for too long. There are plenty of other pretty penniless young women who attend events such as Ascot with the sole intention of bagging themselves a rich lover.'

This time the edge of contempt in his voice was unmistakable and Rachel flushed. 'I'm not with Diego because he's wealthy,' she said tightly.

'Of course you are,' Guy drawled in a coldly amused tone. 'I can spot a common little gold-digger a mile off.' He lifted his hand to her throat and traced his finger over the diamond choker. 'I see that you have expensive tastes, but you are quite clearly not one of us. Diego might have dressed you in haute couture, but I'm afraid nothing can disguise your lack of breeding,' he added bluntly.

Humiliation engulfed Rachel, robbing her of a reply to Guy's outrageous comments. A cheer went up as the leading horse on the track swept past the finishing post. The sun was blazing in the cloudless sky but she felt icy cold and she gripped the balcony rail as Guy moved away from her and melted into the crowd who had spilled out of the box to watch the race. Part of her wanted to follow him and demand an apology for his disgusting suggestion that she was a gold-digger but, as she stared down at her designer dress and her hand strayed once more to the diamonds around her neck, her stomach lurched with the realisation that, by accepting Diego's gifts of clothes and jewellery, she had sold herself to him.

Last night's sex had been amazing but she had been aware of a subtle change in his attitude towards her—a new boldness in his demands and an expectation for her to fulfil his every fantasy. She had felt flattered that he was so turned on by her wearing her new sexy underwear, but now she wondered sickly if he believed he had paid for her to please him.

What had happened to her fiercely guarded independence? she wondered, fighting the nausea that swept through her. How could she have sacrificed it for a sexual liaison that she had known from the outset would never mean anything to Diego? The trials for the British showjumping team were coming up and she should be spending all her free time practising on Piran, but instead she had been on the brink of agreeing to take off to New York with a man who had never given any indication that she meant anything to him outside the bedroom.

Rachel bit her lip and forced herself to face the truth. The reason she had been contemplating going with him was because she had hoped that their affair would develop into something deeper—that Diego would fall for her as she had fallen for him. Ever since he had invited her to Ascot she had been kidding herself that there must be a reason why he wanted to introduce her to his friends. And when he had asked her to accompany him to New York she had taken it as proof that he was starting to feel something for her and regarded her as more than a casual sex partner.

Guy Chetwin's scathing comment that she was 'not one of us' made her realise what a fool she had been. Diego would never want more than a brief affair with her. The social divide between them was enormous, but it was not just that—it was Diego himself. At this moment he was chatting and laughing with the other guests, drawing people to him with his effortless charm. But she recognised that he was essentially a loner who guarded his emotions and never allowed anyone too close. In all the time they had spent together, he had never spoken of his family and had steered their conversation firmly away from his personal life. She did not really know him at all, she realised miserably.

Lost in a sea of dark thoughts, she was unaware that he had joined her until his deep-timbred voice sent the familiar quiver down her spine.

'You are cold, *querida*,' he murmured, running his hand lightly over her arm and noting the tiny goose bumps on her skin. 'Shall we go inside? Jasper Hardwick has gone down to the Royal Enclosure, by the way.' He frowned when Rachel made no acknowledgement of his presence. 'You seemed to be getting on well with Guy,' he said lightly, irritated with himself for the ridiculous spurt of jealousy he'd felt when he had watched them standing close together. 'What were you talking about?'

Rachel gave a brittle laugh. 'Your friend Guy accused me of being a gold-digger,' she said tightly. 'He believes I'm only with you because I want to get my grubby hands on your money.'

Diego's eyes narrowed on her angry face. 'I'm sure you must have been mistaken…' he began slowly.

'I wasn't,' Rachel interrupted him fiercely. 'According to Lord Chetwin, Ascot is a popular hunting ground for pretty penniless women who are looking for a rich stud. He thinks I sold myself to you. And that's what you think too, isn't it, Diego?' she demanded shrilly, hurt and humiliation threatening to shatter her tenuous grip on her self-control. 'The clothes and the necklace—they were payment for my "services".'

'I do not regard them as *payment* for anything,' he growled. 'You needed something to wear today…'

'So that I would be socially acceptable to your wealthy friends,' Rachel said bitterly. 'But apparently the posh frock and the diamonds don't disguise my lack of breeding.'

Her voice had risen once again. Diego frowned when heads

turned in their direction. 'This is ridiculous,' he snapped.
'There has clearly been a misunderstanding. I'll find Guy and
explain that you are my…'

He hesitated, and in the tense silence that quivered between
them Rachel's stomach churned. 'Your what, Diego?' she
asked huskily. 'Perhaps this is a good time to clarify our relationship…and discuss our future.'

Diego stiffened. The conversation was sounding ominously like the ones he'd had with previous lovers, when the
word *commitment* reared its ugly head. His dark brows
winged upwards. 'Our future, *querida*?' he said in a dangerously soft tone. 'I'm afraid there is little to discuss.'

'Then why did you ask me to go to New York with you?'
In her heart she knew the answer, but she needed to have it
spelled out. 'Was it really just for sex?'

Yes, damn it, he thought furiously. He wasn't prepared to
admit to himself, let alone to Rachel, that he had been looking
forward to showing her around one of his favourite cities.

'Don't knock it, Rachel,' he said coldly. 'I haven't heard you
complaining. You've enjoyed our affair as much as I have. I
thought we could continue to enjoy each other for another
month while I'm in the States, but to be frank, I never considered that it would lead to any kind of permanent arrangement.'

Rachel tried to ignore the tearing pain in her chest. 'I see,'
she said quietly.

'*Dios!*' he growled harshly, infuriated by the note of hurt
in her voice, and by the unexpected feeling of guilt that tugged
at his insides. 'I made it clear from the start that I'm not in
the market for any kind of committed relationship.' If it was
emotion she was looking for, she had come to the wrong
man—because his had died with Eduardo. He was cold and
empty inside, but in a strange way he welcomed the aching
loneliness. It was what he deserved—a punishment and a
pain that would last a lifetime.

'I thought you were happy with a no-strings affair,' he said tersely. His frustration bubbled over. 'What were you expecting, Rachel—a marriage proposal?'

'Of course not,' she snapped, stung by his scathing tone. 'But, to go to New York with you, I would have to give up my job, my financial security, and probably my dreams of winning a place in the British Equestrian team. That's a lot to ask of me, Diego, when all you're offering in return is a month in your bed.'

Honesty forced Diego to acknowledge the truth of her words, but he was furious that she had backed him into a corner. Rachel's message was clear—commit to some sort of relationship or I won't come to the States with you. Fine, he thought grimly. He'd never been dictated to by a woman in his life, and he wasn't going to start now.

'But that's all I am offering, *querida*,' he said coldly. 'Take it or leave it.'

Rachel was unprepared for the surge of pain that swept through her. This was it. It was over—the ending of their affair as sudden and unexpected as its beginning. It didn't have to be the end, a voice whispered urgently in her head. She could smile and shake back her hair—look him boldly in the eyes and agree to his terms. Fantastic sex with no emotions involved for another month. But emotions *were* involved, she acknowledged heavily. Her emotions. She was falling in love with him—and she had to end it now, before her heart suffered serious damage. She was not like her mother. She would not sacrifice everything for a man. Not even this man.

Tears burned the back of her throat but she would rather die than cry in front of him. 'I'll leave it,' she told him, proud that she sounded strong and in control when she felt anything but. 'And I think it would be best if I leave immediately—before any of your other friends accuse me of being a gold-digger,' she added bitterly.

'I'll speak to Guy,' Diego said tersely. 'I have no doubt he'll be anxious to apologise for his mistake.'

'Forget it,' Rachel said dully, suddenly bone weary. 'I don't care what he thinks of me. I just want to go.'

Diego stiffened. If she thought he would beg and plead, she was mistaken. His eyes narrowed on her delicate face and he remembered how she had writhed beneath him last night, her cheeks flushed and her mouth reddened and swollen from his kisses. She was beautiful, and he could not deny that he desired her. But beautiful women were ten-a-penny, he reminded himself grimly, and desire was transitory.

'Very well. I intend to enjoy the rest of the day's racing, but I'll arrange for a chauffeur to take you back to London.' Perhaps a couple of hours on her own would bring her to her senses, he brooded sardonically. After a cooling off period he was confident she would change her mind. The sexual alchemy between them was too intense for either of them to walk away until it had burned itself out. 'We'll spend tonight at the flat and I'll drive you back to Gloucestershire tomorrow.' He swung on his heel and strode off, but then paused and glanced back at her motionless figure. 'Come with me now,' he ordered impatiently. 'I'll escort you to the car.'

CHAPTER SEVEN

'I'LL see you later,' Diego told Rachel brusquely as he shut the car door. When the limousine pulled away she turned her head and stared back at him, desperate to imprint his face on her mind one last time—because she had no intention of being at the flat when he returned.

Back in London, it took her less than twenty minutes to change into her jeans, hang up her Ascot outfit in the wardrobe with the other clothes Diego had bought her, and place the diamond choker back in its velvet box. By the time he walked into the penthouse and discovered it empty, she was at Paddington Station, boarding a train to Gloucester.

Rachel spent the following few days on tenterhooks, waiting for Diego to return to Hardwick, certain that he would be furious with her for running out on him. She had made it clear that she was ending their affair, but could she trust herself to resist him if he tried to persuade her back into his bed?

In the event her sleepless nights were for nothing. Diego was due to spend one more week at Hardwick Polo Club, but on Monday morning, when she arrived at the stables, she learned from the other stable-hands that he wasn't coming back and had already flown to his polo school in the States.

'How was your trip to Cornwall?' Alex asked her.

'Cornwall…?' She stared at him blankly, her insides churning at the knowledge that Diego had gone and that she would never see him again.

'To see your dad—Diego told us you'd gone to visit him for a few days,' Alex said cheerfully.

'Oh…yes…it was fine,' she mumbled, shaken that Diego had lied on her behalf. He had known she hadn't wanted anyone at Hardwick to find out about their affair and the realisation that he had taken steps to protect her from being the subject of gossip caused her heart to splinter.

She had done the right thing in refusing to go to New York with him, she reassured herself that night as she tossed restlessly beneath the sheet, unable to sleep in her airless caravan. In a few weeks' time Diego would return to his native Argentina—and she would have had to come back to England and start all over again, looking for a job and somewhere to live. Another month in his bed was all he had ever offered, and she would never forget the hard expression in his eyes when he'd challenged her to 'take it or leave it'.

The days after she had ended her affair with Diego stretched slowly into weeks, and eventually the whole summer dragged by, but the curious lethargy that had settled over Rachel grew steadily worse. Life seemed to have lost its sparkle, and the aching loneliness inside her was not eased by spending time with her friends, or even riding Piran. She seemed to be running on autopilot and even though she threw herself into work and socialising, and competing in various showjumping events, nothing could alter the fact that she missed Diego desperately.

In early September she won a place with the British Show Jumping Team to compete in the European championships. Peter Irving was delighted and she forced herself to act as though she was excited. Competing at a national level had been her lifelong ambition, but instead of feeling euphoric she felt flat and tired, and angry with herself that she was still pining for a man who had probably forgotten all about her.

Diego had been busy for the past weeks. Rachel had read in various riding magazines of his success in polo matches in Barbados, Singapore, and most recently at the US Open Polo Championships in Palm Beach, Florida, and she had felt sick with misery when she'd stared at the photo of him surrounded by gorgeous glamour models. The nauseous feeling continued to plague her. She'd probably picked up one of the many viruses that seemed to be around in the autumn, but decided to mention it to her doctor when she went to collect a new supply of her contraceptive pill.

'Everything else is normal?' the doctor queried. 'When was your last period?'

Rachel frowned. Since she had been on the pill her periods were so light that they often only lasted for a day and she never made a note of them. Her last pill-free week had been three weeks ago, but now that she thought of it, she could not recall needing to buy tampons for ages.

'I think I might have missed a couple,' she said slowly, puzzled rather than concerned. 'But the same thing happened last year, and it turned out that I was anaemic.'

'Well, I can arrange a blood test. And it might be an idea to do a pregnancy test—just to rule it out,' the doctor murmured when she caught Rachel's shocked expression.

'I *can't* be pregnant,' she said forcefully. 'I've never, ever forgotten to take a pill.'

She repeated the statement to the surgery nurse when she handed in her urine sample. 'I'm sure there's nothing to worry about,' the nurse replied soothingly. 'Take a seat in the waiting room and the doctor will call you in to discuss the result in a few minutes.'

Rachel tried to ignore the nervous flutter in her stomach.

Of course she wasn't pregnant. She'd lost weight over the past weeks rather than gained it and was thinner than ever. It was true that she was more tired than usual, and had been for weeks, but that wasn't surprising when she had been sleeping badly—her dreams regularly haunted by Diego.

It was just a blip in her cycle, she reassured herself. But the grave expression on the doctor's face when she walked into the consulting room filled her with dread.

'It must be a mistake,' she croaked minutes later, so utterly devastated by the news that she was expecting Diego's baby that she could barely speak.

'Did you have a stomach upset at any time?' the doctor queried. 'Being sick can reduce the effectiveness of the pill— as can certain antibiotics.'

Rachel shook her head but the reference to antibiotics triggered a memory. 'I was bitten by a horse,' she said slowly, 'and at the casualty unit I was given a course of antibiotics to prevent the wound infecting. That couldn't have led to me falling pregnant—could it?' she asked desperately.

'I'll check with the hospital to see which antibiotics you were given, but it's the most likely reason. More important is the fact that you are definitely pregnant, and I'm going to arrange for you to have a scan to determine when you conceived.'

When you conceived… The words thudded in Rachel's brain. It was now the end of September, and she had ended her affair with Diego on Ladies' Day at Ascot, which this year had been the nineteenth of June. That meant that she must be nearly four months pregnant—possibly more, she thought sickly, remembering how she had been bitten by Earl Hardwick's horse and started the course of antibiotics on the day after she had made love with Diego for the first time.

'I don't look pregnant,' she said desperately, staring down at her flat stomach.

'A scan will tell us more,' the doctor said firmly.

And it did. Four days later Rachel stared disbelievingly at the grainy image on the screen while the nurse pointed out her baby's heartbeat and explained that she was eighteen weeks pregnant.

'The baby is only six inches long at the moment. There's plenty of time for you—and he or she—to grow,' the nurse said cheerfully when Rachel—still clinging to the forlorn hope that it could all be a mistake—pointed out that she did not have a bump or any other visible signs that she was pregnant.

How hadn't she known? she wondered as she lay in bed in the caravan that night, her mind whirling. She felt as though her body had let her down by withholding the usual signs of pregnancy. But the signs had been there, she acknowledged grimly. It was just that she'd put her uncharacteristic tiredness and mood swings down to the fact that she was in love with a man who lived on the other side of the world and wanted nothing more to do with her.

The doctor had told her that taking the pill during the early stages of her pregnancy would not have harmed the baby. She had also quietly pointed out to Rachel that if she did not wish to continue with the pregnancy they would have to act fast. Rachel's response had been immediate—she could not contemplate a termination—but she felt neither joy nor excitement at the prospect of having a child.

'Tell the father, and give his name to the Child Support Agency if he refuses to cough up with some money,' her mother advised when, in sheer desperation, Rachel phoned her. 'Bringing up a kid alone is tough, I can tell you.'

Liz Summers could offer no practical help. She had left her third husband for an Irish artist and was moving to Dublin, taking Rachel's twin half-sisters with her, and she had made it clear that she did not view the prospect of being a grandmother with any enthusiasm. Rachel shuddered at the idea of asking Diego for money. She did not want anything from him, but he had the right to know that she was expecting his child, she acknowledged heavily. The only trouble was she had no idea how to contact him. She knew he owned a ranch, but Argentina was a big country.

Eventually her brain clicked into gear and she found the number of his polo school in New York on the Internet but, when she phoned, the receptionist refused to give his address in Argentina, and instead took Rachel's name and promised she would pass on the message for him to phone her. But he didn't ring, and as the weeks passed Rachel stopped rehearsing how she would break the news that she was expecting his baby and faced up to the fact that she was five months pregnant; she would not be able to continue with her job at the stables for much longer—or keep her place with the British Show Jumping Team—and that a cramped caravan was not a suitable place to bring up a child.

It was raining in Gloucestershire—sheeting rain that teemed down the car windscreen faster than the wipers could clear it. Diego's mouth compressed as he negotiated the winding lanes leading to Hardwick Hall, and not for the first time he wondered what he was doing here when he could be on a plane to Argentina.

He had recently been in Thailand, competing in a series of polo matches, and he missed the heat and sunshine. Back home, the temperature in Buenos Aires would be thirty degrees centigrade, but here in England the display on the car dashboard was registering a measly three degrees and the late November sky was a dismal slate grey. A series of business meetings in London had necessitated him staying at his Thames-side apartment for the past couple of weeks, evoking memories of the last time he had been there with

Rachel, and his curiosity to know why she had tried to contact him had finally got the better of him.

He drove straight past the entrance to the Hardwick estate. The groom he'd spoken to when he had phoned the stables had explained that Rachel no longer worked there, but that she was still living in the caravan on Irving's farm. Why had she left Hardwick and the job he knew she loved? he brooded. And where did she now keep her horse?

Diego frowned, irritated with himself for his interest. From the moment he'd walked into his apartment after the day at Ascot and found her gone, he had dismissed her from his mind, furious—and, if he was honest, piqued—that she had been the one to end their affair. It was a novelty he had not enjoyed and he'd felt a certain amount of satisfaction when the receptionist at his polo school in New York had passed on a message that a Miss Rachel Summers had requested that he should phone her.

It was almost two months since Rachel had tried to contact him, and he had been too busy travelling to polo competitions around the world to return her call. But, to his annoyance, she had lurked in his subconscious. Had she called because she wanted to resume their affair? He was about to find out, Diego thought grimly as he drove through the farmyard and up the muddy track.

The caravan looked even smaller and older than he remembered. Maybe she had decided that being the mistress of a multimillionaire wasn't so bad after all, he brooded cynically. Not that he had any intention of taking her back. But, to his intense irritation, he could not control the sudden quickening of his heartbeat as he walked up the caravan steps and rapped on the door.

'Hello, Rachel.'

Rachel was suffering from a flu virus. For the past three days she'd had a pounding headache, a sore throat and aching limbs, and her temperature must be sky high, because now she was hallucinating.

'*Diego?*'

She could barely comprehend that he was here, and she was horrified by the effect his sudden appearance was having on her. Her heart was pounding and she felt breathless and dizzy, but none of these symptoms were the result of her pregnancy—or the flu virus, she acknowledged dismally.

The sight of him after all this time seared her soul. He was even more gorgeous than she remembered, his tanned skin gleaming like polished bronze and his silky dark hair brushing his shoulders. She wanted to touch him, felt a desperate urge to throw herself against his chest and have him close his arms around her and hold her safe. But when had she ever been safe with Diego? she asked herself bitterly. He was the reason that every one of her dreams had turned to dust.

'What do you want?' she croaked.

Diego frowned and glanced over her shoulder at the packing boxes and the pile of clothes that littered the floor. 'To talk to you,' he said tersely. 'Can I come in? This is obviously a bad time, but I'm flying home tomorrow.'

The last thing Rachel wanted to do was invite Diego into her caravan, and their 'talk' was likely to be explosive, she thought grimly, but the rain was soaking his hair and shoulders and dully she stepped back to allow him inside. It was amazing how much clutter she'd collected over the last five years, she thought ruefully, hastily shifting a pile of old riding magazines so that he could sit down.

Even sitting, Diego seemed to dominate the tiny living space. He stretched his long legs out in front of him and Rachel felt a fierce tug of longing as her eyes skimmed his black designer jeans and the superbly cut tan leather jacket that he wore over a black fine-knit sweater. He looked as incongruous as he had done the first time he had visited her caravan and, as she recalled the passion that had flamed between them on that occasion, colour flooded her pale cheeks.

But there was no hint of the feverish desire that had burned in his amber eyes that day. He was looking at her with an expression of faint distaste that grew more marked as his gaze moved down from her lank hair, scraped back in a ponytail, to her voluminous sweatshirt. His eyes were cold and hard. Rachel had forgotten how autocratic he could look and she was suddenly glad that the sweatshirt concealed the still quite small bump of her pregnancy.

'Why are you here?' she mumbled, her voice thick with cold.

'I received the message you left with the Ortega Academy in New York that you wanted to speak to me,' Diego replied laconically. 'Was it something important?'

Rachel gave a harsh laugh, her temper flaring at his patent disinterest. 'Do you care if it was? I called you two months ago.'

His eyes narrowed at the accusation in her voice. 'I've been busy.'

She recalled the newspaper photo of him surrounded by the promotional models and felt sick. 'Yes, I imagine you have.'

'From the look of it, so have you,' Diego commented, glancing at the packing boxes. 'Can I take it you've finally decided to move to somewhere more habitable?'

'There's nothing wrong with living in a caravan,' Rachel said tightly, infuriated by his scathing tone. 'It's just that it's not a suitable place to bring up a baby…'

Every muscle in Diego's body tensed. His heart had frozen into a solid block of ice on the day Eduardo had died, and he had believed that nothing could ever touch him or stir his emotions. Now, as a torrent of feelings swept through him, he realised that he had been wrong. He was astounded by Rachel's startling statement but, to his surprise, his overwhelming reaction to the news that she was carrying another man's child was one of gut-wrenching disappointment.

The silence between them simmered with tension. This was not how Rachel had ever envisaged telling Diego that she was expecting his baby, she acknowledged wryly. The words had spilled out of her mouth and the moment she'd uttered them she'd stiffened, waiting fearfully for his reaction. His expression was unfathomable, but after a few moments he gave a faint shrug and got to his feet.

'I see,' he murmured coldly. 'Well, I think that's my cue to leave.' He turned towards the door but then glanced back at her, his lip curling in a look of utter contempt. 'You didn't waste much time hopping into another man's bed, did you, Rachel? Who is the father, by the way—your red-haired stable-boy? Tell me, did you get together with him after you walked out on me, or were you sleeping with both of us at the same time?'

Rachel flinched at his deliberate crudity and a curious numbness seeped through her body. She had never kidded herself that Diego would welcome the news of her pregnancy, but he was looking at her as though she was the lowest lifeform on the planet. She licked her suddenly dry lips and forced her throat to work. 'It's not Alex's baby,' she said quietly. 'It's yours.'

Anger coursed through Diego's veins like molten lava. What kind of a fool did she take him for? 'How can you possibly be carrying my child when we split up months ago? If your boyfriend won't face up to his responsibilities, that's your problem. It has nothing to do with me.'

Rachel had been so shocked by Diego's furious denial that he was the father of her baby that her brain temporarily ceased functioning. But, as he pulled open the door and she realised he was actually going to leave, she jerked back to life. Anger burned inside her, turning the ice in her blood to fire. Trembling with rage, she gripped the hem of her sweatshirt and dragged it over her head, and felt a swift spurt of satisfaction at the undisguised shock in his eyes when he stared at her swollen stomach.

'This is your baby, Diego,' she said fiercely. 'I'm seven months pregnant. I didn't even know until I was almost five months, and when I found out, I tried to contact you. I thought you had a right to know.'

Diego shook his head, his eyes glacial. 'I don't believe for a second that I'm the father. And if you think I'm going to pay out for another man's child, think again.'

'Alex is my friend. We have never been lovers,' Rachel cried angrily.

Diego threw her another look of withering scorn and strode down the caravan steps. 'Then you must have trapped some other poor fool,' he snarled. 'But I tell you now, *querida*, you're not dragging me into your web of deceit.'

He was going—marching across the field and leaving footprints in the mud. Rachel stared disbelievingly at his retreating form and for a few seconds she thought—let him go and good riddance. But then the baby kicked and she automatically put her hand on her stomach and felt the hard bulge of a tiny foot or elbow. It wasn't the baby's fault that it had been conceived by sheer fluke. Yet Diego had turned his back on his child, had utterly rejected the possibility that he was the father. Anger surged through her once more and she gripped the edge of the door frame, peering through at the rain that fell relentlessly from the leaden sky.

'You are the father, Diego. It couldn't be anyone else because you're the only man I've ever slept with.'

He carried on walking without altering his pace, but then halted abruptly and swung back to stare at her, his face as cold and hard as if he had been hewn from granite. 'What did you say?' he queried in a dangerously soft tone.

'The first time we made love…I was a virgin,' she faltered.

'Liar.' The single word cracked through the air like a gunshot. 'I would have known,' he added arrogantly before he swung on his heel and disappeared down the track.

CHAPTER EIGHT

RACHEL was lying. She had to be. He had not been her first lover. Diego stared moodily out of the hotel window at the wintry landscape. He hated England at this time of year—cold, grey and as dismal as his spirits. He was due to catch a flight to Buenos Aires later today and he was impatient to be on his way but, to his fury, he could not forget the image of her standing in the doorway of her dilapidated caravan, crying out to him that he was the father of her child.

The waitress who had served him at dinner last night sashayed over to his table and smiled at him. He noted that she had unfastened the top three buttons of her blouse, and when she took out her pad to take his order she deliberately leaned close to him.

'Would you like the full English breakfast, Mr Ortega? Bacon, sausage, egg, fried bread…'

Diego's stomach churned. He hadn't slept last night and this morning his appetite was non-existent. 'I'll just have more coffee, thank you.'

'Are you staying long?' The waitress looked at him guilelessly from beneath her lashes. 'I could always show you around, if you like.'

The girl was pretty and blonde, and eight months ago he would probably have been sufficiently interested to take up her offer. Now, all he could think of was another blonde with big cornflower-blue eyes that had watched him when she'd thought he hadn't noticed.

When he had first arrived at Hardwick, Rachel had been feisty and hot-tempered, but she had also been shy and wary and had gone to great lengths to hide her awareness of him. She had responded to him when he had kissed her with a passion that had inflamed his desire, but when he had taken her to bed that first time he had been faintly surprised by her hesitancy, he recalled grimly.

Santa Madre! Was it possible he had taken her virginity that night? And, in return, had he given her a child? He frowned, remembering his frustration when he'd realised he did not have any protection—and the sweet flood of relief when she had assured him she was on the pill. He had been so hungry for her that he had ignored the voice of common sense in his head reminding him of his golden rule that contraception was his responsibility.

Clearly she had lied to him, but it did not necessarily follow that he was the father of her baby, he reminded himself darkly. She could have had other lovers after him. It was possible that she was less than seven months pregnant. But as he pictured her swollen belly, clearly outlined beneath the clingy top she had been wearing under her sweatshirt yesterday, he acknowledged with a heavy sense of finality that her pregnancy was well advanced.

Anger coursed through him—directed as much at his own stupidity as Rachel's duplicity. He would demand proof that the child was his before he paid her a penny—because of course money was what she wanted. And then he would…what? Walk away? Could he really go back to Argentina and get on with his life, knowing that his own flesh and blood was being brought up in a field? He did not want a child, and yet if Rachel was to be believed his child would come into this world in a matter of weeks. A mixture of frustration and fury gnawed in his gut, but at the same time he could not deny a sense of wonderment at the idea of being a father.

Diego had no memory of his own father. According to his mother, Ricardo had left her for some harlot he'd picked up in Buenos Aires when he and Eduardo were babies. Lorena Ortega had married a good-for-nothing gigolo—a fact that Diego's grandfather had frequently pointed out, before adding in the same breath that Diego was just like his father.

He could almost hear the old man now, taunting him that he was a feckless, unreliable playboy. Such was Alonso Ortega's hatred of his son-in-law that after Lorena had divorced Ricardo Hernandez she had abided by her father's wishes and changed her name, and that of her two sons, back to Ortega. Alonso would not have been surprised that Diego had fathered an illegitimate child. Like father, like son, he would have decreed, had he still been alive. But his grandfather would have been wrong, Diego thought fiercely, pushing his half-drunk cup of coffee aside and jerking to his feet. If he really was the father of Rachel's baby, then he would accept his responsibilities and do what needed to be done.

Moving house was stressful at the best of times, and Rachel had discovered that moving, after spending the previous night alternating between rage and tears after her confrontation with Diego, and with a soaring temperature and a throat that felt as though she'd swallowed broken glass had sent her stress levels through the roof.

Not that she had actually moved into a house, she acknowledged as she stared around the shabby bedsit on the top floor of the Rose and Crown. But the room was marginally bigger and warmer than the caravan, and she was grateful to Bill Bailey, the landlord, for offering it to her for a very reasonable rent.

Thanks to Bill, she also had a job working as a waitress in the pub's restaurant, at least until the baby came. Being on her feet for hours every evening made her legs and back ache, but since she could no longer ride she could not afford to be choosy about where she worked. Job opportunities for an unmarried pregnant stable-hand were not exactly thick on the ground, she thought ruefully. Since she had left Hardwick Polo Club the news of her pregnancy had flown around the village, and speculation that Diego Ortega was the father of her baby had been fuelled by Jasper Hardwick.

What she was going to do when the baby was born, she had no idea. Earl Hardwick had said he would abide by the terms of her employment contract and keep a job for her at the polo club, but in reality she knew she could not return to work at the stables when she had a baby to care for and her low wages would not cover child-care fees. She was struggling to survive now on the small amount of maternity pay she was entitled to, and without Bill's kindness she did not know how she would manage.

The future was beginning to loom frighteningly close when she considered that she was due to give birth in the middle of February and it was already late November. One thing was certain—she would have to manage on her own, she thought grimly. Diego had made it abundantly clear that he wanted nothing to do with her, or the baby that he refused to believe was his.

She sat on the edge of the bed and glanced wearily at the boxes that Bill had carried up the three flights of stairs to the attic flat. She really should start to unpack, but she was so cold that her teeth were chattering and she curled up in a ball, dragged the duvet over her and fell instantly into a restless doze.

Even while she was asleep her head was pounding. The insistent hammering was going right through her brain, but then suddenly, blessedly it stopped.

'So you *are* here—the landlord said you were in. I've been knocking for five minutes. Why didn't you open the door?'

Rachel winced as the angry growl penetrated her skull, and she forced her eyes open and peered groggily at Diego. 'What are *you* doing here?' Her voice sounded over-loud in her ears—she was unaware that it had emerged from her raw throat as a hoarse whisper.

There was a frown of concern on Diego's face as he hunkered down next to the bed and placed his hand on her brow. '*Dios*, you're burning up with a fever,' he muttered. 'Don't go back to sleep, Rachel; I need to get you to a doctor.'

'I saw my doctor two days ago,' she told him, fighting her way out of the duvet because she was now boiling over. 'I've just got a flu virus, that's all, but I can't take any of the usual cold remedies because of the baby.'

The mere mention of the baby caused Diego's brows to lower ominously—although, even when he looked angry, he was still the most gorgeous man she'd ever set eyes on, Rachel thought bleakly. Today he was wearing pale denim jeans and a thick oatmeal sweater topped by a suede car-coat, and he looked so powerful and ruggedly good-looking that her insides melted. She pushed the duvet aside and as his eyes skimmed over her she felt horribly self-conscious of her stomach, clearly defined beneath her maternity top.

'What do you want?' she demanded tersely.

God alone knew—because he certainly didn't, Diego thought grimly. All he knew was that the sight of Rachel looking so heart-wrenchingly vulnerable evoked a curious ache in his chest. He forced himself to ignore it and stood up, no flicker of warmth in his amber eyes as he stared down at her.

'I want the truth,' he said harshly, his accent sounding very pronounced. 'I will ask you one more time. Who is the father of your child?'

'You can ask me a hundred times and the answer will still be the same,' Rachel snapped. How dared he doubt her word? She glared at him, stiff with pride and anger, unaware of how fragile she looked with her hair spilling around her shoulders and the hectic, unhealthy flush on her cheeks. 'You are.'

Diego's jaw clenched as bitter anger swirled inside him. Anger at himself for having been such a gullible fool, and anger at her for…for walking out on him, he owned grimly. He had felt as though he'd been kicked in the gut when he had returned to his London apartment after Ascot and found she'd gone. And now, months later, she was insisting that her body was swollen with his child. 'I want proof,' he said icily. 'I did some research last night and discovered that it's now possible to run a DNA test while a child is in the womb. You'll have to give a blood sample, and from that the baby's DNA can be detected with no risk to either of you.'

'I don't need to prove anything,' Rachel snapped furiously. 'You were the first and only man I've ever had sex with and, like it or not, this baby is yours.'

An unexpected surge of possessiveness swept through Diego at the idea that he was Rachel's only lover. She could be lying, but he could not dismiss his memory of her rapt expression that first time he had made love to her, the look of startled wonder in her eyes when he had eased into her and joined their bodies as one. But, if she had been a virgin, why hadn't she told him?

'Did you plan to get pregnant?' he growled angrily.

Rachel was so shocked by his accusation that for a moment she could not speak. 'Did I *plan* it?' she said in a tight, cold voice. 'Do you think I *want* to be pregnant?' Blinding, burning rage swept through her. 'I have lost everything,' she told him bitterly. 'The job that I loved, my home—my horse.' She swallowed the lump that formed in her throat every time she thought of Piran. 'I had won a place with the British Show

Jumping Team, but obviously I had to stand down.' Her voice faltered. 'I couldn't deprive Piran of his chance to compete in the European Championships, and fortunately Peter Irving managed to find another rider to take my place. Piran now lives on his new owner's farm in Norfolk—too far away for me to visit him,' she said thickly.

She closed her eyes wearily, blocking out Diego's startled expression. 'No, I didn't plan it, and I didn't lie to you. I was on the pill but it didn't work properly—something to do with the antibiotics I was prescribed after I was bitten by that horse. It was just…bad luck,' she said quietly. 'But it's my problem, Diego, and I'll deal with it. I don't want anything from you. I'll manage fine on my own.'

Diego's brows drew together. The conversation wasn't going as he had envisaged. He had expected Rachel to be pleased to see him, grateful that he had given her another chance to convince him that he was the baby's father. And he *was* convinced, he realised with a jolt. Even without a DNA test, his instincts told him that the child she was carrying was his—but, instead of seeming pleased that he was here, she was prickly and belligerent, and plainly unhappy about being pregnant.

His eyes were drawn to her swollen stomach and he felt a curious sensation in his chest, as if his heart were expanding. His child was growing inside her. If she was seven months along, then the baby must be fully formed—his son or daughter, and the next Ortega heir. He felt an overwhelming urge to reach out and touch Rachel's abdomen, to feel his child move. But something in her angry stare warned him that she would not allow him the liberty of touching her, not when there was this yawning chasm of mistrust between them.

'How do you intend to manage?' he queried, glancing around the shabby room with its collection of old furniture and wallpaper peeling in places from the walls.

Rachel moved over to the window and looked down on the paved back yard where the pub guard dogs—two massive black Rottweilers—were prowling. She certainly wouldn't be able to put the baby outside in the pram for some fresh air, she thought ruefully. It was yet another reminder that her situation was far from ideal.

'I'm thinking about having the baby adopted.'

For the second time in his life Diego felt as though he had been kicked in the stomach. Discovering that he was going to be a father had been shocking enough, but Rachel's calm statement sent the oxygen rushing from his lungs. 'How could you even contemplate such a thing?' he grated savagely. 'Do you think I would allow you to hand my child over to strangers?'

Something pinged in Rachel's chest at the possessive way Diego had said 'my child', and for the first time since her pregnancy had been confirmed she pictured the baby as a little human being rather than an alien growing inside her and altering her body-shape out of recognition. Up until now she had viewed her unplanned pregnancy as a problem—a huge life-changing problem that she felt ill-equipped to deal with. But now, suddenly, she was intrigued by the little person that she and Diego had created. Was the baby a boy, with dark hair and his father's tiger-like amber eyes? she wondered. And could she really give birth to this baby and then give it away?

Diego was staring at her as if she were a despicable mass murderer, and she knew she sounded defensive when she snapped, '*Your* child, Diego? Yesterday you were adamant that the baby's father was one of my legions of lovers.'

'And today I am prepared to accept the likelihood that the child is mine,' he bit back tersely. He shook his head, utterly taken aback by the idea that she did not intend to keep the baby. What kind of life would this child have, he wondered grimly, deprived of that most fundamental requirement—a mother's love? He knew what that felt like. From as far back as he could remember, his mother had disliked him and had reserved all her love for Eduardo. His grandmother had told him before she had died that his birth had taken everyone by surprise. His mother had not known she was expecting twins and his arrival into the world had been a traumatic experience for her after Eduardo's uncomplicated birth. According to *abuela* Elvira, Lorena had failed to bond with her second-born son, and as Diego had grown up his resemblance to his father had caused his mother to reject him even more.

His eyes were drawn to Rachel's belly and he felt a surge of empathy with the child she carried within her. 'Don't you want our baby, Rachel?' he queried harshly.

He was doing it again—stirring her emotions with the words *'our baby'*. Rachel bit her lip as she thought back over the past few months when she had almost resented the child she had never expected to conceive. 'It's not that I don't want it,' she said shakily, 'but, more importantly, I want what is best for the baby.' She glanced around the dingy bedsit. 'I don't have the means to bring up a child, but there are hundreds of couples who are desperate for a baby, and who are in a better financial situation to give it a happy, secure upbringing with two parents who will love it.'

'Are you saying then that you do not think *we* can do all those things?'

Rachel gave Diego a scathing glance. 'There is no we, Diego. Until yesterday you didn't know I was pregnant, and I had no way of contacting you. If you hadn't shown up, you would never have known you had fathered a child.'

The idea that Rachel could have had his baby and handed it over to adoptive parents made Diego's blood run cold. He was startled by the feelings of protectiveness and possessiveness that swept through him, and by the realisation that he would love his child unconditionally.

'Tell me honestly,' he demanded harshly. 'If you were in a situation where you could bring up the child properly, would you want to keep it? Would you love it?'

It was so unexpected to hear cool, controlled Diego talk about love, in a voice deepened by emotion, that tears stung Rachel's eyes. 'Of course I would love it,' she whispered, images of a tiny dark-haired infant swirling in her mind. Did Diego believe she had contemplated putting her baby up for adoption lightly? 'Of course I would.'

'Then there is only one thing to be done.' For the first time in twenty-four hours, a feeling of calm settled over Diego— an acceptance of the inevitable and a realisation that there could only be one resolution to the situation. Since Eduardo's death, he had deliberately avoided relationships where his emotions might become involved, but he would not abandon his child, and he could not spend the rest of his life running away. 'You will marry me, Rachel, and we will bring our child up together in Argentina.'

Rachel's legs suddenly felt like jelly, although whether because of shock at Diego's outrageous statement or the effects of the flu virus, she did not know. Possibly both, she conceded as she sank weakly down onto the bed. A dozen responses whirled in her aching head, but one thought took precedence over all the others.

'My mother married my father because she was pregnant with me—and, trust me, it really didn't work. I have no intention of repeating my parents' mistakes,' she told him fiercely.

For a moment he made no reply, just stood watching her intently as if he was determined to read her mind. 'As a matter of fact, my mother and father married for the same reason,' he said coolly. 'I have no memories of my father—apparently he walked out when my twin brother and I were babies. But clearly a shotgun wedding didn't work for my parents, either.'

Rachel gave him a startled glance. It was the first time he had ever mentioned his family and she was annoyed with herself for wanting to hoard any small snippet of information about him. 'I didn't know you have a twin. Are you identical?' It seemed impossible that there was another man as dynamic and possessing the same powerful magnetism as Diego in the world.

'We were alike, but not identical,' he said abruptly.

'Were?' Rachel murmured hesitantly.

'My brother died ten years ago.'

Diego's tone warned Rachel not to pursue the subject, but she caught the flare of pain in his eyes and her heart contracted. To lose a twin must be devastating. She thought of her twin half-sisters from her mother's third marriage. Emma and Kate were five now. They shared such a close bond that each seemed to know what the other twin was thinking, and when they spoke they frequently finished each other's sentences. She could not imagine how one of her sisters would function without the other, and she wondered how Diego had coped with his terrible loss.

During the month they had spent together she had believed him to be the wealthy, successful but emotionally shallow playboy he liked to portray. The passion they had shared had been electrifying, but she realised now that she hadn't known the real Diego Ortega at all.

'If a marriage of convenience didn't work for either of our parents, why suggest it when you know it's doomed to failure…?' she began, but he cut her off.

'What did you want more than anything when you were growing up, Rachel?'

'A horse,' she said tersely, wondering where the conversation was leading. She cast her mind back over her childhood and shrugged. 'Actually, what I wanted more than anything was to be my friend Clare—to live in a normal family with a mum and dad who weren't for ever screaming abuse at each other. Clare's parents liked each other, and I've always thought that that's how marriage should be—an equal partnership, friendship…'

'It seems that we share the same views on marriage,' Diego said quietly. 'As a child, I too wished that I had two parents who loved and cared for me.' Rather than a mother who despised him because he was a constant reminder of the man who had broken her heart. 'I think that for the sake of our child we could be friends, Rachel, and have the kind of marriage you described.

'We were friends once,' he reminded her when she stared at him in stunned silence. 'Until the day we went to Ascot, we had a good relationship.' They had shared a closeness that he had neither sought nor expected and, although he hated to admit it, he had missed her when she had abruptly ended their affair. 'I ended my friendship with Guy Chetwin, by the way. And threatened him with legal action if he ever insulted you again,' he added grimly.

Diego would be a dangerous adversary, Rachel thought with a shiver as she stared at his hard face. But she felt a little thrill of pleasure that he had defended her. It was true that they had shared friendship, as well as incredible sex while he had been at Hardwick, but for her it had been more than that. She had fallen in love with him. But when they had argued at Ascot he had bluntly told her that he had never planned on their affair leading to any kind of permanent relationship. It would be emotional suicide to marry a man who would never love her.

'Getting married is a mad idea,' she muttered. 'It would never work.' Her head was pounding worse than ever and every muscle in her body was aching with the effects of the flu virus. She wished Diego would go away and leave her alone, but he was looming over her, big and powerful and with a determined glint in his eyes that made her heart sink. He was difficult enough to fight at the best of times and right now she was in no fit state to do battle with him.

'So what do you suggest?' he demanded forcefully. 'You are carrying the heir to the Ortega fortune. I want our child to be born legitimately, and I am determined to take an active role in its life. Can you really deny the baby his or her birthright?'

Could she? What right did she have to deprive the baby of its father? And how could she think straight when her head was about to explode? 'I don't know what to do,' Rachel admitted weakly. She closed her eyes—as if by blotting Diego from view she could make him disappear. She had never expected him to reappear in her life, and she was even more stunned by his avowal that he wanted his child.

'It's not just a question of getting married,' she muttered. 'I'd have to move to the other side of the world to a strange country…'

'Argentina is not a strange country,' Diego assured her, his mouth curving into a sudden smile that made her heart turn over. 'It is a beautiful, vibrant country and I promise you will fall in love with it, *querida*.'

He was startled to see a tear trickle from beneath Rachel's lashes, and he felt a pang of guilt. She was clearly unwell, and he knew that in all fairness he should wait until she was feeling stronger before he demanded an answer to his proposal. But life wasn't always fair, and he had no compunction about seizing his opportunity. He wanted his child, and that meant he would have to persuade Rachel to marry him.

He dropped down onto the bed and tugged her into his arms, faintly surprised that she put up no resistance. This quiet, biddable Rachel would not be around for long. Once she had recovered from the virus that had caused her to look like death he was certain her usual feistiness would return, but for now she simply rested her head against his chest while he stroked his hand through her mane of long blonde hair.

He had forgotten how silky it was, and how soft her skin felt beneath his fingertips when he brushed a tear from her face. He liked her new rounded shape, and as he tightened his arms around her so that her full breasts were pressed against him he felt the slow burn of desire ignite inside him. *Dios!* She was heavy with child and burning up with a fever, yet he was more turned on than he had been for months. His desire for her was an unexpected complication—but perhaps not, he mused as he shifted position in an effort to ease the throb of his arousal. He had no great yearning to marry, but there was a child to consider, and at least he knew that he and Rachel were sexually compatible.

'Let me take care of you and the baby,' he murmured, brushing his lips over her hair.

His words struck a chord deep inside Rachel, and the feel of his strong arms around her evoked a desperate longing for him to protect her. If she was honest, she was scared witless about the future and she was tired of putting on a brave face and assuring herself and everyone that she would cope as a single mother. She did not want to do this on her own, and she did not want to give up her baby, she acknowledged, feeling a knife skewer her heart at the thought.

If she had been feeling herself she might have put up more of an argument against marrying Diego, but she felt physically and emotionally drained. He had offered to take care of her and right now those words, uttered in his deep, sensuous voice, drove her doubts to the back of her mind.

'When were you thinking of getting married?' she croaked, her hand straying to her stomach.

He placed his hand next to hers and she saw the faintly startled look in his eyes when he found that her bump was solid. 'I'll make the necessary arrangements immediately,' he said coolly. 'We don't have much time.'

CHAPTER NINE

THEY drove up to Diego's London apartment that day. Rachel slept for most of the journey and spent the following week in bed, so weakened by the virus that she did not even have the energy to argue with Diego when he brought meals to her room on a tray and stood over her until she had eaten enough to satisfy him.

She was dismayed by how little resistance she put up when he bossed her around, and how much she enjoyed being fussed over—even though she knew his concern was for the baby rather than her. She had been fiercely independent for so long that it was frightening to realise that she was turning into one of those pathetic women who meekly gave way to their husband on everything—and they weren't even married yet! But when Diego smiled at her she felt as though her insides were melting, and when he leaned over her bed to plump up her pillows she ached for him to lower his mouth to hers and kiss her until kissing was no longer enough for either of them and he traced his hands over her eager body.

But he never did. He was attentive and charming now that he had won the marriage argument, but nothing in his manner suggested that he found her sexually attractive.

It was hardly surprising, Rachel conceded three weeks later, on the morning of their wedding, when she donned the pale blue maternity dress and matching swing-coat which had cost a fortune from a top design house. The coat was cleverly cut to disguise the fact that she was heavily pregnant but she still felt like a ship in full sail, and there was nothing sexy about her big round football stomach, she decided ruefully.

Diego had arranged for Jemima Philips, the stylist who had helped Rachel choose an outfit for Ascot, to accompany her on a shopping trip for her trousseau. The irony of searching for a maternity bridal outfit six months after she had last been in London buying sexy underwear to seduce Diego was not lost on her. At least she had stuck to her guns and refused to buy a dress that was white, cream or overtly bridal, she mused. She was not a blushing bride, and Diego was far from a loving groom. They were marrying for purely practical reasons—although the doubts that Rachel had conveniently ignored while she had been ill were multiplying at a frantic rate now that she was better.

'We can be good parents to the baby without being married,' she had reasoned when he had informed her that they would be flying to Argentina immediately after their civil wedding. But the results of the DNA test which Diego had insisted on had proved beyond doubt that he was the baby's father, and he was utterly determined that his child would be born legitimately.

'So what do you suggest?' he demanded when she admitted that she was having second thoughts about becoming his wife. 'That I should set you up in an apartment in Buenos Aires—where you don't know a soul—so that I can visit my child on alternate weekends? Or were you thinking of remaining in England and sending our son or daughter over to Argentina for the school holidays? If that's the kind of life you want for our child then I'll fight for custody and bring the baby up in Argentina on my own.'

'You wouldn't win custody,' Rachel said faintly, shaken by the cold implacability in Diego's eyes. He had been so nice to her when she was ill, and she had been pathetically eager to grasp any sign that he might care for her a little, but this was the real Diego, hard and powerful and used to having his own way.

His smile held no warmth as he said, 'Losing isn't in my vocabulary, *querida*. I can afford the best lawyers, and the fact that you had considered putting the baby up for adoption would be a strong argument against allowing the child to remain with you.'

'But you know I only considered it because I felt the baby would have a better life with adoptive parents than I could give it,' she cried. 'I have only ever wanted what is best for the baby.'

'Then stop fighting with me,' Diego told her bluntly. 'It's not good for your blood pressure.'

The wedding took place at Westminster Register Office at eleven o'clock on a wet Friday morning, and was witnessed by Diego's chauffeur and the housekeeper from his London apartment. Rachel had turned down his offer to invite her family, explaining that her parents could not be in the same room together without old hostilities resurfacing.

It was a stark reminder of the pitfalls of a marriage of convenience. What would happen if in two or three years' time, she and Diego could not bear the sight of each other? She would never put her child through the misery of divorce and torn loyalties, she vowed fiercely. Somehow this marriage that had begun so inauspiciously had to work, and for the baby's sake, she would try her hardest to settle in a new country with a man who did not love her.

As they stood in the waiting room before their marriage ceremony Diego suddenly disappeared and returned moments later to hand her an exquisite bouquet of yellow roses. 'It is customary for a bride to have flowers on her wedding day,' he said quietly when Rachel could not hide her surprise.

Theirs was not a conventional marriage and she had not even thought about flowers, but for some reason Diego's unexpected gesture moved her deeply and she blinked hard to dispel the sudden rush of tears that filled her eyes.

'Thank you. They're beautiful,' she murmured huskily, remembering how he had given her yellow roses when he had visited her caravan after she had been thrown from her horse and the passion that had flared between them when he had kissed her. She wondered if he remembered too, but his closed expression told her nothing and she felt sick with nerves when they stood before the registrar and made their vows. Diego looked impossibly handsome in a charcoal-grey suit, his dark hair brushing his shoulders, and she felt a sharp stab of longing for him to take her in his arms and kiss her as she longed to be kissed instead of brushing his cool lips over hers in a perfunctory gesture.

Immediately after the ceremony Diego assisted her into the waiting limousine for the journey to the airport. The same doctor who had performed the paternity tests on the baby had signed a special consent to allow Rachel to fly, even in her advanced stage of pregnancy. In truth, her heart had sunk a receiving the permission, the last hope for legitimately refusing to go along with Diego's plans removed.

'You won't be able to take your bouquet onto the plane,' he told her when she refused to leave it at the register office.

Rachel felt a fierce reluctance to part with her one memento of her wedding day, and while Diego was looking out of the window she quickly untied the yellow ribbon that secured the roses and slipped it into her handbag.

As the car joined the queue of Christmas getaway traffic into Heathrow, he turned back to her and handed her a small velvet box. 'Your wedding gift,' he murmured, wondering why the wariness in her eyes made him want to pull her into his arms and hold her close.

She was still pale, he noted. There had been a moment during the wedding ceremony when he had feared she would refuse to go through with it, and tension had churned in his gut. But after a few agonising seconds she had made her vows and now, for the first time in days, he could relax.

He had achieved what he wanted; his child would be born in Argentina and would bear the Ortega name. And he had a wife whom he desired more than any other woman, Diego acknowledged with a self-derisive smile. If someone had told him six months ago that he would spend night after sleepless night fantasising about making love to a woman in the later stages of pregnancy, he would have laughed. But it was no laughing matter. He wanted to lie next to Rachel and run his hands over her swollen stomach where his child was growing; he longed to cradle her breasts, which were no longer small but enticingly full, and he ached to gently part her pale thighs and position his body between them.

But something deep inside him told him it would be wrong to suggest that she shared his bed. She was no longer his mistress but the mother of his child, and he had a responsibility towards her that he'd never had for any other woman. Added to that, she was still recovering her strength from the flu virus, as well as coping with the demands of pregnancy and, although she tried to hide it, she was patently nervous about moving to a country she had never even visited before. The last thing she needed was a husband demanding his marital rights, and he would just have to control his urges and give her time to adjust to her new life.

'Open it,' he murmured when Rachel remained staring at the box as though she feared it might explode.

With fumbling fingers she flipped open the lid and caught

her breath at the sight of an oval sapphire surrounded by diamonds which sparkled with fiery brilliance against the velvet surround.

'It's incredible,' she said faintly, because he was plainly waiting for her to say something. The ring was the most spectacular piece of jewellery she had ever seen and she couldn't imagine what it must have cost. But money was no object to Diego and she did not kid herself that he had bought her a ring for sentimental reasons.

Her doubts were confirmed when he murmured, 'I know you should have had an engagement ring before the wedding but it's a bespoke piece which I had made to match a necklace of the same design. We've been invited to numerous social functions in Buenos Aires over the Christmas period, and you'll need some jewellery.'

He lifted her hand and slid the ring next to her wedding band. It felt heavy and, although it fitted perfectly, it looked too big and cumbersome on her slender finger. It certainly wasn't something she would have worn when she had worked at the stables, but she was unlikely to be mucking out loose boxes any time soon, Rachel thought dismally.

She remembered how Diego had insisted on her wearing a designer outfit and an eye-catching diamond choker to Ascot. She had felt as though he had bought her—a feeling made worse when Guy Chetwin had accused her of being a gold-digger. Would Diego's friends in Argentina share the same view? she thought worriedly.

'How far is your ranch from Buenos Aires?' she asked curiously.

'The Estancia Elvira is about a hundred kilometres north of the city. It takes a little over an hour by road, but I usually commute by helicopter.'

'Commute?' Rachel frowned. 'But you live at the.. *estancia*, don't you?'

'No, I prefer to live in town,' Diego said shortly. 'I have a penthouse apartment in the Puerto Madero district of Buenos Aires. There are fantastic views over the port and the city from the forty-second floor, and the shops and nightlife are excellent.'

Rachel's spirits dipped. She disliked heights, loathed shopping, and she didn't relish hitting the nightclubs at her advanced stage of pregnancy. But presumably Diego enjoyed an active social life in Buenos Aires. Would he expect her to accompany him on nights out, she wondered, or did he intend to visit nightclubs without the encumbrance of a heavily pregnant wife?

'But we will stay at the *estancia* sometimes, won't we?' she pressed. The only occasions during their stay in London that Diego hadn't seemed like a stranger was when they had discussed his polo pony breeding programme, and she had been looking forward to living on his ranch, close to the horses.

He gave a faint shrug. 'Perhaps I will take you after the baby is born, but for now it will be better to live in town, close to the amenities. The roads are good, but the *estancia* is still a long way from the hospital.' And it still held too many memories, Diego thought heavily. When he was at the stables he concentrated solely on the horses, but at the *hacienda* where he and Eduardo had spent their childhoods he was bombarded with scenes from the past, and he would swear he had sometimes heard his brother's voice echoing through the corridors. There were too many ghosts at the ranch house, and he did not need reminding of how he had failed Eduardo.

The flight to Argentina took fourteen hours, with a brief stopover at Sao Paolo airport in Brazil. As the plane began its descent over Buenos Aires, Rachel was shocked by the scale of the city and the hundreds of skyscrapers stretching for as far as she could see. It was a stark contrast to the small village in Gloucestershire where she had spent most of her life, and she felt a jolt of panic at the thought of trying to find her way around unfamiliar streets when she didn't speak a word of Spanish.

The heat and humidity when they walked out of the airport building to the waiting car was another shock after the cold winter they had left behind in England.

'The penthouse is fully air-conditioned,' Diego explained when she waved her hand in front of her hot face and asked if it was always this warm. 'The apartment block has a private pool, and there is a gymnasium if you want to get your figure back after the baby is born.'

Rachel stared down at her big stomach and wondered if it would ever go back to its pre-pregnancy flatness. Would Diego show an interest in her again if she worked out and regained her slender shape—or had his desire for her died completely? They had never discussed the physical aspect of their marriage, and as they'd spent their wedding night on the plane the question of sex hadn't come up. Would it tonight she wondered, her heart rate quickening. Would Diego expect her to share his bed now that she was his wife?

She had her answer when they stepped out of the lift, dizzying forty-two storeys from ground level, and Diego ushered her into his penthouse home. Jet lag and nervous tension had combined to make Rachel feel limp with tiredness and her eyes were huge in her pale face as she followed him from room to room, wondering how the cream velvet carpet and silk sofas would fare once the baby grew into an inquisitive, sticky-fingered toddler.

'You look exhausted,' Diego commented tersely, assuring himself that it was natural for him to feel concerned for Rachel, as well as for the baby. He scooped her into his arms, ignoring her yelp of surprise, and strode down the hall. 'I' show you to your room and you can rest for a few hours. Tonight we'll eat at one of my usual restaurants and if you're up to it I'll give you a tour of the local area.'

Rachel nodded, her heart racing from the all too brief pleasure of being held against his chest. When he lowered her onto the pretty pink bedspread she wished he would stretch out next to her, but he quickly straightened up and moved away from the bed.

'We won't be able to eat out once the baby is here,' she murmured. When she had stayed at the cottage with him at Hardwick, Diego had frequently arranged for dinner to be delivered from a nearby restaurant, and it seemed that he still had an aversion to the kitchen.

'I realise that and I have already advertised for a cook. I suppose I will have to become more domesticated,' he said, sounding distinctly unenthusiastic at the prospect. Was he already regretting bringing her here? Rachel wondered, watching him prowl around her room like a caged tiger. There was something wild and primal about Diego and she could not imagine him settling down to a life of cosy domesticity. But he had insisted on marrying her, she reminded herself. And, for the baby's sake, they would both have to adjust and make the best of it.

To her amazement, adapting to her new life in Argentina did not prove as hard as Rachel had anticipated. Diego had withdrawn from his next polo tournament because it would have meant immediately flying to the Bahamas, and he gave her several guided tours of Buenos Aires, although he insisted on taking frequent breaks at street cafés so that she could rest.

'You'll find that Buenos Aires is a cosmopolitan city, with a strong European influence,' he explained as they strolled around the district of La Boca, where the unusual tin houses were painted in rainbow colours. 'The Portenos—as the

citizens of Buenos Aires are called—are a multicultural
people, and you will hear Italian and German spoken just as
much as Spanish.'

It was a pity she did not speak any of those languages,
Rachel mused. Diego had been shocked when she had
admitted that she had never travelled outside England, and she
felt ill-educated and unworldly when he revealed that he had
visited practically every capital city in the world. Bustling
vibrant Buenos Aires was light years away from anything
she'd ever experienced, but she enjoyed their trips to the
famous Plaza de Mayo with its beautiful fountains, and the
spectacular pink Presidential palace, and her heart had leapt
when Diego linked his fingers through hers as they strolled
through the old district of San Telmo, exploring the narrow
streets lined with antique shops and artists' studios, pausing
to watch dancers perform a breathtakingly sensual tango in
one of the little courtyards.

Rachel was captivated by the raw energy of the city, but
she was less enthusiastic when they went shopping. The
Avenida Alvear housed many of the top designer establish-
ments and Diego whisked her into Prada, Louis Vuitton and
Versace, where she was fitted for several stunning but ludi-
crously expensive maternity evening gowns.

'I won't need maternity clothes in a few weeks,' she
argued, praying it was true and that she wouldn't spend the
rest of her life resembling a beach ball.

'I've already explained that we've been invited to various
events over Christmas,' Diego replied. 'And tomorrow night
one of my closest friends, Federico, and his wife Juana are
throwing a party to celebrate our marriage.'

Rachel's mind flew to the one and only other social event
she had attended with Diego. She had felt horribly out of place
at Ascot, among his wealthy friends, and here in Argentina
her inability to speak Spanish would surely be another barrier

'You'll like Rico and Juana,' Diego assured her, feeling a curious tugging sensation on his heart at her dismayed expression. 'Their daughter Ana is two years old, and Juana has just announced that she is expecting another child.'

Federico Gonzalez and his wife lived in a large Spanish-style house in a leafy suburb of the city—and were as friendly and charming as Diego had promised. Juana was pretty and plump. 'I piled on *pounds* when I was expecting Ana,' she confided to Rachel, 'and now there's another baby on the way. But fortunately Rico says he likes me curvy.'

Rachel was grateful that Juana was so down-to-earth because most of Diego's other friends were cultured socialites, members of the jet set whose wealth and sophistication made her feel horribly gauche. They politely hid their curiosity about her and took care to speak to her in English, but she knew nothing about fine wines or opera, and even less about politics, and found that she had little in common with them.

Among themselves the other guests chatted in Spanish, and as Rachel listened to the babble of incomprehensible words she felt increasingly isolated. She looked around for Diego and saw him walking towards her.

'Where did you disappear to?' he murmured when he reached her side.

'I went up to the nursery with Juana to meet little Ana. She's the sweetest baby,' Rachel said, her face softening as she thought of the cherubic toddler, who had still been wide awake, playing with her nanny. It seemed hard to believe that soon she would be holding her own baby. This time last year she'd had no idea that Diego would storm into her life, but now here she was, heavily pregnant and the wife of a man who had only married her to claim his child.

'Not long now,' Diego said softly, watching the play of

emotions on her face. He could not take his eyes off Rachel tonight. He had read in one of the many pregnancy and child-birth books he'd been studying that pregnant women often glowed, and he had wondered what that meant. Now he knew.

She had caught the sun while they had been walking around the city and her face was lightly tanned, her cheeks flushed a soft rose-pink that emphasised the dense blue of her eyes. Her blonde hair was rich and lustrous, tumbling around her shoulders, and the dress she had chosen for tonight—layers of blue chiffon that skimmed her bump—was a perfect foil for the sapphire and diamond necklace that matched her engagement ring.

But her loveliness was more than a designer dress and jewellery, he mused. She was serene and slightly distant, as though her thoughts were focused on the child she carried and Diego found that he wanted to be included in that special secret bond between mother and baby.

'No,' Rachel murmured, wondering if he was tired of her looking like an elephant and impatient for the baby to arrive. As if on cue, the baby kicked, the movement clearly visible beneath her dress. Diego looked startled.

'Was that…? Doesn't it hurt?'

'Not really, but the kicks are definitely getting stronger.'

Diego was staring at her stomach with an absorbed expression that, for some inexplicable reason, made Rachel want to cry.

'May I?' he asked huskily, moving his hand over her stomach.

Wordlessly, Rachel nodded. The warmth of his palm through her dress was enticing. It was so long since he had touched her body. Her heart began to thud and her breathing quickened. The baby kicked again. Did he or she recognise its father? she wondered mistily. She met Diego's gaze and her heart contracted at the emotion blazing in his amber eyes. Unquestionably, he would love his child. But what about her? a voice in her head demanded. Would she ever be anything to him other than the mother of his baby?

'He's obviously going to have a career as a footballer,' Diego murmured as the distinct shape of a tiny heel drummed against his hand.

'*She* might be a ballerina,' Rachel retorted.

He threw back his head and laughed. 'One thing's for sure, he or she is destined to be stubborn and argumentative—just like their mother.'

Rachel blushed but lifted her chin. 'I suppose you'd like me to be amenable and biddable and agree with everything you say,' she muttered crossly.

'I'd like to see the day you become amenable,' Diego choked, his eyes gleaming with amusement. He paused and then said quietly, 'I like you just the way you are, *querida*.'

Rachel did not know how to respond to that startling statement, but the warmth in Diego's gaze filled her with a tremulous hope that maybe they could work things out between them. She hesitated for a moment and then voiced the fear that had been gnawing at her all evening. 'Will we bring our child up to speak English or Spanish? Juana speaks to her daughter in Spanish… naturally…' She broke off, unable to explain how she'd felt when it had hit her that Diego would undoubtedly wish for his child's first language to be Spanish. It was bad enough that she could not chat to his friends, but the idea that she would be unable to communicate with her own child was terrible.

'I imagine we will bring him or her up to be bilingual,' Diego replied.

'That's fine for you, because you can speak both languages fluently.' Rachel bit her lip. 'You'll be able to chat away to our child in Spanish, but I'll be left out—and when we go to parents' evenings at school I won't know how he or she is progressing…' Her voice rose slightly. She was swamped by the very real fear that she would spend her life alienated from her environment and her baby, and tears flooded her eyes. 'Diego…I need to learn Spanish, but I was hopeless at languages at school. I failed French abysmally.'

Her vulnerability tore at Diego's insides. Unlike the many women he had met who could turn on the tears when it suited them, Rachel rarely cried. She gave the impression that she was strong and independent, but he suddenly appreciated how frightened she must have felt, moving to a new country with different customs, lifestyle and language.

'I will teach you Spanish, *querida*,' he promised gently. 'And with me as your tutor you will not fail.' He lifted his hand to her face and wiped away her tears. 'Every day we will spend an hour where I will show you the written language but, more importantly, we will talk in Spanish and you'll be surprised at how quickly you pick it up.'

He drew her into his arms and inhaled the delicate fragrance of her perfume. 'This is your first lesson. *Me siento muy orgulloso de mi hermosa esposa.* Do you want to know what that means?'

Rachel nodded, her eyes locked with his dark gaze and her heart beating too fast.

'It means—I am very proud of my beautiful wife.'

'Oh…' She did not know what to say, but suddenly words seemed unimportant as Diego lowered his head and brushed his mouth over hers in a butterfly caress that left her aching for more. She wrapped her arms around his waist, afraid that he intended to pull away, but instead he traced the shape of her lips with his tongue and then claimed her mouth once more in a slow, drugging kiss that stirred her soul.

'From now on you tell me immediately if something is troubling you,' he ordered when he eventually lifted his head and they both dragged oxygen into their lungs. 'I am your husband, Rachel, and it is my duty to care for you and protect you.'

His smile stole her breath, and she tried to ignore the little flutter of hurt that he regarded his role as her husband as a duty. It was unrealistic to hope he would fall in love with her as she loved him, she reminded herself. But they had been friends, as well as lovers, during their affair—and only a few moments ago he had told her that he liked her. That was a start, wasn't it?

Diego was shocked by how sweetly seductive it had felt to press his body against Rachel's soft curves. He had hardened the moment he had taken her into his arms, and the urge to lead her out into the dark garden where they would be alone and he could run his hands freely over her gorgeous pregnant shape was almost overwhelming. Calling on all his willpower, he eased away from her and stroked his finger lightly over her swollen mouth.

'I'll go and find us some drinks. Will you be all right on your own for a few minutes?' He needed to bring his raging hormones under control.

'Of course.' Rachel watched him stride across the room, her heart sinking when she noted the many admiring glances he drew from the female guests. His stunning looks made him a magnet for the opposite sex but, to give him credit, he seemed unaware of the interest he aroused.

A waiter appeared at her side, offering a selection of sweet pastries, and she could not resist the sugar-covered *churros*, which were similar to small English doughnuts, or the little layered cakes filled with chocolate that the waiter told her were called *alfajores*.

'I'm going to be the size of a house if I keep eating these,' she said guiltily to Juana, who had just joined her.

Juana gave a faint smile but her eyes were troubled. 'Rachel... Lorena Ortega has arrived and she's asked to meet you.' Juana grimaced. 'Lorena is Diego's mother. I had to invite her to the party, of course, but she told me she wasn't coming. I can't believe she's turned up.' Juana looked even more awkward. 'I expect you know that Diego and his mother don't get on. They never did, not even when Diego was a child, and of course after the accident…well…' Juana broke off. 'It's no secret that Lorena adored Eduardo and rejected Diego. The thing is, she's asked to see you alone. But you don't have to. I wanted to warn Diego she's here, but Federico has dragged him off to admire his new toy—and, knowing my husband and cars, they could be hours.'

Rachel shrugged. 'I'm quite happy to meet Diego's mother.' If she was honest, she was intensely curious to meet Lorena Ortega because Diego had never spoken about her.

She followed Juana along the hall and into what she guessed was Federico's study.

'Lorena, this is Rachel,' Juana said as she ushered Rachel into the room.

Diego's mother must have been a beauty in her youth, and even now she was older she had retained her classically sculpted features and enviably slim figure. But her face was lined, her mouth set in a permanent droop of dissatisfaction and her dark eyes were dulled. She was also drunk, Rachel realised as she stepped into the room and waited while Lorena drained a glass of spirits and set the glass down with an unsteady hand.

'So you're Diego's little wife.' Her eyes roamed over Rachel and she gave a mirthless laugh. 'And you're pregnant. Well, I'm surprised it hasn't happened before now. My son's list of mistresses is legendary.'

She waved her hand imperiously, indicating that Rachel should sit down, and refilled her glass with brandy. 'Would you like a drink?'

'No, thank you.' Rachel instinctively moved her hand to her stomach.

Lorena's eyes narrowed. 'You're just a child—a child who, no doubt, was seduced by a man who should have known better.'

Rachel shook her head. 'That's not true,' she said firmly. 'Diego didn't seduce me. I knew what I was doing.'

Lorena shrugged. 'Your loyalty is touching, but I fear it won't be repaid. I was your age when I met Diego's father. I was young, naïve, hopelessly in love. But Ricardo was a playboy and an opportunist, and he didn't want me—he wanted my money. My father saw him for what he was immediately, but by then it was too late. I was pregnant, and blinded by love for Ricardo. I was grateful when he offered to marry me.

'I didn't know about his other women, not at first,' Lorena spat, seemingly unaware of Rachel's shocked silence in the face of her venomous diatribe. 'But as the months and my pregnancy progressed and I became grossly huge, Ricardo no longer bothered to keep the reason for his frequent trips to Buenos Aires a secret.

'I have always thought that if there had only been one child, if there had only been Eduardo, I would have retained Ricardo's interest,' she confided to Rachel, an unnerving wildness in her eyes. 'But what man would want to make love to a woman whose body is swollen and ugly? I did not have one baby, I had two, and giving birth to Diego nearly killed me.'

'But you can't blame Diego for that, or for your husband's infidelity,' Rachel said in a startled voice. 'How could anyone blame a baby for anything?' She bit her lip, remembering how in the weeks after she had learned that she was pregnant she had almost resented the child she had conceived by accident. She had blamed the baby for the fact that she could no longer ride or work at the stables, and for having to give up Piran. Fortunately she had come to her senses, but it was clear that Lorena Ortega's resentment of her son had begun before he had even drawn breath.

Lorena lifted her glass to her lips and took another long

swig of brandy. 'If there had only been Eduardo…' she muttered, her voice slurring. She suddenly looked up and stared
at Rachel with glazed eyes. 'Diego is a man like his father,
mark my words. I believe there is an English expression—
don't expect a leopard to change its spots? Diego has never
remained faithful to one woman for long, and you're a fool
if you think he'll start now.

'Diego was always wild and reckless,' Lorena continued
morosely, 'while Eduardo was the finest son a mother could
wish for. But now Eduardo is dead—,' her voice broke and
she drained the brandy in another gulp '—and it's Diego's
fault. Diego sent him to his death…'

'What do you mean…?' Rachel's heart was beating so fast
she could barely breathe. She gasped, frantically trying to
snatch air into her lungs, and when she heard a sound from
behind her she jerked her head around.

Diego walked into the room. '*Hola, madre.*' His eyes
swung suspiciously from Lorena Ortega, and the half empty
bottle of brandy in front of her, to Rachel's pale face and he
grimaced. 'I see you have been celebrating my marriage to
Rachel. Is it too much to hope that you've been drinking to
my good health?' he drawled sarcastically.

'Perhaps I have been commiserating with your wife on her
choice of husband,' Lorena snapped.

'And no doubt warning her that I am a serial womaniser
like my father was?'

'Well, that's the truth, isn't it, Diego?' Lorena glared at her
son, and Rachel was shocked by the bitterness in the older
woman's eyes. 'You and Ricardo were from the same mould.
He even died in the arms of one of his harlots. I always knew
cocaine would kill him.'

Diego strolled across the room and slid his arm around
Rachel's waist, drawing her against him. She made no resistance, glad of his support, his strength and air of calm in contrast to his mother's emotional intensity.

'I'm taking Rachel home now,' he said quietly. 'It's been a long evening and I'm sure she must be tired.'

Rachel was so shocked by Lorena's startling accusation that Diego had somehow been involved in his twin's death that she said nothing and simply allowed him to steer her across the room. He halted in the doorway and glanced back at his mother. 'My child is your grandchild, *madre*. Do you not think you should try to forget the past and be a part of the baby's life?'

Lorena gave a harsh laugh. 'I will never forget,' she said viciously. She threw Diego a look of such loathing that Rachel gasped. 'Eduardo will never marry or have a child.' Hysteria edged into her voice. 'Everything was snatched away from him…'

The colour drained from Diego's face and Rachel was shaken by the flare of agony in his eyes. But he quickly masked his expression and nodded to his mother. '*Adios, madre*,' he murmured quietly, before he swept Rachel out of the room.

CHAPTER TEN

ON THE drive back to the penthouse Rachel could not face talking so she closed her eyes and pretended to be asleep. But she could not dismiss the image of Lorena Ortega throwing brandy down her throat and staring at Rachel with her wild eyes—and, worse than that, the look on Diego's face when Lorena had spoken of his twin brother, Eduardo. It was clear Lorena believed that Diego was somehow to blame for Eduardo's death. But when Rachel peeped through her lashes at Diego's grim face she dared not ask him for an explanation.

But whatever dark thoughts had been troubling him on the journey across town, he seemed to have dismissed them when they arrived back at the apartment.

'I knew you would like Juana,' he commented as he crossed to the bar in the lounge. Rachel knew he hadn't drunk alcohol all evening, and it was understandable that he would want a nightcap, but as he half filled a glass with brandy she was reminded vividly of his mother, and she could not restrain a shiver.

'Would you like a drink? I'll make you some tea.' He gave her the confident smile of a man who was no longer a stranger to the kitchen, and who had now mastered the intricacies of the teapot to make her tea first thing in the morning and every evening.

'No, thank you. I'm going straight to bed,' Rachel replied dully.

Diego frowned, noting how stiffly she held herself. She had seemed relaxed in the car and he'd assumed that meeting his mother hadn't bothered her as much as he had feared it might. Clearly he had been wrong.

'What's the matter, Rachel? Although I don't really need to ask,' he said grimly. 'Perhaps I should rephrase the question, and ask what my mother said to you.'

Rachel bit her lip, hearing again Lorena Ortega's cry that Diego had sent his brother to his death. It couldn't be true—could it? It had just been the drunken ramblings of an embittered woman. But why did Lorena hate her surviving son so much? She did not have the nerve to come straight out and ask Diego how Eduardo had died, and instead she dwelled on the other things his mother had said, in particular her assertion that Diego was a womaniser as his father had been.

'She said that your list of mistresses is legendary—and that you will never remain faithful to one woman,' she mumbled.

Diego's brows winged upwards and he gave her an arrogant stare. 'And of course you believed her—even though you had never met her before and it was obvious she'd had too much to drink? Thank you for your faith in me, *querida*,' he said icily.

It was impossible to believe she had hurt him, Rachel thought shakily—not when he was staring down his nose at her as if she were something unpleasant on the bottom of his shoe. She wanted to assure him that no, she hadn't believed a word his mother had said, but she could not forget the newspaper photo of him surrounded by gorgeous glamour models at the US open polo tournament, or the boldly flirtatious glances some of the women at the party had sent his way tonight.

'Have you had other lovers since me?' she burst out.

'I don't think that's any of your business.' His expression was glacial. 'You walked out on me, remember?' Nothing on earth would induce Diego to admit that he had felt gutted when she had abruptly ended their relationship.

His arrogance fuelled Rachel's temper. She had a sudden flashback to when she had been eight years old and she had watched her mother sobbing uncontrollably because she had discovered that Rachel's father was having an affair with his secretary. She wasn't prepared to live her life like that, always looking over her shoulder and wondering…

'I don't care how many women you slept with before we were married,' she told Diego fiercely. 'But now I am your wife, and if you think I will turn a blind eye to your extra-marital activities, think again.'

Diego surveyed her with an air of mocking amusement which did not disguise his anger. 'Perhaps I should remind you that you are hardly in the position to impose stipulations or make demands regarding our marriage,' he drawled. 'I married you for my child, and I will retain custody of the child should I ever decide to end our marriage.

'But I can see no reason why it should come to that,' he murmured in a marginally softer tone when Rachel paled. 'We both want to be good parents and give our child the stability that was missing from our own childhoods.' He reached out and ran his fingers through her hair, his brows lifting arrogantly when she tensed. 'Despite the impression my mother has given you that I am a lecherous playboy like my father, I give you my word that I am prepared to be a loyal and faithful husband.' His other hand snaked around her waist and he jerked her up against his chest, his eyes no longer icy, but blazing with a sensual intent that made Rachel catch her breath.

'I have been patient, *querida*, waiting for you to regain your strength after your illness, and giving you time to settle here in Argentina. But now it is time to make this marriage real, so that you can be in no doubt about my intention to please my wife in all the ways I know she likes best.'

'Diego…' Embarrassed colour scorched Rachel's cheeks as she remembered her unabashed enjoyment of the many and varied ways he had made love to her during their affair. But her startled protest was muffled beneath his mouth as he lowered his head and claimed her lips in a devastating assault that obliterated her fear that his desire for her had died.

It had been months since he had kissed her properly, and so much had happened since then. She had learned that she was carrying his child—and he had been so angry when she'd told him, which in turn had fuelled her resentment and mistrust of him. But right now none of that seemed to matter. Her body had been denied him for so long, and it paid no heed to the warning voice in her head which taunted that sexual desire was not love—not for him, anyway. For Rachel it was inextricably linked—and that left her wide-open to being hurt.

Frantically she firmed her lips against the fierce thrust of his tongue, but Diego changed tactics and, instead of trying to force her lips apart, he began to tease her with soft, beguiling kisses, tasting her and sipping her so that her resistance slowly melted away. Her arms crept around him. He was so strong and powerful and she felt safe with him, and yet at the same time she knew she was in mortal danger of succumbing to his potent masculinity.

He trailed his lips over her cheek and down her throat to the pulse jerking wildly at its base. Every nerve-ending on Rachel's body sprang into urgent life and she gasped when he lowered his head to the deep valley between her breasts.

'I love what pregnancy has done to your body,' he murmured huskily, his breath feathering her skin. He closed his fingers possessively around one full breast, and Rachel felt her nipples swell and harden. 'You are more beautiful than ever, *querida*.'

Rachel laid her hands on his chest and felt the heat of his body through his shirt, and her senses swam as she caught the scent of his aftershave mingled with the subtle drift of male pheromones. Whatever had happened in his past, he was with her now and had vowed to be faithful to her. He did not love her, but he wanted to make love to her—and she could no longer deny her need for him, she acknowledged, sighing her pleasure when he captured her mouth once again.

She could not fight the insidious warmth spreading through her veins, the heaviness of her breasts and the dragging ache between her legs. Slowly she opened her mouth to him and heard his low groan as he slid his tongue deep into her moist warmth and explored her until she was trembling. It seemed the most natural thing in the world for him to sweep her up into his arms and stride down the hall to the master bedroom, and when he laid her on the rich burgundy silk bedspread she threaded her fingers through his long, dark hair and tugged him down on top of her.

He wanted her, and nothing else seemed important— because she wanted him too, her desperation to feel his satiny skin beneath her fingertips so great that she tore open his shirt with feverish haste and skimmed her palms over the bunched muscles of his abdomen.

'Slowly,' he bade her huskily, amusement at her eagerness mingling with a feral hunger he had never experienced with any other woman. 'We must be careful of the little one.'

But Rachel did not want to be careful. The baby was safely cocooned inside her, and she was burning up with need. She shifted obligingly onto her side so that Diego could unzip her dress, her breath coming in shallow gasps when he drew the material down to expose her sheer black lace bra.

'*Bella*,' he growled, dull colour flaring along his magnificent cheekbones as he stared down at her proudly erect nipples straining against the lace. He swiftly unfastened her bra and groaned his satisfaction when he cupped her naked breasts in his hands and felt their plump softness. 'It has been a long time since we were together, and I want you very badly,' he warned her.

Rachel wanted to tell him that her hunger was as urgent as his, but the words were trapped in her throat when he bent his dark head to her breast and took one rosy crest into his mouth, the sensations he evoked as he sucked making her twist her hips in a blatant invitation. She had relived him making love to her every night since they had parted, but her dreams had been no substitute for the feel of his hands and mouth sliding over her body. Her breasts were so acutely sensitive that when he transferred his mouth to her other nipple and teased the swollen peak with his tongue she cried out and anchored her fingers in his silky hair to hold him to this task of pleasuring her.

Heat flooded between her thighs and she was desperate for him to touch her there, but reality briefly impinged when he began to tug her dress over her hips.

'Leave it on,' she implored him, her face flaming. 'I look like a whale.'

'No, you don't. You are exquisite,' Diego said deeply as he allowed her dress to float to the floor and ran his hand possessively over the hard swell of her stomach. '*Dios*, Rachel, you carry my child within you, and you will never look lovelier than you do now.'

He kissed her mouth, and she sensed tenderness, as well as passion. The sensual sweep of his tongue dismissed the last lingering doubts, and she lifted her hips so that he could slide her knickers down her legs, sighing her pleasure when he gently parted her and probed delicately between the slick wet folds of her womanhood.

'Please, Diego—now,' she whispered, and the undisguised need in her voice shattered his restraint so that he jumped up and stripped out of his clothes before stretching out on the bed beside her.

The sight of his arousal still had the power to steal her breath. He was a magnificent bronzed demi-god, and Rachel gave a shiver of anticipation as she ran her hands over the dark whorls of hair that covered his chest, and followed the path over his flat stomach and lower, to where his throbbing erection was pushing impatiently against her belly.

How were they going to do this? she wondered, her heart sinking as she stared down at her stomach.

Diego noted her faint frown and smiled, his amber eyes gleaming. 'Like this,' he murmured as he helped her move to the edge of the bed so that her feet rested on the floor. He stood up, nudged her thighs apart and positioned himself between them, slid his hands beneath her bottom and, as he lifted her, he eased forwards and carefully entered her. He filled her so deeply that Rachel gave a little sob of pleasure, but he misunderstood and immediately stilled.

'Am I hurting you?'

'Only if you stop. I'm not breakable, I'm strong and fit and I want you to make love to me properly,' she told him, clutching his shoulders and urging him to thrust deeper still. 'Please, Diego, don't stop…don't stop.'

The sensation of having him move inside her was so exquisite that she wanted it to never ever end. He drove into her again, a little faster, a little harder, setting a rhythm that made her blood thunder through her veins as the nagging ache deep in her pelvis grew and grew. The pleasure was intolerable, it couldn't last, and suddenly she was there on the edge of ecstasy, and the spasms that began as tiny ripples deep inside her radiated out in an explosion of sensation that made her cry out as she shuddered with the intensity of her climax.

Only then, when he had taken her to the heights, did Diego's control falter. She was so tight and hot, and so generous, lifting her hips to meet the thrust of his. He was afraid of hurting her, but she was urging him on and he gripped her buttocks and drove into her one last time, felt the exquisite spasms of her vaginal muscles squeeze him and with a groan his control shattered and he pumped his seed into her.

For a few moments he rested his weight on her, his breathing ragged and his heart-rate gradually slowing. But he was aware that this must be uncomfortable for her and he drew her back up the bed, curling his arm around her as she laid her head on his chest.

She felt as though she had come home, Rachel thought dreamily. The sound of Diego's steady heartbeat beneath her ear was wonderfully familiar, and in the golden afterglow of sex she felt the same sense of closeness to him that she had loved during their affair. She loved him, and she finally accepted that there was no point in trying to fight her feelings for him. And, as she lay in his arms and felt him stroke her hair, she felt a wild sense of hope that he might care for her a little.

'How many women have you slept with since me?' she whispered, hating herself for sounding so needy, but needing to know.

He stiffened, and in the taut silence Rachel was sure he could hear the overloud thud of her heart. Slowly he turned his head on the pillow and met her gaze, a curious expression in his eyes that she could not define.

'None,' he grated, his mouth twisting into a self-derisive grimace. 'Dammit, Rachel. Sex with you was always explosive—as I've just proved,' he drawled. 'I don't mind admitting that you turn me on more than any other woman.

'Happy now?' he asked dryly when she could not hold back her smile.

Oh, yes! Happier than she'd believed possible. The fact that Diego hadn't made love to half a dozen beautiful models while they had been apart did not mean that he actually felt anything for her, she reminded herself. But at least she could banish the jealous demon from her head. There was only one other thing that was bothering her. She felt reluctant to bring up the subject of his brother, but she could not forget Lorena Ortega's accusation—and there was probably a simple explanation.

Diego watched the play of emotions on her face and wondered if she was aware that he could read every nuance. 'What is it, *querida*?'

'How did Eduardo die?'

'*Dios*, what made you ask that?' His reaction was instant and savage, his face hardening as he jerked away from her.

'I'm sorry, I was just curious,' Rachel stammered, wishing she had kept quiet as the harmony between them was shattered. 'It was just something your mother said…' She bit her lip and shrank back on the pillows as Diego leaned over her and pierced her with an icy stare that made her blood run cold.

'What did my mother say?' he demanded in a dangerously soft tone.

'She said that Eduardo's death was…was your fault. But I know that can't be true,' she whispered, her heart thudding painfully beneath her ribs when Diego did not immediately refute Lorena's allegation.

'But it is true, Rachel,' he said quietly, his voice no longer full of anger, but flat and lifeless. 'I was responsible for Eduardo's death. Not deliberately,' he continued, his gut clenching when he saw the flare of horror in her eyes. 'Eduardo was my twin; we were like two halves of a whole, and when he died…' Diego broke off, reliving the pain that had been almost unendurable when he had dragged Eduardo's lifeless body from the river. 'When he died, I wished I had died too,' he admitted rawly. 'But I did not die, and I have had to live with the knowledge that because of my hot temper, my wildness and irresponsibility which—as my mother constantly reminded me throughout my youth—were traits I inherited from my father, I caused the death of the person I loved most in this world.'

He would carry his guilt to the grave, Diego acknowledged silently, as he jumped up from the bed and dragged his clothes on. It ate away at him and tainted everything he did, hovering like a spectre over every moment of happiness and reminding him that he had no right to be happy when, because of him, Eduardo had been robbed of his life. Eduardo would never hold his wife in his arms and run his hands over her stomach that was swollen with his child. He would never experience the excitement of being a father, or look at his wife across a crowded room and feel a surge of pride that she was his woman and his alone.

Rachel's eyes were huge in her pale face, but her expression of curiosity had been replaced by one of compassion that tore at Diego's insides. He did not want compassion, did not deserve it. What right did he have to lie next to her in the blissful aftermath of making love, and feel a contentment he had never known before?

Suddenly he could not bear to be near her. She was so beautiful with her golden hair tumbling around her shoulders and her creamy breasts pouting at him invitingly, causing the familiar ache in his groin. He did not deserve her when Eduardo had nothing. And he would not give in to the temptation to confide in her that, far from being the hard, emotionless man he portrayed, he was a bloody mess. It was better to keep her at a distance and deal with his pain alone. Better to strengthen the barriers he had erected against the warmth of her smile.

'Where are you going?'

He had reached the door, but turned back at the tremulous sound of her voice. 'I'm leaving for a polo tournament in South Africa early in the morning. I don't want to disturb you, so I'll sleep in the spare room.'

'South Africa! Why didn't you tell me before now?' Rachel asked shakily. It was crazy, but she couldn't help thinking that Diego was running away from her.

He shrugged, refusing to admit that up until five minutes ago he had decided to pull out of the competition so that he could stay with her. 'You know I play all over the world. I'm afraid you'll have to get used to me disappearing at short notice.'

'But how long will you be gone? We have things to discuss,' she said desperately. 'Your brother…'

'What happened with Eduardo does not concern you,' Diego told her grimly. 'The only thing you need to think about is the baby. I will be away for less than a week, but I have arranged for Juana Gonzalez to come to the apartment to give you Spanish lessons. What with that and your antenatal classes, you will be too busy to miss me, *querida*,' he taunted.

Rachel flushed. Did he know that she would be counting the minutes until he returned? she wondered in an agony of embarrassment. And, if so, did he also guess that she was utterly besotted with him?

She sat up and pushed her hair over her shoulder, feeling a minute sense of triumph when his eyes lingered on her breasts and dull colour flared along his cheekbones. 'I'm sure I won't give you a second's thought,' she said coolly. 'Have a good trip.'

Diego came home from South Africa on Christmas Eve. He greeted Rachel with cool politeness and she went to bed alone soon after he arrived and wept silently into her pillow, wishing she could recapture the closeness they had briefly shared the night he had made love to her.

The following morning she was taken aback to find a pile of gifts beneath the Christmas tree, and she stiffly thanked him when she unwrapped a breathtaking pearl and diamond necklace and matching earrings, a solid white gold bracelet and a platinum ring set with an emerald the size of a rock. The jewellery must have cost a fortune, but she could not tell him that what she really wanted was the most priceless gift of all and the one thing, it seemed, he would never give—his love.

They spent Christmas Day with Federico and Juana, and in the following days attended numerous lavish parties thrown by Diego's many wealthy friends. Rachel grew used to being the focus of interest—it seemed that everyone was curious about the woman who had tamed Diego. Little did his friends know that once they returned to his apartment Diego invariably disappeared into his study, making no attempt to disguise the fact that he was avoiding her, Rachel thought bitterly, or that that they slept in different beds.

Once the festive period was over he settled into a routine of leaving home at dawn and travelling by helicopter to his ranch to the north of Buenos Aires. Rachel filled the long days while he was away chatting to Juana, who visited regularly or invited Rachel back to her home. She attended antenatal appointments and birthing classes and shopped in earnest for baby clothes and nursery equipment, amazed by the amount of paraphernalia required for one small baby.

But the heat and humidity of the city left her exhausted. She was thirty-six weeks pregnant and was convinced that if her stomach grew any bigger it would explode. Perhaps Diego spent all his time at the Estancia Elvira to avoid seeing her waddling around the apartment, she thought dismally. He had said that he found her pregnant shape beautiful, but she certainly did not feel beautiful, she felt huge and clumsy and horribly hormonal, which at least explained her tendency to burst into tears when no one was around to see.

It was understandable that she felt homesick, she thought one morning when she stepped out of the air-conditioned apartment onto the balcony and felt as though she had walked into a furnace. But in reality she hadn't had a proper home in England for years apart from her dilapidated old caravan. She wasn't so much homesick as horse-sick— which was ridiculous when she was married to a man who owned one of the largest polo pony stud farms in Argentina. She longed to visit the *estancia* and see the horses but, although she had asked Diego several times when he would take her, he had always made some excuse.

But Diego had said that the *estancia* was not much more than an hour's journey by road, she brooded as she stared out over the endless expanse of skyscrapers that stretched up to the sky like concrete giants, their hundreds of windows winking in the brilliant sunlight. If she left now she should arrive at the Estancia Elvira by late morning. Filled with a sudden restless excitement she ignored the niggling backache that had woken her in the early hours, threw a few basic necessities into a bag and put a call through to the chauffeur, Arturo.

Diego had spent the morning in the paddock, working with one of the *gauchos* to introduce a couple of four-year-old colts to the ball and mallet which were used in polo. But now the midday sun was at its hottest and it was time to give the ponies a break.

'The chestnut mare is showing particular promise,' he spoke to the *gaucho* in Spanish as they rode the horses back to the stable block.

Carlos nodded. 'Another good horse from the Estancia

Elvira, huh, boss?' He paused and stared curiously along the dirt track at the figure some way in the distance. 'Boss…I think we've got a visitor.'

'There are no appointments today.' Diego broke off as he followed the *gaucho's* gaze, and then he swore savagely. '*Santa madre!* That woman would test the patience of a saint!' he growled before he urged his horse into a gallop and thundered along the track.

'What the *blazes* are you doing here?' he demanded when he halted in front of Rachel. She looked achingly lovely in a yellow sundress that left her slim shoulders bare and softly skimmed her rounded stomach. Her hair was caught up in a ponytail, secured with the yellow ribbon she always wore, but stray tendrils had escaped and curled around her face and Diego could not prevent his eyes from focusing on her soft pink mouth. 'You look like a buttercup,' he muttered, staring at her dress.

'More like a butter-pat,' she replied with a rueful glance at her sizeable bump.

'You should have stayed in town. The baby…'

'The baby isn't due for another month,' Rachel said serenely. In the past weeks Diego's preoccupation with the baby's well-being had driven her mad. She was sure he would wrap her in cotton wool and forbid her from leaving her bed if he had the chance, no matter that her obstetrician had assured them the baby's heartbeat was strong and Rachel's pregnancy was progressing normally.

She looked up at him, astride his horse. His dark hair brushed his shoulders and his hard-boned face was so beautiful that her heart turned over. 'It's so hot in the city, and I wanted to breathe fresh air and feel a breeze on my face. It's beautiful here,' she murmured, lifting her arms wide to encompass the view of two thousand acres of prime grassland, the horses grazing in the distance and the sprawling white-walled *hacienda* which was further up the track, surrounded by blue-flowered jacaranda trees.

'The sun is hot here too,' Diego growled impatiently, 'and I see you failed to have the good sense to wear a hat. You'd better get up to the house. The housekeeper, Beatriz, will be pleased to see you,' he said in a tone which clearly implied that he was not.

'I've already met her,' Rachel told him. 'When I first arrived, one of your ranch-hands showed me around the stables and then took me to the house. But Beatriz isn't there now. She told me she was going to visit her sister who lives on another farm.'

Diego nodded. 'I'd forgotten. She goes every week.' He looked up the track towards the *hacienda*. 'I need to take the horse back to the stables. Will you be all right to walk to the house—I'll meet you there as soon as I can?'

'Of course I'll be all right,' Rachel assured him firmly. She certainly was not going to mention that her backache was now acutely painful, she thought as she walked slowly up to the house. She had probably slept awkwardly and pulled a muscle, but she had to admit that she would be glad to sit down in the cool shade of the veranda that ran right around the *hacienda*.

At least Diego had not immediately demanded that she should return to the city. The chasm that had opened between them when she had asked him about his brother's death was growing wider each day, and she knew she had to try and make him talk to her. She just prayed that here at his childhood home she would be able to reach him, and that one day soon he would smile at her again instead of treating her with a cool indifference that broke her heart.

CHAPTER ELEVEN

THERE was no sign of Rachel when Diego walked into the *hacienda*. He strode down the hall, his boots echoing on the terracotta stone floors as he searched the various big airy rooms on the ground floor. Little had changed over the years. The house seemed to be trapped in a time-warp, he brooded when he reached the kitchen and stared at the copper cooking pots hanging on the wall and the huge wooden table that Beatriz still scrubbed every day.

How many times had he and Eduardo sat at that table, eating *empanadas*—delicious meat-filled pasties—and watching Beatriz prepare the evening meal? He remembered how the cook used to give them a big bowl of peas to shell, and Eduardo had carefully prised open the pods while he had fired his peas at Beatriz until she had waved her wooden spoon at him and told him he was the devil's child.

Beatriz had been joking, but he was sure his mother and grandfather had truly believed he was one of Satan's offspring, he thought grimly. He had understood from an early age that his startling resemblance to his father had provoked his mother's hatred of him, but he hadn't cared. He'd had Eduardo and that was all that mattered...

Diego turned abruptly and strode out of the kitchen, taking the stairs to the second floor two at a time. He did not want to be here. He wanted to find Rachel and take her back to the city, where the ghosts were still in his head but he was not surrounded by visual reminders of the past.

'Rachel…' he called impatiently.

'I'm in here.'

He followed the sound of her voice and halted in the doorway of the bedroom directly across the hall from the master bedroom.

'What are you doing?' he demanded, frowning at the sight of her taking clothes out of a small suitcase and stowing them in a drawer.

'Unpacking,' she replied brightly. 'I brought enough things with me so that we could stay for a few days. Beatriz said that you keep spare clothes here, and it seems silly to rush back to town.' She did not add that she had planned to put her things in Diego's room, hoping he would realise that she wanted to share his bed, but that her nerve had failed her at the last minute. From the deep frown furrowing his brow, her decision had probably been unwise, she thought with a sinking heart.

'Silly or not, that's what we're doing,' Diego said harshly. 'I have no wish to stay here, and you are a few weeks away from giving birth and need to be close to the hospital. You'd better repack while I tell Arturo to bring the car down to the house.'

'You can't. I sent him back to town,' Rachel murmured, steeling herself for Diego's angry response when his eyes glittered dangerously. 'Diego…we can't carry on like this,' she said shakily.

His brows rose. 'Like what?'

She quailed beneath his haughty stare, but forced herself to go on. 'You…so cold…and distant.' How would he feel if he knew she cried herself to sleep every night? 'I don't understand what happened in your past, but while it hangs over us we can't begin to have a future. I thought we were friends, she whispered when he said nothing. 'In a few weeks our baby will be born—the baby we vowed to give the happy childhood that neither of us had. But how can we, Diego, when there is this terrible silence between us?'

Tears clung to her lashes, and the sight of them tore at Diego's insides. Rachel was right; they could not carry on avoiding his past. He hated the silence that hovered between them like a poisonous gas cloud, and he missed her laughter and her cheerful chatter, but more than anything he was swamped with a loneliness that felt like a knife in his ribs when he lay in bed every night and wished that she was curled up next to him, all warm and soft and so sexy that he ached for her.

Her cornflower-blue eyes were fixed on him, waiting. But he had never spoken about Eduardo's death to anyone and he could not face her as he revealed the guilt he had carried for ten long years. He swung away from her to stare unseeingly across the grasslands that surrounded the *hacienda*.

'I don't remember a time when my mother ever loved me,' he said harshly. 'She adored Eduardo but, as I grew older and my physical resemblance to my father became more marked, she seemed to hate me more. She had loved my father, you see, but his infidelity broke her heart and left her deeply bitter.

'My grandfather, Alonso, had always thought that my father had married Lorena for money. After their bitter divorce he persuaded her to revert back to her maiden name, and she also changed my and Eduardo's name to Ortega. But although I carried the family name, my grandfather—like my mother—believed that my resemblance to my father was more than just skin deep,' Diego continued bleakly. 'He made no secret that he intended to make Eduardo the sole heir to the Estancia Elvira.'

'That must have been hard,' Rachel said quietly. 'It would be understandable if you had been jealous of Eduardo.'

Diego shook his head. 'I was never jealous of him. He was my twin, and he was as much a part of me as one of my limbs. We spent all our time together, and shared everything. I didn't care what anyone else thought about me and, to be honest, Lorena and Alonso's dislike of me upset Eduardo more than it did me.

'But I rowed frequently with my grandfather. No matter what I did, and how hard I tried to please him and my mother, in their eyes I was a feckless playboy like my father.' Diego paused and raked a hand through his hair. 'On the day Eduardo died I'd had a furious argument with Alonso because he disapproved of my decision to become a professional polo player. I was in a foul temper,' he admitted grimly. 'It was a crazy idea to go out in my kayak when the river was swollen after the spring rains, and Eduardo tried to dissuade me. But I wouldn't listen, and eventually I shouted at him to leave me alone.'

Diego's throat felt raw, as if he had swallowed barbed wire but now that he had started talking he could not stop the torrent. 'It was our first and only argument,' he said huskily. 'My last words to Eduardo were words of anger, and to my dying day I will never forget the expression of hurt on his face when I pushed him away.

'I continued up to the river alone, unaware that Eduardo had followed me. I didn't realise until I reached the bottom of the rapids, and turned and saw his empty boat carried along on the white-water.'

Lost in his private hell, he was unaware that Rachel had moved until he felt the light touch of her hand on his arm. 'Eduardo drowned?' she queried gently.

Diego nodded jerkily. 'The water was wild that day, and I imagine his boat must have overturned in the swirling current. We had both ridden the rapids many times before and knew what to do, but he must have hit his head on a rock. I got to the bank and raced back up the river…but I was too late.' His voice cracked. 'Eduardo was dead when I dragged him from the water.'

Oh, my love! Rachel wished she could say the words out loud, wished she could offer some sort of comfort to Diego, but the agony in his eyes told her that nothing could ease the devastation of losing his twin. Instead, she threaded her fingers through his and clung to him, and after a few moments he tightened his hand around hers.

'My mother was naturally distraught when I carried Eduardo's body back to the *hacienda*.' Diego spoke in a clipped tone as he fought to control the emotions surging through him. 'And my grandfather…' he closed his eyes briefly '…my grandfather accused me of deliberately causing Eduardo's death so that I could inherit the Estancia Elvira.'

'No!' Rachel could not restrain a cry at Alonso Ortega's cruelty. 'He must have known how much you loved your twin. And no one could have predicted that Eduardo would die in the river. It was a tragic accident.'

'An accident that I could have prevented,' Diego said harshly. 'Of course I did not mean for him to die, but if I had not been so headstrong, and Eduardo had not been so loyal, he would be alive today. He took his boat on the river to try and protect me—even though I had yelled at him.' His jaw clenched. 'You cannot know how that makes me feel,' he ground out, his voice throbbing. 'My grandfather was right. I killed my brother as surely as if I had stabbed him through the heart.'

'Diego, you can't believe that.' Rachel forced back the tears that were threatening to choke her. 'Everyone makes their own choices in life, and Eduardo *chose* to follow you down the river. It's a terrible thing that he died, but I don't believe he would have wanted you to spend your life racked with guilt.' Or to have become so emotionally damaged that he never allowed himself to become close to another human being, Rachel thought sadly. Diego had buried his heart with his twin, and it was little wonder he seemed so cold and aloof when his mother and grandfather had blamed him for Eduardo's death.

'That's why you don't live at the *estancia*, isn't it? There are too many memories of the past,' she said softly.

For the first time since he had bared his soul to Rachel, Diego forced himself to look at her, certain he would see disgust in her eyes for what he had done. But there was only understanding in her bright blue gaze, and a deep compassion that brought a lump to his throat. At least she did not hate him as his mother and grandfather had done, and she seemed determined to absolve him of blame. But he blamed himself—and he always would.

'Sometimes, when the wind whistles through the trees, I swear I can hear the scream my mother gave when she saw Eduardo's body,' he said in a low tone. 'After Eduardo's funeral I couldn't bear to be here and I moved away, played polo in just about every corner of the earth. But every night my dreams brought me back to the *hacienda* and I saw his body, lying grey and lifeless.'

Diego gave a faint shrug. 'I had no contact with my mother and grandfather during all that time, but when Alonso died four years ago I discovered that he had made me his heir. Coming back here was…hard.' Words could not explain how hard it had been to return to his childhood home, he thought grimly. 'At first I resolved to sell the *estancia*—but I couldn't. Eduardo loved this place, it was his birthright, and to sell it would have felt like the ultimate betrayal.'

He glanced down at Rachel's upturned face and thought how beautiful she was. Tears shimmered in her eyes, and he realised with a jolt that her tears were for him.

'Do you understand now why I can't live here?' he asked

jerkily. 'This should have been Eduardo's home.' And Eduardo should have had a beautiful wife and a child. His eyes were drawn to Rachel's swollen stomach. He knew she was finding these last few weeks of her pregnancy tiring, but she never complained, in the same way that she had not complained about moving to a new country and starting a new life. He had never told her how much he admired her for the way she had coped, he brooded. He had simply shut her out, as he shut everyone out. She deserved more than that, but he could not give her more. He was empty inside.

'Rachel...' While he had been wrapped up in his own thoughts she had turned very pale, and he saw a spasm of pain cross her face. 'I'm sorry,' he said gruffly. 'I know you hoped to stay here.'

She shook her head. 'It's all right. I think you are wrong to blame yourself for Eduardo's death, and I also think he would have wanted you to be here,' she said gently. 'But I understand why you would prefer to go back to the city, and I'm sorry I sent Arturo away.'

Rachel managed a faint smile, wanting to reassure Diego, but she felt another curious sensation in her lower stomach like the one she had felt a few moments ago, and she caught her breath as a sudden searing pain tore through her, so intense that she doubled over.

'What's wrong?' Diego demanded urgently. 'Are you in pain?'

'It's nothing,' she muttered, standing upright as the spasm passed. 'I think it must have been one of those practice contractions, in preparation for the real thing. The lady at the birthing class said you can have them for weeks before the birth. They're called Braxton Hicks contractions.'

'*Santa madre!* I don't give a damn what they're called,' Diego said explosively. 'I just don't want you having them here, miles from anywhere.' He dragged his hand through his hair. 'Wait here while I go and call Arturo. I've left my mobile at the stables and the only phone in the house is downstairs.' He strode across the room but paused in the doorway and turned back to her. 'Rachel...thank you.'

She understood immediately that he was thanking her for not denouncing him as a murderer as his mother and grandfather had done. Tears pricked her eyes but she gave him a wobbly smile. 'Go and make that call.'

She heard him thunder down the stairs and wanted to call out that there was no need to panic, but just then another spasm ripped across her abdomen and she stifled a cry. She hadn't expected the practice contractions to be so strong and did not relish having them for the next few weeks. Her backache was agony and another spasm, worse than the two previous ones, almost made her legs buckle. She bit down on her lip so hard that she tasted blood, and tried to breathe calmly. But as the contraction finally passed she became aware of wetness between her legs and a bolt of fear shot through her as she realised with a sense of numb disbelief that her waters had broken.

Diego slammed down the phone and swore savagely before he ran back upstairs. 'Arturo will be a while. There's been a serious accident on the freeway and he says the traffic is...hell,' he finished slowly, his brain struggling to comprehend the sight of Rachel sitting on the bed, her head thrown back on the pillows and her legs drawn up.

'*Dios!* What are you doing?'

Sweat was pouring down her cheeks and her face was screwed up in an expression of agony, but it was the note of fear in her voice that made his gut clench as she gasped 'Diego...I think I'm in labour.'

The paralysis that had temporarily gripped Diego's muscles eased. 'No, *querida*, it's just the practice contractions,' he reassured her. 'The baby's not due for another four weeks.'

'But it's coming now.' Pain ripped through Rachel's body and she could not hold back her cry. 'My waters have broken. The baby's coming, I know it is.' She stared up at him desperately, tears pouring down her face. 'I'm scared. It's too soon. And we can't get to the hospital.'

Diego quelled the fear coursing through him and knelt beside the bed, taking one of her hands in his. '*Querida*, even if you are in labour, first babies don't arrive that quickly. All the books say so. Arturo will come soon and we'll get you to the hospital, I promise.'

In reply Rachel let out a scream that tore at Diego's insides, and he watched in helpless disbelief as she tensed, her fingers clutching spasmodically around his hand. 'Our baby hasn't read the book,' she sobbed when she was able to speak. 'Diego, please…please, you've got to take my knickers off.'

The note of terror in her voice forced Diego to control his own fear. Rachel was in pain and he had to help her. Without another word, he jumped up, pushed her dress up to her waist and removed her underwear.

'*Santa madre,* I can see the head,' he said harshly. 'Rachel, I must get you to the hospital. The helicopter…'

'I'm not giving birth in a helicopter,' she gasped, her face screwing up once more as another contraction built to a crescendo of unbelievable pain. 'Oh, Diego, this is all my fault. I shouldn't have come, and I've put the baby in danger. There's no one here to help, but I can't give birth on my own,' she wept.

'You're not going to give birth on your own, *querida.*' Diego's voice was strong and calm, soothing Rachel's terror. 'I'm going to call the emergency services, but if they don't arrive in time I will deliver the baby.'

'Can you?' she asked waveringly, staring up at him with tear-drenched blue eyes.

There was no room for doubt, no time to remember that

he had failed Eduardo. 'I can do anything,' he said steadily. 'Trust me, *mi corazon*.'

From then on Rachel lost all sense of time and the world became a blur of pain that sucked her under and threatened to overwhelm her. Her only anchor to reality was the sound of Diego's deep voice encouraging her and telling her that she was doing brilliantly, that she was the most amazing woman in the world.

'I want to push,' she groaned as the pain became deeper. 'Diego...I can't bear it...'

'Easy now, *querida*, easy now.' He spoke to her gently, as he would a frightened colt, trying to control the wild excitement flooding through him as he realised his child was about to be born. But something wasn't right. 'Rachel...' his voice was suddenly urgent '...the cord is around the baby's neck. You mustn't push yet. Do you understand me? You must wait.'

Racked with pain, Rachel put her arms above her head and gripped the rungs of the wrought iron headboard as she tried to recall the advice from her birthing class to pretend she was blowing out a candle. Short little breaths, short little breaths... 'I can't hold back,' she cried, panting as she desperately fought the primal urge to push.

'It's all right.' Diego snatched air into his lungs. 'Push now, Rachel.'

And, with a guttural scream, she did. Diego stared in utter wonder as the baby's head and shoulders emerged, followed by a tiny slippery body, and as he held his son in his hands his throat burned with the tears that slid unchecked down his face.

'We have a son,' he said in an awestruck voice. 'Rachel we have a son.'

He looked up and saw the tears running down her cheeks. Wordlessly she held out her arms and, as he placed their child in her hands, their eyes met and held and he could not hide the emotions that were storming through him.

A thin cry broke the intense silence and as Rachel looked down at her tiny son she felt a tidal wave of love for him that swept away the doubts and fears she had harboured during her pregnancy. Nothing was more important than her baby, she thought mistily as she instinctively held him to her breast and felt a piercing joy when he suckled. He was worth every second of pain, and although he had been conceived by accident he was the most wanted, most adored baby in the world.

She looked up at Diego and her heart contracted when she saw that his face was wet. He was not emotionless, she thought sadly, but he had been so terribly hurt, and she did not know how to heal him. Her mind reran the birth, the frightening power of the contractions that she had felt were tearing her in two, and Diego's calmness and strength as he had held her. It could have gone terribly wrong, she thought shakily, remembering his sharp command not to push because the cord was round the baby's neck. Instinctively she hugged her newborn son to her and swallowed the lump in her throat.

'Our son owes you his life,' she said softly.

Pain flared in Diego's eyes. He could not tear his gaze from Rachel. Her hair was lank with sweat and she looked utterly exhausted, but her smile as she looked down at her son was the most beautiful thing he had ever witnessed. She was incredible, he thought deeply. And it had taken him far too long to appreciate how lucky he was to have her in his life—but he did not deserve her when Eduardo had nothing.

Rachel could sense Diego drawing away from her, retreating behind the barricades he had built around his heart, and she wanted to reach out to him and assure him that she would never hurt him as his mother and grandfather had done. But there was no time—and too much to say—and the sound of footsteps running up the stairs heralded the arrival of the para-medics.

'You had an amazingly quick labour for a first baby,' the paramedic commented when she had cut the cord and cleaned the baby, before wrapping him in a blanket. 'What are you going to call him?'

'I'm not sure,' Rachel murmured, stroking her finger over her son's petal soft cheek and his mass of downy black hair. 'I want him to have an Argentinian name.' Because Argentina would always be her child's home, she acknowledged. She had glimpsed the look of possessive pride on Diego's face as he had handed the baby to her, and she had known then that whatever happened between them, Diego would never part with his child. 'You choose,' she said shyly, giving Diego a tremulous smile. She wondered if he would want to name their son after his twin, but she did not like to suggest it.

After a second he said, 'Alejo is a good strong name—which complements his good strong lungs,' he added wryly, recalling his surprise that such a tiny baby had made such a loud protest when the nurse had washed him.

'Alejo Ortega,' Rachel tried it out and smiled down at the infant now sleeping in her arms. 'It's perfect.' He was perfect, and she would never ever leave him—which meant that she and Diego were stuck with each other, she thought sleepily, unable to fight the wave of exhaustion that swept over her.

'Are you happy?' she asked suddenly, staring at Diego and searching for some sign that would give her hope. But the wealth of emotion that had blazed in his eyes at the moment of Alejo's birth had disappeared, and the smile he gave her was cool and impersonal as he leaned over her and brushed his lips lightly over her cheek.

'Of course I am happy,' he murmured. 'You have given me a son. What more could I want?'

Me, Rachel wanted to cry. You could want me. But she said nothing and prayed he would think her tears were of happiness for her baby.

CHAPTER TWELVE

ALTHOUGH Alejo appeared in perfect health, despite his abrupt
entry into the world, he was four weeks' premature and the
paramedic was anxious to get him to the hospital in Buenos
Aires as quickly as possible. Rachel did not argue. Her baby's
well-being was paramount, but once she was in the ambulance
she smiled down at her tiny son and whispered, 'You knew
where you wanted to be born, didn't you, my angel. Now we
just have to persuade your daddy that you should grow up on
the Estancia Elvira.'

She spent a week in the exclusive private hospital Diego
had booked, but felt a fraud when the nurses fussed around
her because, apart from being a bit tired, she felt absolutely
fine. Alejo had a mild case of jaundice—not unusual in premature babies, the doctor assured Rachel—but after photo-
therapy treatment, where he lay beneath an ultraviolet lamp,
the baby quickly recovered and demanded feeding every two
hours with a shrill cry that could not be ignored.

Back home, Rachel did her best, and Diego assisted in every
way he could and frequently paced the nursery floor at two in
the morning with his tiny son nestled into his shoulder. But, after
a month of virtually no sleep, Rachel was hollow-eyed and painfully thin, and was inconsolable when the midwife suggested
that she should supplement Alejo's feeds with baby formula.

'He was a low birth weight because he was early, but this baby is going to take after his father,' the midwife told her, glancing at Diego's six feet four frame. 'Alejo will do just fine on bottled milk; it's you I'm worried about,' she said, her beady eyes skimming over Rachel. 'You've lost too much weight.'

'I'm naturally thin,' Rachel defended herself. Privately she was amazed that her once huge stomach was now as flat as it had been before she'd fallen pregnant, and that she was already able to wear her jeans again. But she was exhausted and permanently anxious about Alejo, and her disappointment that she could not breastfeed him properly was made worse when Diego announced that he had hired a nanny.

'I don't need a nanny. I want to care for my baby myself,' she snapped, before bursting into tears.

'Post-baby blues are very common for new mothers in the first weeks after the birth,' the midwife had explained to Diego when he had managed to snatch a word with her out of Rachel's earshot. But he could not allow the situation to continue. Rachel was wasting away before his eyes and something had to be done.

'Ines will give Alejo his evening feed and be responsible for him during the nights,' he told Rachel implacably.

'Why can't I give his evening feed?' Rachel demanded sulkily, hating the idea of someone else looking after her baby, but at the same time acknowledging that most days she couldn't think straight because she was so tired.

'Because in the evenings you will do your hair and make-up and change into one of the new dresses I ordered for you, and we will go out for dinner.' Diego's eyes gleamed with determination at Rachel's mutinous expression. 'You're not just a mother, *querida*. You are also a wife, and you have a husband who wants to spend some time with you.'

Rachel was so stunned by this statement that, once she had

met Ines, and discovered her to be both friendly and highly experienced in child care, she stopped fretting about leaving Alejo for a few hours. It was good to wear normal clothes again, instead of maternity dresses. Diego had taken her for fittings at several of the top design houses and now her wardrobes were full of smart day-wear and exquisite evening gowns that showed off her slender figure.

The first evening they went out she was armed with a mobile phone and a spare in case Ines needed to contact her, but when she sat opposite Diego in one of the city's most exclusive restaurants it struck her that this was the first proper date they had ever been on. They had eaten out regularly when she had first arrived in Argentina, but then she had been preoccupied with her pregnancy. Now she no longer felt fat and ungainly, and in her sexy new clothes she felt like an attractive woman for the first time in months.

Had Diego even noticed? she wondered, peeping at him over the top of her menu. He glanced up from the wine list and she smiled at him and shook back her hair, excitement shooting through her when she saw his eyes linger on the low-cut neckline of her dress. Her breasts were a lot smaller than during her pregnancy, she thought ruefully. But the flare of heat in his eyes was unmistakable, and heat pooled between her thighs as she wondered if tonight he would ask her to share his bed for the first time since Alejo's birth.

They enjoyed a leisurely meal and, although their conversation revolved around their new son, Rachel felt closer to Diego than she had done for weeks. He seemed more relaxed tonight. Earlier in the day, when he had helped her bath Alejo, he had told her how he and Eduardo had delighted in flooding the bathroom at the *hacienda* when they had been young boys. Seizing the moment, she had encouraged him to recount more tales from his childhood and he had done so, laughing at the memories of the escapades he and Eduardo had got up to. Afterwards, when they had tucked their son into his crib, Diego had looked at her intently.

'I had forgotten all the good times I shared with my brother,' he admitted. 'Or maybe I deliberately pushed them away because they were too painful to recall.'

'Are they painful now?' she'd asked softly.

He had sounded faintly surprised as he replied slowly, 'No—they're good memories, and I don't want to lose them.'

They lingered over coffee and in the soft glow of the candle flickering on their table Diego's eyes gleamed like polished gold. 'You look stunning tonight,' he murmured. 'You have regained your figure, and that dress shows off your tiny waist perfectly.'

'Thank you.' Rachel's heart was beating so hard she was sure it must be visible beneath her blue silk dress. She held her breath when he reached across the table and took her hand in his, idly rubbing his thumb over the pulse jerking in her wrist.

'I have a present for you—a little token of thanks for giving me my adorable son.'

At the sight of the small velvet box Rachel quickly schooled her features into one of appreciation, but when Diego opened the lid to reveal a band of diamonds and brilliant blue gems she gave a gasp of genuine delight. 'Oh, Diego, it's lovely.'

'The sapphires are from Sri Lanka and are a lighter blue than most other sapphires,' he explained. 'They are the colour of your eyes, *querida*.' He slid the ring onto her third finger, next to her wedding band. 'I noticed that you don't wear your engagement ring because it catches on Alejo's clothes. This is small and dainty, and I think it suits you better,' he said with a smile.

'I love it,' Rachel assured him. She loved him too, but she swallowed the words and picked up her coffee cup, unable to disguise the slight shake of her hand.

Diego glanced at his watch. 'It's getting late. I'll ask for the bill.'

'We don't have to leave yet. Maybe you would like a liqueur,' she said quickly, wishing that the evening would never end. 'I'm not the least bit tired.'

'I'm glad to hear it,' Diego said gravely, conscious of the strong, deep thud of his heart. 'I was wondering if I could interest you in a game of chess when we get home. Argentinian rules,' he murmured dulcetly, his eyes glinting wickedly as soft colour flooded her cheeks.

'I think you mean your rules,' Rachel choked, unable to hold back a smile as she remembered the chess games they had played during the heady days of their affair back in Gloucestershire. 'When I play chess with you I seem to lose my clothes.'

Diego walked around the table and drew her to her feet. 'That is the plan, *querida*,' he murmured, before he bent his head and brushed his mouth over hers in a kiss that left her aching for more.

They did not speak on the drive back to the apartment, but the silence shimmered with sexual tension that was almost tangible. Diego kissed her again when they stepped into the lift, and did not take his lips from hers until they reached the forty-second floor.

'I should check on Alejo,' Rachel whispered as he swept her up into his arms and carried her purposefully towards the master suite.

'Ines is in charge during the nights,' Diego said firmly. When he claimed her mouth once more Rachel could not resist him, and curled her arms around his neck as he strode into the bedroom and kicked the door shut behind them.

He might not love her as she loved him, but he cared for her, she was sure of it, she thought as he drew the straps of her dress over her shoulders and slowly revealed her breasts.

He had given her an eternity ring, and Diego of all people would not have made such a gesture lightly.

'I thought we were going to play chess,' she teased as her dress slithered down her thighs and pooled at her feet.

'Revised rules,' he murmured against her throat. 'No playing board or pieces, and we both lose our clothes.'

He made love to her with exquisite care, conscious that it was only six weeks since she had given birth.

'You were so brave when you had Alejo,' he said deeply, shuddering at the memory of her lying on the bed, torn apart with pain. He would have given anything to have changed places with her and spared her the ordeal, and he had felt so helpless, but Rachel had coped brilliantly and had left him awed by her physical and mental strength.

'I wasn't brave, I screamed my head off,' Rachel said ruefully. 'I was so glad you were with me.' Her heart jolted when she met his gaze and saw an expression there that she could not define. But then he claimed her mouth once more in a drugging kiss, and she parted her lips and welcomed the bold sweep of his tongue, every nerve-ending in her body tingling with anticipation. He traced his hands over her breasts and her flat stomach, and then slipped between her thighs and stroked her gently through the sheer lace of her knickers.

'Diego…' It wasn't enough, not nearly enough. She was shaking with need, and she tugged frantically at his shirt buttons so that he laughed huskily at her eagerness and quickly stripped out of his clothes. He drew her panties down and then lifted her and laid her on the bed, desire pulsing through him as he nudged her legs apart. She was wet for him, but he was intent on arousing her fully and he bent his head and flicked his tongue over her taut nipple, heard her gasp of pleasure and transferred his mouth to her other breast. She had given him so much, he acknowledged as he gently parted her and slid his finger between her velvet folds, caressing her until she arched her hips. Rachel was like a golden light in his life, which had been dark for so long, and because of her gentleness and understanding he was slowly coming to terms with his past.

'Diego…now…please,' Rachel implored him as his wickedly inventive fingers made her quiver with longing to feel him deep inside her.

'I don't want to hurt you.'

'You won't…' She stretched her legs wide and sighed her pleasure when he eased into her, his hard length filling her while her heart flooded with love for him. After all that had happened to him, he might never be able to love her, but she understood now why he sometimes appeared distant, and she would always be there for him, no matter what.

He kissed her again, his mouth fused with hers while he drove into her in a steady rhythm that grew quicker and more intense with each deep stroke, until Rachel hovered on the edge of heaven, waiting for him to join her. She saw his head go back, the cords on his neck standing out as he gave one final thrust, and he cried her name as they fell together, their bodies trembling with the intensity of their passion. And, in the aftermath, Diego traced his lips over her cheek and hair and closed each of her eyelids with a gentle benediction, and she fell asleep in his arms, unaware that he lay watching her for long into the night.

For the next week Rachel was happier than she had ever been in her life. She spent her days caring for her darling son, but her nights were Diego's, and she certainly wasn't complaining about the dedication he showed to making love to her.

But her bubble burst when she woke one morning and saw him walking out of the en suite bathroom dressed in his riding gear.

'I'm sorry, sweetheart, but it's time for me to go back to work,' he murmured as he leant over the bed and dropped a soft kiss on her mouth. 'I'm due to play in a tournament in Brazil, and the sponsor's called to ask me to fly to Sao Paulo a couple of days early.'

His words came as an unwelcome reality check to Rachel. 'You intend to continue with your polo career, then?' she said slowly.

Diego looked surprised. 'Of course. Why wouldn't I?'

'It's a dangerous sport, and I thought…now that there is Alejo to consider, you might retire from competitions.'

He gave a faint shrug. 'Polo is no more dangerous than many other sports. Playing polo is what I do, Rachel,' he said a touch impatiently when she stared at him with an air of reproach that tugged at his insides. For the past ten years his career had been the one thing he'd been proud of, and if he was honest he had made polo his life. He hadn't thought about retiring, but he admitted to himself that he had left it this late to announce that he was flying to Brazil because he was reluctant to leave Rachel.

'Alejo will miss you,' Rachel said dully, trying to hide her disappointment that Diego would continue to spend much of his life travelling around the world to play in matches, and seemingly intended to leave her behind.

'I will miss him too…' Diego hesitated. 'When I come back, the Estancia Elvira is hosting a national tournament. I thought you would like to come with Alejo, and we'll spend a few days there.'

Rachel nodded and forced a smile, but during the following week while he was away she could not shake off the nameless dread that something would shatter her newfound happiness. Diego was an experienced player, she reminded herself. But he was also a dangerously confident rider who took risks other players would not dare.

* * *

Diego's flight from Brazil was delayed and he did not arrive at the *estancia* until the day of the national tournament. Arturo had driven Rachel to the *hacienda* two days earlier, the car laden with Alejo's stroller and crib and a mountain of other baby paraphernalia.

The housekeeper, Beatriz, adored the baby, and once Rachel had fed Alejo and settled him in his crib she went to find her husband. The stables were a hive of frantic activity and she searched desperately for Diego, her heart pounding when she caught sight of him striding across the yard, looking utterly gorgeous in pale jodhpurs and a black shirt and boots. She loved him so much it scared her, she acknowledged as she forgot any pretence of acting cool and hurtled into his arms.

'Can I take it you missed me, *querida*?' he asked, his amber eyes glinting with amusement that swiftly turned to hunger as he claimed her mouth in a passionate kiss and she responded unrestrainedly.

'Of course I did,' she admitted shyly, unable to lie to him or hide her emotions any longer.

He set her down on her feet and stared at her, his expression suddenly so grave that her heart lurched painfully in her chest. 'Rachel...we need to talk,' he said in a strained voice. 'But not now,' he added with a grimace. The grooms were leading the polo ponies out and the babble of voices, horses neighing and the general air of pre-match excitement made conversation impossible. 'I have to go.' He dropped a brief, hard kiss on her lips and strode away to mount his horse, leaving Rachel staring after him, wondering what it was that he needed to say to her.

Had he realised that she was in love with him, and intended to warn her that he could never feel the same way? She already knew that, she reminded herself. But all the joy she'd felt at seeing him again had faded, and her heart felt like lead when she walked down to the polo field.

The national championships had attracted a huge crowd of spectators who filled the stands, while in the refreshment marquees the champagne was flowing. Rachel made her way to the opposing team's end of the pitch where, as top goal scorer, Diego was sure to be in action. The horses were snorting and pawing the ground and as soon as the umpire bowled the ball into play they began to thunder down the pitch.

It was exciting and terrifying to watch and, although Rachel had never played polo, she knew just how much skill was needed to halt a horse in full gallop, turn on a sixpence and hurtle off again, all the while trying to hit a small ball with a wooden mallet. Diego was an outstanding player who rode with a fearlessness which bordered on recklessness. He dominated the game and Rachel struggled to keep sight of him as he raced up and down the pitch so fast that his horse's hooves sent lumps of turf flying up into the air.

The accident happened so fast—and yet to Rachel, watching Diego's horse collide with another pony, he seemed to fly out of his saddle in slow motion, there was a tangle of legs and his horse hit the ground and rolled over, appearing to crush Diego beneath its massive body. For a few seconds a shocked silence gripped the crowd and then the air reverberated with cries and shouts, a woman screaming. Rachel did not realise at first that the screams were coming from her throat, she was simply calling Diego's name over and over as she fought to scramble over the barrier onto the pitch and was held back by a pair of strong arms.

'The paramedics are already with him,' one of the *gauchos*, Hector, said urgently. 'You can do nothing Señora Ortega. Go back to the *hacienda* and I will bring news as soon as I have a report of his injuries.'

'I can't leave him,' Rachel cried desperately. 'I want to be with him.'

But Hector shook his head grimly, and Rachel felt sick with fear. She knew the risks. Only a few months ago a top polo player from the US team had been killed during a match. She pressed her hand to her mouth to hold back her sobs. 'I have to go to him,' she choked.

'Go to your son, *señora*,' Hector told her harshly. 'I will come when I have news.'

Another of the ranch hands drove her back to the house. Rachel went without argument, knowing that Hector was right—there was nothing she could do for Diego, and she needed to be with her baby. The minute hand on the clock moved with excruciating slowness. Half an hour passed, an hour. Beatriz wept silently into her apron, but Rachel felt frozen inside as she fed and changed Alejo and forced herself to smile for him, while a voice in her head insisted—*he's not dead, he's not dead.*

The sound of tyres on the gravel drive made her heart stop beating and she rushed to the door, expecting to see Hector, her legs threatening to give way when Diego walked up the veranda steps, his shirt covered in dust and a livid purple bruise along one cheekbone, but otherwise apparently uninjured.

'Hello, *querida*.' Diego's gaze settled on her ashen face and red-rimmed eyes and he felt a pain in his chest that had nothing to do with his riding accident. When he had hit the ground and realised that he was about to be crushed by his horse, his one thought had been that he hadn't told Rachel what she meant to him—and in that split second he had known how desperately he wanted to live.

'I thought you were dead,' Rachel whispered, her throat feeling as though she had swallowed barbed wire. 'I watched the horse go down and I was sure you must have been crushed.'

'I saw it fall and knew I had to decide which way to roll,' he replied. 'Fortunately, I made the right choice. I'm fine,' he assured her gently when she stared at him as if she still believed he was a ghost. 'A couple of cracked ribs and a few bruises, including this beauty—' he ran his finger over his purple cheek '—but nothing to worry about.'

Nothing to worry about! The glib phrase hammered in Rachel's head as she recalled the worst hour of her life, when she had gone almost insane with worry, and her temper simmered.

She marched up to him, hiding her fury behind a sympathetic smile. 'Does the bruise on your cheek hurt?'

Diego gave a faint shrug. 'It's sore, but I'll live. Rachel…'

Her hand whipped through the air and cracked against his other cheek. 'Well, there's a matching bruise. Trust me, it doesn't hurt nearly as much as the pain I felt when I saw…when I thought…' Rachel's voice broke and tears streamed down her face as if a dam inside her had burst and released the flood of emotions she had tried to suppress during the agonising wait for news.

She stepped back, her eyes clashing with Diego's stunned gaze, and she felt sick when she saw the imprint of her fingers on his skin. But she was so angry—angrier than she had ever been in her life.

'How dare you put me through that?' she yelled at him. 'How dare you taunt death to come and claim you because you don't care if you live or die? I watched the way you rode today, with complete disregard for your safety. I know you still blame yourself for Eduardo's death. It was a tragic accident, Diego. It was not your fault. Yet you seem determined to be a martyr for the rest of your life.'

She paused to drag oxygen into her lungs, her whole body trembling, while Diego stood as still as if he had been carved from granite. 'Sometimes I wish I didn't love you,' she said brokenly. 'But I do, damn you. I do.'

She saw the sudden blaze in Diego's eyes and knew she had gone too far. He was probably furious with her. And, as usual, her tongue had run away with her. Blinded by tears, she spun round and hurtled up the stairs but, before she was halfway to the top, Diego caught up with her and she gasped when he snatched her into his arms. She could not bear to face him, not when she had revealed her feelings for him, and she beat her fists against his chest in fury.

'Go away. Leave me alone.'

'I can't do that, *querida*. I will never leave you again,' he vowed as he strode down the landing and kicked open the door to the master bedroom. 'You are my wife and we will never be apart again, not even for one night.' His voice throbbed with emotion, but as Rachel lifted her startled eyes to his face he brought his mouth down on hers and kissed her until she sagged against him and parted her lips so that his tongue could slide between them.

It was a kiss of possession and determined intent, his lips moving on hers with bruising force as the storm between them raged out of control. Tears were still pouring down Rachel's cheeks as she relived her terror that she had lost him for ever, and she kissed him back hungrily, needing to taste him and know that he was really here and not some figment of her imagination. His hands roamed up and down her body, curving around her bottom to drag her against his pelvis, and then up over her hips and waist until he cupped her breasts in his palms.

Wild excitement coursed through Rachel when he tugged open the buttons running down the front of her sundress and bared her breasts to his burning gaze. The feel of his hands on her naked flesh felt so good, so right, and she wanted him so very badly. But nothing between them had changed, and the warning voice in her head battled with her feverish need for his possession.

'Diego…' He lifted his mouth from hers and she shivered when he trailed his lips over her jaw and down her throat. Her heart was breaking and if he took her to bed now she feared it would destroy her. 'I don't want to have sex with you.'

'I don't want to have sex with you, either, Rachel.'

'You…don't?' She thought she had suffered as much pain as she could bear, but his rejection was agony.

Diego cupped her face, his hands shaking, and stared intently into her eyes. And suddenly the words that he had wanted to tell her for so long were not difficult to say. 'I want to make love to you,' he said deeply. 'But first I need to tell you…that I love you, *querida. Te amo*, Rachel. *Tu eres mi vida, mi amor.*'

He brushed her tears away with his mouth and Rachel trembled when she saw the tenderness, the *love*, blazing in his eyes. 'If I'm honest, I think I fell in love with you when I scooped you up after you'd been thrown from your horse,' he told her softly, smiling faintly at the stunned disbelief in her eyes. 'You were tiny and beautiful, and so argumentative. I'd never met anyone like you before, and the month we spent together was the happiest of my life. But you proved just how different you were from my previous lovers when you walked out on me.

'It hurt,' he admitted gruffly. 'And I was so furious that you had the power to hurt me that I went to New York utterly determined to forget you. But I couldn't get you out of my mind, and when I heard that you had tried to contact me I seized on my business trip to London as an excuse to visit you.'

'And found me seven months pregnant with a child you refused to believe was yours,' Rachel murmured.

He winced. 'You did not deserve my anger, or my foul accusations, *querida*. At first I felt a fool for falling into the age-old trap, but when I calmed down I knew you had told the truth when you said you had been a virgin—and then I was angry with myself that I had not been more gentle that first time.

'Don't cry any more, *mi corazon*,' he said softly, grazing his lips over her damp cheeks. 'I never want to make you cry again. I felt that it was wrong to love you when I had robbed Eduardo of his future. And my guilt had been reinforced by my mother and grandfather, who accused me of being responsible for his death. I can never escape the fact that if I had curbed my temper that day, Eduardo would still be alive,' he said quietly. 'But you made me realise that my brother would not want me to waste my life in bitter recriminations and deny what is in my heart.'

More tears filled Rachel's eyes when she saw that Diego's lashes were wet. He would never fully recover from losing his twin, and his mother and grandfather had made his pain even greater. He had been alone for so long, but he would never be alone again.

'What is in your heart?' she whispered.

'You,' he said simply, his voice breaking with emotion as he enfolded her in his arms and held her so close that she could hear his heart beating unsteadily. 'You and Alejo are my reasons for living and I will love you both until I die.'

'Oh, Diego…' She stretched up on tiptoe, flung her arms around his neck and pressed desperate kisses to his damp lashes, his bruised face, and hovered over the sensual curve of his lips. 'I love you so much it *hurts*.' She kissed his mouth and felt a piercing joy when he groaned and kissed her back with a tender passion that promised love and commitment that would last for eternity.

'Make love to me,' she pleaded, and he laughed joyfully, his mouth on her breast as he pushed her back onto the bed and covered her with his big body.

'With pleasure, *mi amante*.'

Their clothes were an unwelcome barrier he swiftly removed, and his amber eyes glittered with desire as he stared down at her pale, slender body and then nudged her thighs apart and moved over her. 'I love you, my Rachel,' he whispered against her mouth as he entered her. And he repeated the words over and over, making love to her with his heart, mind and body and with all the love inside him until they reached the heights together and drifted slowly down to lie blissfully content in each other's arms.

Diego idly wrapped a strand of Rachel's hair around his finger. 'I think we should make the Estancia Elvira our permanent home. It will be good for Alejo to grow up here,' he murmured, his heart turning over at the undisguised happiness on her face. She was so beautiful, and he loved her so much. He would never let any harm come to her or his son, he vowed fiercely.

'Are you sure you want to?' she said softly.

'I'm certain.' There were no ghosts here now, only happy memories of Eduardo. 'My competition days are coming to an end, and I want to be more involved with the day to day running of the ranch. Besides, once you've seen the present I've bought you, I doubt I'll ever be able to drag you away from the stables.'

Rachel smiled at him. His love was the only gift she wanted, but curiosity got the better of her. 'What present?'

'A showjumper—seventeen hands, black, apparently his name means "dark"...'

'Piran?' Rachel gasped. 'Really? Oh...Diego...' she buried her face in his neck, feeling as though she would explode with joy '...I love you.' Words were so inadequate to express what she felt, but he understood.

'I know, *querida*. And I love you too. Always and for ever.'

* * * * *

BAD BLOOD

A POWERFUL
DYNASTY,
WHERE SECRETS
AND SCANDAL
NEVER SLEEP!

VOLUME 1 – 15th April 2011
TORTURED RAKE
by Sarah Morgan

VOLUME 2 – 6th May 2011
SHAMELESS PLAYBOY
by Caitlin Crews

VOLUME 3 – 20th May 2011
RESTLESS BILLIONAIRE
by Abby Green

VOLUME 4 – 3rd June 2011
FEARLESS MAVERICK
by Robyn Grady

8 VOLUMES IN ALL TO COLLECT!

MILLS &
BOON

www.millsandboon.co.uk

BAD BLOOD

A POWERFUL
DYNASTY,
WHERE SECRETS
AND SCANDAL
NEVER SLEEP!

VOLUME 5 – 17th June 2011
HEARTLESS REBEL
by Lynn Raye Harris

VOLUME 6 – 1st July 2011
ILLEGITIMATE TYCOON
by Janette Kenny

VOLUME 7 – 15th July 2011
FORGOTTEN DAUGHTER
by Jennie Lucas

VOLUME 8 – 5th August 2011
LONE WOLFE
by Kate Hewitt

8 VOLUMES IN ALL TO COLLECT!

MILLS
BOON

www.millsandboon.co.uk

Meet the three Keyes sisters—in Susan Mallery's unmissable family saga

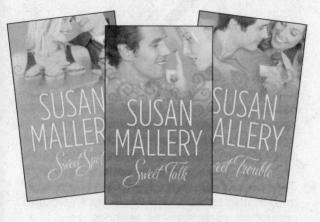

Sweet Talk
Available 18th March 2011

Sweet Spot
Available 15th April 2011

Sweet Trouble
Available 20th May 2011

*For "readers who can't get enough of
Nora Roberts' family series"—Booklist*

MILLS
BOON

www.millsandboon.co.uk